10-28-70

Thanks for coming to my
retirement party.

Sincerely,

Henry D. Swanson

Countdown

for

Agriculture

by

HENRY F. SWANSON

i

First Printing 1975
Library of Congress Catalog Card Number: 75-14857

Printed in the United States of America

by
DESIGNERS PRESS OF ORLANDO, INC.
Orlando, Florida

HISTORY PUT IN PERSPECTIVE

"ALL THE WORLD'S A STAGE, AND ALL THE MEN AND WOMEN MERELY PLAYERS; THEY HAVE THEIR EXITS AND THEIR ENTRANCES AND ONE MAN IN HIS TIME PLANS MANY PARTS . . ."

SHAKESPEARE

HISTORY IS AN ATTEMPT OF THE HUMAN SPIRIT TO SEE HUMAN ACTIVITIES IN PERSPECTIVE SO THAT MANY CAN PARTICIPATE IN ALL AFFAIRS MORE MEANINGFULLY.

A CALL TO FAITH
RACHEL HENDERLITE

WHEN I WANT TO UNDERSTAND WHAT IS HAPPENING TODAY OR TRY TO DECIDE WHAT WILL HAPPEN TOMORROW I LOOK BACK. A PAGE OF HISTORY IS WORTH A VOLUME OF LOGIC.

OLIVER WENDELL HOLMES, JR.

NO SINGLE MAN MAKES HISTORY. HISTORY CANNOT BE SEEN, JUST AS ONE CANNOT SEE GRASS GROWING.

BORIS PASTERNAK

A GENERATION GOES, AND A GENERATION COMES, BUT THE EARTH REMAINS FOR EVER:

ECCLESIASTES 1:4

TABLE OF CONTENTS

ILLUSTRATIONS

PAGE

ACKNOWLEDGEMENTS

Secretly, a great many people nurture the idea that someday they would like to "write a book". However, to bring such an idea into being requires the cooperation and assistance of many individuals. To all of those individuals who helped me convert an idea into reality, I am sincerely grateful.

I am especially indebted to the late County Agent K. C. Moore for having provided the motivation and direction for pursuing such an idea. It was his parting remark as he handed me his 20 years of narrative reports of his activities that put me to thinking. His request that he hoped "someone would document these agricultural events" has stayed with me some eight or 10 years. Moore's plea, coupled with Bicentennial activities, convinced me an idea's time had come.

Motivation, without editorial direction and encouragement, is like faith without works — dead. Here again I was fortunate to have several individuals who gave of their time and encouragement as I labored with the events in what I hoped would be of reader interest.

Dr. J. F. L. Childs, who had helped me previously with the "Citrus Bagman" responded graciously when informed of my desire to write a history of Orange County's agriculture. He agreed to edit and guide me on this venture because he too felt a historical account of agriculture was a high priority Bicentennial "must". His hours of editing and helpful suggestions are sincerely appreciated.

We also want to acknowledge the assistance and encouragement of Dr. and Mrs. Ralph L. Miller rendered to me as they read the various drafts of this manuscript.

The secretarial help rendered for various sections of the manuscript by Mrs. Carmen Hayden, Mrs. Julia Gilbert, Mrs. Betty Kelly and Mrs. Achsah Proctor Swickard to type and re-type pages of manuscript on her own time at night and week ends was truly an inspiration when the going was tough.

Photographs by Agent Thomas MacCubbin and retired Sentinel photographer C. W. "Barney" Barnes helped personalize the history. "Barney's" assistance in securing a printer and assisting in the picture layout was a great help in "putting it all together".

Finally, after all of the above was contributed by these individuals, a sponsor was needed to underwrite the publication of this manuscript. We are indebted to the Orange County Farm Bureau for their financial support in getting the history published. Special recognition goes to President Henry W. Land and Publication Chairman John Talton in giving the necessary leadership for action.

Thanks goes to Jerry J. Chicone, Jr. for heading up the Book Promotion and related activities.

In conclusion, I want to recognize my wife Billie as the greatest helper of all. For without her understanding and encouragement I would never have found the time to do what Agent Moore "hoped" someone would do someday.

HENRY F. SWANSON
April 1975

CHAPTER I

What Happened?

The newcomer to Orange County is impressed with the surging urban development spreading across the local landscape and doubly so if the newcomer arrived by air and had the benefit of that overview. However, his reactions to the details of this growth vary. He is surprised to learn that for over 20 years Orange County was the second leading agricultural income-producing county in Florida. In that same period the county has ranked 64th, 44th, 21st, 20th and 37th in the entire nation for agricultural income. To be ranked among the top 100 agricultural income-producing counties of the nation's 3079 counties is quite an accomplishment.

Impressive as these agricultural statistics are, the newcomer is even more impressed by the changes in land values. After contemplating these changes he invariably asks — "What happened?" This "What Happened" question has been on many lips and no doubt will be asked by future generations. For that reason a discussion of what happened should be recorded for posterity's sake. Opinions as to "What Happened" will differ in some aspects, but all agree that Orange County will never be the same again. To render a broad generalization as to "What Happened", it is the writer's opinion that the changes resulted from the impact of the "military-industrial" complex coupled with a network of major highways that made Orlando the transportation hub to all areas of the state. To put all of this in perspective, however, we must turn the "clock" back to the period prior to World War II.

Before August, 1940, land-use in Orange County was primarily agricultural, citrus, cattle, poultry or truck gardening. As a consequence, land values were based on agricultural productivity. These activities constituted the way-of-life for many of the county's 70,000 inhabitants. It should be noted that air drainage and water relationships of the soil as to water drainage, were the principal factors determining the value of the land for agriculture.

Land values were also closely associated with local weather patterns. Land in a moderately warm location and at least moderately well-drained was valuable for citrus production. Citrus returned the highest income per acre and good citrus land consequently commanded the highest price. The southwest area of Orange County met most of these basic criteria and became the site of the largest citrus acreage.

Vegetable production or truck farming yielded the next highest agricultural return. Soils for this agricultural crop must be level and have a high water table which the grower can control by installing the drains. Even more than citrus, vegetables depend upon the weather and are vulnerable to heavy losses during periods of cold weather. Soils meeting the requirements for vegetable production were located mostly south of Lake Apopka in the Oakland-Winter Garden-Ocoee area and the county's vegetable production of pre-World War II days was confined to that area. Later, the mucky-peat soils north of Lake Apopka were developed for the production of vegetable crops and after World War II the industry moved to that area. Since citrus and vegetable production both require mild winters, these two crops were said to farm the weather as well as the land!

Land that met neither the requirements for citrus or vegetable production because it was cold and poorly drained was used for cattle pasture or just to hold the county together. Land of this description had little or no agricultural value and it could be bought for 25¢ to $2.00 an acre in the 1930's! Thousands of acres were sold for taxes at 25¢ an acre in the 1930's.

Because thousands of acres of Orange County land met the water and temperature requirements for citrus, this crop became the county's largest and most important agricultural enterprise. Although citrus prices varied considerably from year to year due to market conditions and the weather, so much acreage was devoted to this crop its economic importance was never seriously challenged. However, vegetables and dairying frequently exchanged places for the No. 2 agricultural position. So until the early 1940's these three big income producers — citrus, vegetables and dairying were the backbone of the local economy. Poultry was commonly in fourth place with cattle and ornamental plants falling well down the scale of values.

Such was the land-use situation in Orange County prior to August, 1940. At that time the emerging military-industrial complex began to change the entire economic life of the county and the land values with it. Although no one recognized it at that time, the die was cast when the first military convoy rolled into Orlando in August of 1940 and took over the Orlando Airport. It was primarily a housekeeping operation at first but when the base was formally dedicated as the Orlando Army Air Field in December of 1940, it was evident that the military had come to stay. After Pearl Harbor, military activities at the Orlando base multiplied rapidly. This generated a need for a second base of operations in the county and in 1942 Pine Castle Army Air Field was officially activated as a secondary field for the Orlando Army Air Base. The Pine Castle field provided the facilities where B-17 Flying Fortresses developed the strategic bombing techniques used in World War II.

These two military bases brought thousands of servicemen into the area around Orlando. Many servicemen stationed at these two bases during the war years were impressed with the mild weather, many lakes, nearby beaches and scenic landscape. For many of them it was a case of "love at first sight" and this was the selling factor which induced thousands of these ex-servicemen to return to the area after the war. The massive influx of thousands of ex-servicemen and their families into the Orlando area after World War II started a development trend that has continued to this day. Basically, it is this trend that brought about the changes in land-use and land values that caused the countdown for agriculture.

Orange County was still agriculturally oriented at the end of the war and absorption of the thousands of newcomers into the agricultural economy was simply impossible. This situation created something new, a "taking in each other's wash" type of economic boom, underwritten primarily by the government. World War II veterans descended upon the county like a swarm of friendly locusts. Overnight their demands arose for houses, goods and services of all kinds. The military operation had stimulated the local economy to unprecedented heights during the war years, and after the war the Home Financing provisions of the G.I. Bill stimulated a boom in home building for returning veterans. Under this Bill many veterans participated in training programs in preparation for new careers. These government programs pumped much money into the local economy and prevented a post-war slump such as occurred in many areas. At this point it appeared that Orange County economy was doing an outstanding job of absorbing the thousands of newcomers. However, demands for residential land were expanding at an ever increasing rate.

Agricultural tracts within or close to the City of Orlando were the first to go. Some of the "city farmers" perceived that the local land values were changing drastically and a few wise prophets recognized this trend for what it was, by selling their property and immediately re-investing in more land. Not every "native" was so perceptive in this matter, however. Many nursed bitter memories of the Florida "boom" in the 1920's, and weren't to be "suckered" into land speculation again. As a result, there are many near-miss millionaires in Orange County today who can look back and say "I could have bought that tract for a song at one time!!"

When the war ended, the military influence on the local economy did not die and fade away, it continued (and still continues) to exert tremendous stimulation on the county's economy. In fact, its influence has been so profound that a brief history of military events is required to put it into perspective. For example, when the Pine

3

Castle base was deactivated in 1946, it quickly became a scene of abandoned runways and dilapidated buildings. However, the closing of the base was only temporary, as future events reveal.

The Orlando Air Force Base (the name changed when the Air Force was created), was reduced to housekeeping activities in 1946. Military and civilian payrolls were reduced sharply and ceased to be major contributors to the local economy. However, the Orlando Air Force Base, and the Pine Castle Air Force Base, were only biding their time and would again be major economic influences on the community. Within four years, the Korean War "revived" both military establishments, and a new era of economic stimulation began. As the Korean War gained momentum in 1950, the sleeping atmosphere of the Orlando Air Force Base swiftly changed to one reminiscent of World War II days. The Pine Castle Air Force Base was reactivated and in April 1951 the Air Training Command set up a transitional school for B-47 training of jet pilot instructors and fighter pilots. Soon another generation of servicemen was becoming "exposed" to the charms of Central Florida and once again military activity began to stimulate the local economy.

COW PASTURE YESTERDAY CAR PASTURE TODAY — Colonial Plaza looking south across Highway #50 (Colonial Drive). Formerly T. G. Lee Dairy pasture — Sentinel Star Photo.

Under the influence of the "revived" military spending, and the big building boom in the early 1950's, urban growth spread rapidly in all directions. Another factor that stimulated growth "in all directions" was the Orange County highway building program.

This program just didn't happen, it resulted from skillful, heads-up planning by a group of farsighted community leaders who understood road politics. Towards the end of World War II, these progressive community leaders were searching for "key" factors which could stimulate growth in the Orlando area. They concluded that roads could open the area for economic growth. To achieve that end, these community leaders evolved a strategy designed to get the jump on neighboring counties for the construction of new highways. It was a political strategy that paid off.

As a preliminary stratagem these leaders gave early endorsement and support to candidates running for state and national office. By supporting winning candidates the promoters managed to have several Orange Countians appointed to the State Road Board. This was to prove most helpful in the Central Florida road building program.

Looking back at the road building program raises the old question of the chicken or egg and whether the new highways "fostered" urban development, or whether urban development created a need for new highways? In any event, new urban developments in the Orlando area created traffic problems. This was a self-serving situation because more traffic naturally demands more roads. Also, the influx of more people provided more "political clout" for establishing priority needs.

To appreciate fully the impact of the local road building program on urban development in the county requires item by item review of several highway developments. Highway # 50 was the first post World War II project that exposed rural areas of the county to development. This major east-west route through the county was completed in 1949. The first major urban development to take advantage of this highway and to "leapfrog" out into the county was the Pine Hills development. Old timers shook their heads in disbelief. They couldn't imagine people living that far out of Orlando, even though it was only a few minutes drive from downtown Orlando on the new road!

The skeptics were wedded to their belief that land values depended on their proximity to downtown Orlando. They were completely unaware a new era had arrived — the drive-in shopping center. As this concept caught on, neighborhood shopping centers sprang up over the countryside and triggered a scramble for land adjacent to major highways. Eager speculators drove up land values in areas previously considered too far out-in-the-woods. Owners of agricultural land outside the city limits were fascinated as potential buyers outbid each other for land.

Traffic problems on Highway #441, the major north-south artery through the couty, necessitated a widening operation. In the mid 1950's community leaders were able to convince State Road Board officials this was a top priority and this improvement further encouraged growth of the county.

At this same time a group of local community leaders began a study of defense-oriented industries in various parts of the country and their impact on the economy of the communities. These leaders were already aware that the military establishments at the Orlando and Pine Castle bases had proved beneficial to the economy. Defense-oriented industries, operating on cost plus 10% contracts had high civilian employment, and were an even better stimulant of local business than military bases.

So with the dollar generating capacity of defense-oriented industries in mind, a task force of community leaders began "beating the bushes" in search of such a plum for the Orlando area. With the assets of a good highway system, two military bases, a good potential civilian work force, adequate water supplies, the task force started their drive for such a complex.

A "block-busting" announcement on September 14, 1956, disclosed the success of their efforts. The magnitude of their success was described the following day in the Orlando Sentinel under the banner headline — "Martin Aircraft comes to Orlando." The banner headline was followed by — "Two million for land, but it's still a guess on how much for the plant." The story behind these headlines was that the 'Glen L. Martin Co. of Baltimore, Md.' had selected a 7,300 acre site in southwest Orange County for their proposed huge defense plant. Some 6,400 acres of this pasture land tract was secured from the estate of Clarence Ziegler, former dairyman and cattleman, who had passed away some six months before. The remaining 900 acres of the Martin Company purchase was obtained from Mrs. Mary Halm.

Reaction to this monumental announcement fell into one of two categories. The enthusiastic response of the promoter-speculator group translated roughly into — "what's in it for me?" and those expecting to "profit" from the many spin-offs this industrial complex shared that attitude. The reaction of the other group was more cautious and translated into — "Wonder what all of this new activity will mean to my present and future way-of-life?" These individuals wanted things to remain as they were and hoped that whatever took place would not affect them adversely.

Of course the businessmen and community leaders were overjoyed at what this defense industry might do for them and for the local business. Community leaders were told that this new industry would "pump" approximately 1-1/2 million dollars weekly into local business. As always some were skeptical of this rosy forecast, so let

6

us tabulate what actually happened. After checking with a Martin Company official, we found that for the 14-year period ending in 1971, 1 billion, 63 million dollars were "pumped" into the local economy, as cash payroll money.

However, this defense plant also had a tremendous impact on land values and taxes. The acquisition of 7,300 acres by the Martin Company immediately changed the basis of all land values in the county from potentially agricultural to potentially urban-use. No longer would Orange County land be automatically agriculture related. From this point on speculation associated with urban-use would dominate the market.

By 1957 a full "military-industrial" complex was stimulating Orange County economy, and when the Martin Company paid approximately $1,950,000 "cash" for some 7,000 acres of pasture, land owners realized that an era of speculation had dawned. When the unheard price of $200.00 per acre was paid for 6,400 acres of pasture land and $750.00 an acre was paid for another 900 acres of pasture land just to "square-off" the Martin tract, landowners, promoters and speculators realized that the lid was off.

Agriculturists, the county's largest group of landowners, realized that their operations had acquired a new meaning. First of all, they were now in the land business and, second, they just "happened" to be in the agricultural business on the side! A similar situation had occurred in Dade County several years before, but Orange Countians never dreamed that they would experience such a gold rush.

At this point, a brief history of the Martin Company site is in order to put former land-use patterns in perspective. Clarence Ziegler and his brother, Alan, began operations in that area of the county in 1923 with a few cows and sixty acres of land. Through the years, Clarence expanded his dairy and beef herds and acquired an additional 8,000 acres of flatwoods land in the process. After Clarence died Alan moved to the Conway area where he established a dairy farm. No doubt Clarence Ziegler would have been amazed to see the huge Martin Company plant in his former pasture and to witness the tremendous changes it brought to the county.

Following the announcement of the Martin Company project, Orange County Commissioners and legislators enacted a series of courageous legislative acts to prevent the county from becoming engulfed in a haphazard building boom. The importance of these legislative acts should be noted because they largely prevented the type of building boom that would have caused a big urban slum as a result of the Martin Company building boom.

These public servants had the foresight and the intestinal fortitude to secure a county-wide zoning act that prevented organized confusion. In 1955, the county passed a limited zoning act, but it only controlled land-use along major highways. Certain courageous community leaders tried to maintain the "City Beautiful" image at least in a limited way during the immediate post-war building boom. To do so required fortitude because telling people what they could or could not do with their land was not at all popular.

When the Martin Company project was announced, these leaders knew the county was in for a tremendous building boom to provide houses for the projected 10,000 employees this defense industry would attract, plus the additional supply and service personnel needs. This building would surely generate some urban slums if controls of some kind were not devised. Needless to say, the proposed controls stirred up a hornet's nest.

However, with some modest land-use controls on the books, Mother Nature entered the scene and created a set of conditions that emphasized a new aspect for water control.

In 1959, the county recorded 63.77" of rainfall roughly 13 inches above the normal annual rainfall. This above average rainfall spelled big trouble for several recent housing developments built in low-ground areas. In 1960, the "wettest" year in over thirty years dumped 17.37 inches of "excess" rainfall on the county. Hurricane "Donna" was responsible for part of this. At any rate, two "back to back" wet years caused flooding to the eaves of houses in some urban developments in the county.

The public was outraged that the County Commissioners had allowed building in these flood prone areas. The County Commissioners realized that something had to be done. They had a County Water Control Act pushed through the legislature which gave them authority to control lake levels to prevent the urban encroachment on to flood prone areas and provided the means of building primary and secondary water control structures. To finance the construction of such structures, this Bill authorized the County Commissioners to levy a special ad valorem tax on all property in the county. This Water Control Act was passed in 1961.

During the 1963 session of the legislature the county negotiated another not overly popular ordinance. This act created a County Planning Department. Now, with a County Planning Department, the Commissioners could work toward some long range goals in good land-use through the use of county zoning.

To facilitate the orderly growth of Central Florida, Orange County joined with six other counties — Brevard, Indian River, Lake,

8

Osceola, Seminole and Volusia, to form the East Central Florida Regional Planning Council. Then in the fall of 1963 Orange joined with Seminole County in a joint planning program because the highway needs of the two counties were so interwoven. By 1963, Orange County was involved in three planning programs — county, bi-county and regional county.

These legislative devices were designed to help policymakers guide the frenzied building boom into a semblance of planned development, but critics, especially the speculators, were quite vocal in their displeasure at these restrictions.

From the time Orange County's boundaries were finally determined (1913) until 1955, no one told the landowner what he could or could not do with the land and water that he owned. Now suddenly when real estate prices for land were soaring, government officials had the audacity to try to play umpire in this new financial ball game. These critics reasoned they owned the land, paid taxes on it, and it was their right to make as much money as they could off of it for development purposes, so how did the county have the right to "nose" in on the deal?

This attitude may not have been the sole factor, but it certainly contributed to the defeat of every legislator and county commissioner in office at the time these growth-control laws were enacted.

Progressive leadership invariably pays a heavy price for farsightedness and these public servants deserve credit for their courageous actions. If some kind of planning and zoning had not been instituted during the "crash period" created by the Martin Company announcement, Orange County would have become far more an urban slum area than it is today.

After the industrial aspect of the military-industrial economic complex moved center stage in 1956 and 1957, the military received very little publicity. In May, 1958, the Pine Castle Air Force Base was renamed McCoy Air Force Base in honor of Colonel Michael N. W. McCoy who was killed in an air crash over Orlando in 1957. The base through the years made many economic contributions to the local economy, and the reader should be aware of these contributions and their effect on urban growth. Although it is financially impossible to measure all of these contributions by McCoy Air Force Base to the local economy over the years, a story about the base's closing gives us a few clues. This story, in the Orlando Sentinel April 30, 1973, revealed the following facts for the 1972 year of operations. "In terms of payroll, McCoy lays out $32.5 million annually. Of that amount, the military receives about $28 million and the civil service employees receive about $4.5 million. Other non-government employees not figured in that total — such as base exchange employees, gas station attendants, officers' and reception clubs' employees — take home just $1 million." The article quoted air force records as to the breakdown of the $32.5 million paid to base employees in 1972 as follows:

$24 million left to spend after taxes and deductions
$900,000 in restaurants
$500,000 in church donations
$3 million for off-base housing
$3.6 million for for groceries, including what they spent at the base commissary
$2.7 million for automobiles
$1.3 million for recreation, plus another $95,000 for boats and motors
$1.5 million for miscellaneous personal items
$2.5 million in savings and insurance

The above figures provide some insight into what a military base, such as McCoy, contributes to the local economy in one year.

As the 1950's drew to a close, those Orange Countians who thought about it, imagined they had everything going for them that any community could wish for — two military bases and a giant defense plant. Few realized that the 60's would bring more expansion, both industrial and urban, than all the previous decades added together. The name "dizzy sixties" accurately describes the frenzy of activity that accompanied these new developments. Community leaders were overwhelmed by the phenomenal success of their efforts to promote the rapid growth of Orange County.

For Central Florida the sixties blasted off with a "bang" when President Kennedy announced the United States was committed to putting a man on the moon within the decade. A veritable beehive of activity was created at nearby Cape Canaveral. The economic "spin-offs" from this activity stimulated Orange County's economy in endless numbers of ways. Brevard County, the "home" of Cape Canaveral, was showered with all kinds of federal money directed towards putting a man on the moon. Orange County leaders feared that they might be displaced from their "kingmaker" role in Central Florida. To forestall that possibility they seized the initiative with promotional activities of all kinds.

When Brevard County coined the slogan "Gateway to the Moon", Orange County needed a slogan also. Towards that end the title, "City Beautiful", was replaced by "Action Center of Florida". To indeed become the "Action Center of Florida", Orange County must become the transportation hub of Peninsular Florida. The community leaders realized this full well, and it meant that major road systems must radiate out of the county along with air traffic as well.

Community leaders realized that Orange County must have a jetport to compete with the hugh NASA operation in Brevard County. However, Brevard Countians also could muster considerable political clout since the space port was in Brevard County, and was responsible for much of the increased air traffic into the Central Florida area.

One might think that the "Action Center" promoters would have difficulty overcoming such handicaps, but anyone with such negative thoughts was immediately banished from the committee. Orange Countians became known for their ability to swing deals that other areas in the state could only hope for. What transpired in the sixties amazed even the most optimistic of the "action" promoters. The jetport tast force realized that time would ultimately decide the air traffic leadership of Central Florida — Brevard or Orange County. However, while searching for a bold concept with which to buy time, the Orange County promoters suddenly realized that Orange County already had a jetport — McCoy Air Force Base! That the runways of this strategic Air Force Base were full of B-52's all primed and cocked with nuclear weapons was no handicap. Two runways that could accommodate jets of any size was simply a necessary ingredient. To harbor such "unthinkable thoughts" as sharing this base with civilian aircraft, was, well unthinkable! However, on September 28, 1963, those harboring such thoughts were treated to a special crow dinner. On that historic date, the east runway of the McCoy Strategic Air Force Base was dedicated as the McCoy Civilian Jetport!

This tremendous accomplishment by the jetport promoters only served to whet the appetite of their counterparts, the highway promoters. The response of that promotional group seemed to be — "Anything you can do, we can do better". You have challenged us to do our part, we intend to round out the highway network to make Orange County the crossroads for all of Florida! As the first step in this campaign, the promoters succeeded in having the Sunshine Parkway (later re-named the Florida Turnpike) routed through Orange County and right past the front door of the Martin Company defense plant. This high speed limited access highway became another spoke in the Action Center transportation "wheel" visualized by the promoters. It linked Orange County with the lower East Coast, with Interstate #75 and points northwest, and it put Orange County in a bargaining position for a similar road across Florida from northeast to southwest. At this same time the new highway (Interstate #4) was "inching" its way from Tampa to Daytona Beach. Orange County promoters saw to it that this highway would traverse Orange County at the angle called for in their "hub" concept.

It was their recommendations that routed I-4 past the front door of the Martin Company, intersected the Turnpike nearby, and angled through the heart of Orlando on its northeasterly course toward Daytona Beach. Upon completion of Interstate #4 in 1965, Orlando had a major highway system that radiated to all points, north, south, east and west. With all of these accomplishments secured — two military bases, a navy sound testing laboratory, a defense plant, a jetport, and a major network of roads covering the county, one might expect the promoters to rest on their laurels and enjoy the fruits of their labors. However, the promoters recognized that the jetport lacked connecting links with the three major highways. Consequently, roads linking it with those highways and with the Cape Kennedy (re-named in the late 1960's) area, were high priority items.

Travelers bound for Cape Kennedy via McCoy Jetport needed fast transportation to the Cape such as a limited access highway or the demand for a regional jetport for the Cape area would continue. In July, 1967, the Martin Andersen Beeline Highway was completed and formally dedicated. It connected McCoy Jetport with State Road #520 near the Brevard County line and the Cape area. Completion of the major highway system through Orange County in the mid 1960's set the stage to "lure" additional growth stimulators to the area.

First of these additional growth stimulators appeared in the fall of 1965. It was the announcement of a new state university (Florida Technological University) to be constructed in East Orange County. This institution of higher learning, Florida Technological University, opened its doors to the first class of students on October 7, 1968. Then Orange County could boast of two educational institutions at the college level. Rollins College in Winter Park, the other college, and one of the oldest institutions of higher learning in Florida, opened its doors in 1885. Orlando community leaders snared Florida Technological University from other counties with the argument that NASA operations at nearby Cape Kennedy and at the Martin Company had brought thousands of engineering and allied professional personnel to the Central Florida area, and that these people wanted and needed a technological university close at hand. The method consisted of getting broad support from community leaders in Brevard, Seminole, Orange, and Osceola Counties on record in support of an appeal for a state university for the area.

Once the policymakers were convinced that such a need was legitimate and well documented, the next question was — "Where

12

should this new university be located?" Selection of the site was placed on the basis of — "Every county on its own and may the best group of promoters win". Other counties knew that persuading was an Orange County talent that none could equal! At any rate, East Orange County was the site finally selected as "The most logical location" for the new state university.

One old sage expressed a popular opinion rather well when he remarked shortly after the university site announcement, "There are very few things Orange Countians fail to get once they have set their minds to it." And "If they had thought for a minute that overland rocket launches were feasible, they would have tried for the Cape project too!"

In regard to the Florida Technological University project it should be noted that the need for a technological university in the area has changed greatly. The great reduction in activity at the Cape after the successful moon launchings and consequent reduction in personnel, considerably diminished the demand for technological training. The campaign to secure the university brought forth newspaper stories that the university could become the M.I.T. of the south, but student enrollment leaned more towards Arts and Sciences and Business Administration. As a matter of fact, the university underwent an identity "crisis". The Technological University name was called misleading and other names were suggested by various individuals. However, the students objected to changing the name and this project has been "shelved" for the present.

When the Florida Technological University project was in the building stage, Orange County leaders took some time out for a period of "soul searching" before tackling their next university project. Up to this time the community leaders had supported the Orlando Junior College, a private endowed Junior College created in 1941 and which had served the community for over 20 years and rejected previous offers of a State Junior College.

At this point, community leaders found themselves divided for once on a public issue. One group wanted a State Junior College like other counties in the state. In the name of supporting private enterprise other community leaders said public funds for a Junior college should not be sought because that would mean the death of the Orlando Junior College. However, those favoring a State Junior College won, and efforts were made to secure a state financed Junior College.

In December of 1966 this effort was successful and a state financed Junior College to be called Valencia Junior College was announced for Orange County. Acquisition of two state financed

13

institutions of higher learning by one county within a period of 18 months must set some kind of promotional record in the educational field! This newly acquired Junior College was temporarily quartered south of Orlando on Oak Ridge Road not far from the Martin defense plant. However, when the site for permanent facilities were completed on Kirkman Road, Valencia Community College moved there in September of 1971. As a result Orange County has two state college level institutions east and west of Orlando, plus a private educational institution, Rollins College, north of Orlando, an education wheel located within a transportation wheel.

Acquisition of these two educational stimulants to growth and the business economy in an 18-month period would have caused less ambitious community leaders to "rest and reflect a while". Not so with Orange Countians. The military input into the local economy had ebbed to a new low. The Orlando Army Air Field (now the Orlando Air Force Base) had diminished to a shadow of its once giant economic muscle in the local economy. By the mid 1960's it was reduced to housekeeping status and rumor mills opined that the base was due for deactivation and permanent closure. Community leaders decided that they must move quickly or this historic site of Orange County's would become a museum of a bygone period.

The community leaders came up with a proposition so bold that it must have made the faint-of-heart gasp. After studying various options that would require continued use of this site by the military, community leaders decided to court another branch of service. This plan called for a rather zig-zag promotional course. The Air Force must agree that they no longer cared to maintain this facility. Without creating military rivalry or suspicion, the promoters would then approach the Navy Department to see if they could be interested in the old Air Force Base. If the Navy responded favorably without tipping its hand to Air Force, the Defense Department had to be cautiously approached to see if they were agreeable to the transfer of property from one branch of service to another.

If and when these in-house contacts were cleared through the maze of inter-service channels, departments and bureaus, then the U.S. Congress would have to sanction this military wedding by providing the necessary funds. This course required secrecy until the Navy agreed to phase out operations at some present unannounced location and agree to "move" to new headquarters at the old Orlando AFB once it had been "rehabilitated" to meet the Navy needs. News that some area might be losing a Navy base to Orlando would naturally raise unfavorable publicity and result in an organized effort to defeat this fancy bit of promotional footwork. So the strategy had to be carefully planned to prevent a news leak that could alert community leaders in the affected area of the Navy base "rustling" scheme.

To less hardy souls this promotional project would have seemed like a "mission impossible" because of the many ramifications involved — Air Force, Navy, Defense Department, Congress all the way up to the Secretaries of these Departments and maybe even to the Commander-in-Chief.

When the plans were finalized and the "news" became public, Maryland realized that the Orange County rustlers were back in the saddle again! Once before Orange County had visited Maryland and taken with them a defense plant and the big payroll connected with it. This time the delegation was after the Navy Training facility at Bainbridge. By the time the Maryland Congressional delegation got "news" of the proposal, the Orange County "rustlers" had won and the only defense the Maryland Congressional delegation could muster was the mournful cry of — "Please don't take our military base".

Orlando promoters have been compared to chess players or even combat officers planning a battle. They do their home work well, plan their moves in advance, operate under strict secrecy, have a list of options, have only positive thinkers and move aggressively to accomplish their objective. The success of these "treasure hunters" was acknowledged in a press release, December 6, 1966, stating that the U. S. Naval Training Center at Bainbridge, Maryland, was being transferred to the former AFB at Orlando. The Orlando Naval Training Center accepted its first class of seamen on July 1, 1968. This unique triple play could well be a military "first" for the history books because in the span of 28 years three different branches of service — Army, Air Force and Navy, had operated the same piece of real estate! Historically, the promotional activities used to secure these "Federally financed economy stimulants" may be another first. Who ever heard of a county "rustling" a defense plant and a military base from another state within 10 years!

Unknown to the community leaders, a group of out-of-state promoters were looking over the county at this time. They were favorably impressed with all its activity and accomplishments. Doubtless the network of major highways in and out of the "Action Center" county with jetport convinced the promoters that they should pitch their tents in this area and share in the action of the Orlando area. The size operation this group planned was indicated in the Orlando Sentinel May 29, 1965, which stated — "In Mystery Land Deals — Industry Pays $5 million". The article went on to say — "More than $5 million worth of land has been purchased here as the site of the "mystery industry" which will provide jobs for 5,000 the Sentinel learned Friday. The total area involved is 27,568 acres

15

priced at $5,018,770, less than $200 an acre. Nelson, Boice, President, and David Nusbickel, his associate, of Florida Ranch Lands, Inc., completed the 47 transactions involved in the sale for an unidentified buyer. The property is located in Southern Orange and Northern Osceola Counties. The Sentinel has known of the prospective industry for some time and that it would employ 5,000 but has been unwilling to identify it." The rumor mills worked overtime with this tantalizing story. Guesses ranged from a giant defense industry to — "We — really — don't know what kind of explanation to share with you." However, the mystery was clarified on November 15, 1965, when Walt and Roy Disney announced that they would build the world's largest entertainment complex on 27,000 acres recently acquired in Orange and Osceola Counties. One could scarcely imagine the magnitude of the impact that this project was to have on future land values, and related developments in the county. Events prior to November 15, 1965, might well be recorded as B.W.D.W. (Before Walt Disney World) and those "after" as A.W.D.W. (after Walt Disney World).

Of the hundreds of possible sites all over the country that might have been selected, it was not mere happenstance that Orange County was selected. According to Disney officials, they had carefully surveyed the entire Southeast and found the Orange County site with its "super" transportation connections to be the logical choice.

When Orange County was selected as the site of a Disney entertainment complex, it seemed wise to ascertain how local interests, especially agriculture, might be affected. For this purpose a letter was written to J. E. Pehrson, Farm Advisor, in Orange County, California.

He responded as follows:

AGRICULTURAL EXTENSION SERVICE
IN ORANGE COUNTY
UNIVERSITY OF CALIFORNIA

December 10, 1965

Mr. Henry Swanson
County Agent
Florida Agricultural Extension Service
2350 East Michigan Avenue
Orlando, Florida 32806

Dear Henry:

Congratulations on your county being selected for the site of another Disneyland development. From now on you will not have to explain where Orlando and Orange County are located. You merely say they are right next to Florida's Disneyland.

16

Here is some of the type of information that you requested in your letter. It may sound like I am rambling, but certain things come to mind as I bring up subjects and I will try and add them if they seem appropriate.

Back in 1950 the population of Orange County, California, was slightly over 216,000. The County had experienced slight postwar growth and each succeeding year saw a 7 to 13 per cent increase until 1956 when it jumped 33 per cent in a single year. During the year the County was inundated with over 111,000 new residents. For the past few years the rate of growth has been averaging between 10 to 12 per cent per year and we now in 1965 have an estimated population of 1,136,000. Along with the population growth has come the expansive growth of city limits and the establishment of new cities. Presently, 90 per cent or more of the population is within city limits. I mention this fact since the city is subject to new growth pressures. It looks for added tax base. One of the most suitable units to bring in is farmland, since it brings in taxes and does not have heavy demands on the services of the city. By this type of manipulation, the home owner is in a sense provided city services at the expense of farmland brought within the limits.

During this same 15 year period, the citrus acreage in the County has gone from a bearing acreage of 62,000, with an additional 3,700 nonbearing acres in acres in 1950, down to just under 20,000 acres in the last report of June 1965. There is one interesting item regarding nonbearing acreage, we actually have 4,700 nonbearing acres listed now. The reason for this increase is the planting of some areas that previously did not have irrigation water available and are located far enough away from urban development to make their capitalization a worthwhile venture. Basically, these are properties under the management of large scale landholders. These people consider their citrus venture an interim use of the land, while it increases in capital value to the point that they feel a suitable fortune can be made on the land. Incidently, the value of property went from $3500 an acre average in 1950 to somewhere between $15,000 to $20,000 an acre at the present time. There are some individual pieces with higher value and some parcels within a stone's throw of Disneyland that have a value of somewhere between $75,000 to $100,000 per acre. However, these are exceptions. Presently, our real estate activity is in a lull. The space age industry having such an important influence on southern California, the speculation rises or falls with the approval of new contracts or their cancellations.

Back in 1950, the County tax rate was about $50 per acre for citrus land. Presently, it ranges from about $75 up. An average figure would be about $100 per acre. Individual parcels within city limits and suitable for future commercial or high value development may have tax rates in excess of $150 per acre. There appears to be a change of philosophy on the part of the assessing agencies in the county. Growers are bracing themselves for substantial increase next year. This change in taxing philosophy is not unique to Orange County. Growers in Los Angeles County have had a similar experience as have a number of urban areas in Riverside County.

One of the things that has come up with urban growth has been the general rise in wage scales as well as competition for labor. Once an area becomes industrialized, it is difficult to retain workers for farm labor which is usually looked down upon when a worker gets a factory job. Presently, unskilled labor is receiving $1.15 to $1.25 an hour plus fringe benefits. Some of which are required in California such as workman's

17

compensation, contribution to social security, plus the cost of any payroll deduction accounting which must be done by the grower. Back in 1950, the rate for hand labor was 90¢ an hour.

A vital concern to any agricultural venture in this state is a supply of irrigation water. During this time, both farm and urban people have worked together to assure themselves of an adequage water supply. Presently, it has meant an increase to farmers since it has been necessary to import more water from the Colorado River to southern California. In the earlier days, the water drawn by pumping was actually depleting the underground basin. This is being recharged with imported water and the cost is being borne by the users which is mainly agriculture. This County is probably unique among southern California counties in having a historical positive attitude towards obtaining adequate water supply. There has been a rise in water cost, however. This comes with the increased labor cost for operating an irrigation district, materials, pumping equipment, power and all the rest. Growers presently are thinking in terms of nearly $50 an acre foot for watering a good portion of the county. Others are fortunate to have some local supplies that keep this down to about $35 an acre foot. Fifteen years ago the cost would have been somewhere between $10 to $15 per acre foot.

Along with the declining acreage there has been a tendency towards declining production as well. A good portion of this we can attribute to our problems of tristeza but on top of this there is an overall air pollution and water pollution problem that comes with more urbanization. A number of cities upstream from this area contribute to the pollution of our Santa Ana River and as a result salinity of irrigation water of local source occasionally reaches levels as salty as the Colorado.

I certainly commend you for your forward approach to "people problems". I think many areas in the United States are being transformed from small towns that are desirable places to live into metropolitan centers with all the social ills that go along with large cities. Unfortunately, most planning is ten to twenty years behind the times as far as integrating free enterprise possibilities of development. It seems we have very few areas that can balance rural and urban characteristics. It either has to be the wide open spaces or just the city. I hope you folks can find a suitable approach to it. Best regards.

Sincerely yours,

/s/ J. E. Pehrson

J. E. Pehrson
Farm Advisor
1000 South Harbor Boulevard
Anaheim, California 92805
Phone: 774-0284 (Area Code 714)

bm

The letter from J. E. Pehrson was mimeographed and sent out to all agriculturists in the county, and to the news media.

Perhaps the first "shock wave" to arise from this announcement was the effect on land prices. Before the Martin Company announcement (September 14, 1956) Orange County land values were equated with the agricultural use of the land. The Martin announcement added a speculative dimension and buyers began to offer prices that astounded the natives. People were just beginning to get the feel of this new game when the Disney thunderbolt struck and set off a wave of speculation which few seemed to comprehend. Two early examples of this could be cited. A small tract (200' X 167') of unimproved land in Southwest Orange County close by the Disney tract sold for $1,750 in January of 1965. After the Disney announcement on November 15th of that year, the still unimproved tract sold for $15,000. Then, seven months later (July 1966) it sold for $45,000!

In the second example, the buyer bought 1,530 acres of swampy land just down the road from the Disney tract for $168,000 in 1964. The year after the Disney announcement (November 1965), land speculators "bid-up" the price on this undeveloped swampy land and four years later it sold for $2,070,000! But that is not all, in 1970 this same undeveloped swampy tract sold to another group for $3,594,000!!

Prior to the Martin Company's land purchase (September 14, 1956), local million dollar real estate transactions were unknown but after Disney's land purchase, the real estate speculators swarmed into Orange County like bees to honey. Big real estate deals became commonplace and in the late 1960's, one company kept a box score, as follows:

The real estate transactions of $100,000 or more in Orange County for 1969 through 1973.

YEAR	SALES OF $100,000 OR MORE
1969	228
1970	219
1971	363
1972	430
1973	438

Million dollar real estate transactions became common and lost their news interest. A couple of million dollar sales per month became the accepted pattern. Several sales topped the 5 million mark and a couple topped 10 million.

Million dollar sales for the period 1969 through 1973 are as follows:

YEAR	SALES OF A MILLION DOLLARS OR MORE
1969	12
1970	15
1971	25
1972	52
1973	66

During this land speculation explosion, orange blossoms lost their attraction. Those who had stayed in the citrus business enjoyed the luxury of watching their land values exceed their agricultural potential by far. Many enjoyed the excitement of watching land speculators bid up the price of land, but others had mixed emotions. One reason for such a reaction was that the tax assessor revised property assessments on the land in proportion to the value based on current market price. Millage rates were increased to provide schools, roads, law enforcement, fire protection, etc., that became necessary becaues of the new population demands. So between increased property assessments and millage rates, the legitimate agriculturist saw all of this as a double-edged sword.

To protect legitimate agriculturists from being forced out of business by speculators that were driving up land prices as well as taxes, the Florida Legislature passed the so-called Greenbelt Law (HB Chapter 67-117). This law went into effect without the Governor's signature May 29, 1967. The law provided that the land owners using their land for bona fide agricultural purposes must file between January 1st and March 1st, annually, for a special agricultural assessment. Owners failing to file for this classification would have their property assessed on the basis of its commercial market value.

In the early years of the law's operation, the County Commissioners in consulting with the Tax Assessor and County Agricultural Agent, would grant or deny applications for agricultural assessment based on their opinion of the bona fide nature of the operation. Several years later (1973) the Tax Assessor was given sole responsibility for determining the bona fide agricultural activity of the applicant.

At first this agricultural assessment appeal could be denied to properties bordered on two or more sides by urban development if the Board of County Commissioners felt the property in question was impeding the orderly growth of the community. If the taxes were changed from agriculture to current market value levels, they could be 10 times or more. Such an increase in taxes generally "convinced" the owner his property was standing in the way and he should put it up for sale.

In 1973 this portion of the law was changed to "being contiguous with urban development". A recovery type provision was added in that year which stated that property purchased for three or more times than its current agricultural assessed rate would no longer qualify for agricultural assessment. Such high prices paid for an agricultural piece of property would automatically raise suspicions of government officials if this new owner was a bona fide agriculturist. On the other hand, was he trying to hide behind agricultural assessment until the time was ripe for him to develop the property for urban use?

Over the years many owners of small tracts of agricultural land, primarily small citrus plantings in and around urban developments in Orange County, were forced to sell because of higher assessments levied against them under the provisions of this Act. Also, there were numerous instances of land speculators trying to hide parcels of land behind agricultural assessments while waiting for prices to rise. Claims were made that a cow or two or a few pine trees made the land-use a bona fide agricultural endeavor and therefore entitled the property to be assessed at an agricultural rate.

On the other hand, if the Tax Assessor had assessed all agricultural land on its speculative market value rather than its agricultural value, agriculture might well have ceased in Orange County during this period of speculative growth. The law allowed those who wished to continue their agricultural businesses to do so even though their lands were considered gold mines by land speculators. Nevertheless, and in spite of these assessment restraints, property values and taxes rose on all Orange County property — agricultural, business, homes, etc.

To illustrate the changes in property assessment and the resulting changes in taxes during a 20 year period, two case histories are cited.

The tax assessment history of a mature 40-acre bearing orange grove located in a warm area of West Orange County is cited as an agricultural case study. The three criteria used to determine assessment rates on groves are — the variety of the citrus trees, their age, and the overall condition of the trees. Orange trees are assessed at a higher rate than a grapefruit or a block of mixed varieties. As a grove matures, its production potential increases up to a point and then levels off. Lastly, the condition of the overall grove and trees is considered. Missing trees, new replants, diseased trees, overall bearing surface are factors used in this consideration.

Using these various criteria, here is how this mature 40 acre bearing orange grove located in a warm location, reflected rising property values and how increased millage rates reflect taxes on this agricultural property during a period of rapid urbanization in Orange County.

Year	Assessment	Taxes Paid	Year	Assessment	Taxes Paid
1955	$16,400	$ 651.08	1960	$34,600	$1051.84
1956	$34,500	$ 810.75	1961	$28,220	$ 919.97
1957	$34,500	$ 838.35	1962	$28,220	$ 962.30
1958	$34,500	$ 886.65	1963	$28,220	$ 962.30
1959	$34,600	$ 889.22	1964	$28,220	$1080.83

Year	Assessment	Taxes Paid	Year	Assessment	Taxes Paid
1965	$66,015	$1,593.60	1970	$53,646	$1,139.49
1966	$66,015	$1,596.24	1971	$53,646	$1,048.78
1967	$46,407	$1,175.21	1972	$53,646	$1,140.00
1968	$46,407	$ 973.25	1973	$53,646	$1,131.96
1969	$53,646	$1,163.31	1974	$53,646	$ 811.66

It should be noted the grove was appraised five times during the 20 year period. Because of the grove's warm location, it escaped serious damage by the severe freezes of 1957 and '58, and the '62 seasons, so freeze damage was not a factor in these appraisals. Had the grove been seriously damaged, the assessments would have reflected that fact. These appraisals reflect the attempt of the Tax Assessor to keep his assessments in line with current market values as required by law. Without question the Greenbelt Law performed a vital function in maintaining these assessments in line with the land's agricultural use rather than some "supposed" urban possibility. Otherwise, the speculative land values would have quickly exceeded the agricultural value of the grove. Although the county millage rate fluctuated in line with the re-appraisals and new properties added to the tax rolls through the years, nevertheless, an overall increase in millage was required occasionally to provide new services for the increasing population. The interplay of these — assessment and millage, resulted in an increase of $12.02 per acre for taxes or a total increase of $480.88 as of the 1973 tax year. However, with the big addition of new property added to the local tax rolls in 1974, the agriculturist benefited and his taxes went down. In this comparison it reflected a total increase of $160.58 or $4.10 per acre as compared to that paid in 1955!

However, the homeowner didn't fare as well as the agricultural property owner during this 20 year period. For example, the increased value on a small house with no improvements or additions during this same period changed as follows:

YEAR	TOTAL ASSESSMENT	HOMESTEAD EXEMPTION	FINAL ASSESSMENT	TAX PAID
1955	$ 4,800	$5,000	0	0
1956	$ 8,800	$5,000	$3,800	$ 86.26
1957	$ 8,800	$5,000	$3,800	$ 92.34
1958	$ 8,800	$5,000	$3,800	$ 94.62
1959	$ 8,800	$5,000	$3,800	$ 94.62
1960	$ 8,800	$5,000	$3,800	$112.48
1961	$ 8,830	$5,000	$3,830	$121.79
1962	$ 8,830	$5,000	$3,830	$126.54
1963	$ 8,830	$5,000	$3,830	$126.54
1964	$ 8,830	$5,000	$3,830	$141.71
1965	$10,649	$5,000	$5,649	$131.00
1966	$10,649	$5,000	$5,649	$131.00
1967	$10,649	$5,000	$5,649	$ 92.30

YEAR	TOTAL ASSESSMENT	HOMESTEAD EXEMPTION	FINAL ASSESSMENT	TAX PAID
1968	$10,649	$5,000	$5,649	$112.36
1969	$10,649	$5,000	$5,649	$114.39
1970	$10,649	$5,000	$5,649	$111.57
1971	$13,223	$5,000	$8,223	$148.01
1972	$13,223	$5,000	$8,223	$153.77
1973	$13,223	$5,000	$8,223	$149.57
1974	$17.631	$5,000	$12,631	$268.41

These two case studies of "what happened" in the assessed valuation and taxes levied on property during a 20 year period of rapid urban growth are items for the history books. For those who are desirous of a more in-depth study of changing land values over a longer period of time, we have a 90 year case history.

We are able to present the history and early tax records on this 40-acre parcel of land in the Piedmont section of Orange County (Sec. 24, Twp. 21, Range 28, NW ¼ of NE ¼ and East of Highway 441) through the courtesy of Mrs. Julia T. Oddo, a daughter-in-law of one of the first owners. In this 40-acre tract the soil types vary widely so that the entire tract was not suitable for citrus. The 14 acres of Blanton soils were planted to citrus quite early.

The remaining 26 acres was St. Lucie soil which is white sand and worthless for citrus. However, during the "citrus boom" of the early 1950's this portion was planted to citrus by the son (Edgar Fox) of the pioneer owner, but the citrus failed as could be expected. Consequently, only about 14 acres was in producing grove during the 50 years. Even this was only a few acres originally, but with the passage of time was expanded 'til all the suitable 14 acres was planted to citrus.

Page McKinney, the first owner of the 40-acre parcel, acquired it as a land grant from President Arthur. In 1884 he sold it for $400.00 to William Burwell and Charles Fox. This purchase price of $10.00 an acre value was based on the agricultural possibilities of the land at that time. The value of the dollar in 1884 as compared to the dollar value of 1974 should be considered along with the price paid at that time. In 1895 Mr. Charles Fox, of New London, Connecticut, bought out his partner, William Burwell, and the property has been in the Fox family continuously since that date. It is one of the oldest one-owner tract of which we have knowledge in Orange County and Mr. Fox was one of the county's pioneer absentee grove owners. After the disastrous 1894-'95 freeze several acres of seedling trees grew back from root sprouts and became the nucleus around which budded trees were planted through the years. As a result, the 14-acre orange grove consisted of several varieties of different ages. The grove was cared for by neighbor and nearby grower, Gust Jackson.

When Charles Fox died in 1927, his son Edgar took over its management. In 1932 Plymouth C.G.A. assumed the care of the grove. Upon Edgar Fox's death in January of 1963, his widow Julia Cox Oddo took over management of the property.

Mrs. Julia Oddo, Greenacre Road, widow of Edgar Fox whose father Charles Fox and Arthur Burwell purchased the 40 acre tract in 1884 for $400.00.

During the period of the Fox's ownership many problems have confronted the 14-acre citrus portion of the tract. In 1927, the new Highway #441 cut several acres from the grove on the southwest corner of the property. In 1955 the widening of #441 removed several additional acres of land and trees.

Weather adversities have made their imprint on the grove during its 80-year history. The severe freezes of 1894-95, 1917, '34, '40, '62, etc. left their "battle scars" on the surviving trees. Then the severe "wet" years of 1959 and '60 flooded several acres and caused the loss of many trees and damaged many more.

Considering the number and condition of the trees in the 14-acre grove and the remaining 20 acres of abandoned grove in the poor soil area, what were the assessed valuations and the taxes paid on this parcel for the past 70 years? The answer to this is as follows:

YEAR	ACREAGE	VALUATION	AGGREGATE TAX
1904	40	$ 100	$ 2.00
1905	40	$ 100	$ 2.20
1906	40	$ 100	$ 2.40
1907	40	$ 100	$ 2.75
1908	40	$ 100	$ 2.65
1909	40	$ 100	$ 2.85
1910	40	$ 100	$ 2.85
1911	40	$ 100	$ 2.95
1912	40	$ 100	$ 2.95
1913	40	$ 100	$ 3.05
1914	40	$ 120	$ 2.82
1915	40	$ 120	$ 3.90
1916	40	$ 120	$ 4.44

YEAR	ACREAGE	VALUATION	AGGREGATE TAX
1917	40	$ 120	$ 4.80
1918	40	$ 120	$ 4.92
1919	40	$ 103	$ 6.70
1920	40	$ 120	$ 6.06
1921	40	$ 140	$ 8.44
1922	40	$ 320	$ 17.16
1923	40	$ 400	$ 25.40
1924	40	$ 400	$ 25.40
1925	40	$ 400	$ 27.00
1926	40	$ 600	$ 37.80
1927	40	$ 540	$ 35.91
1928	40	$ 540	$ 37.80
1929	40	$ 600	$ 45.75
1930	40	$ 600	$ 44.10
1931	40	$ 600	$ 39.00
1932	34	$ 580	$ 37.42
1933	34	$ 500	$ 37.31
1934	34	$ 500	$ 38.56
1935	34	$ 500	$ 34.52
1936	34	$ 500	$ 31.88
1937	34	$ 500	$ 31.81
1938	34	$ 500	$ 32.81
1939	34	$ 500	$ 33.93
1940	34	$ 500	$ 35.43
1941	34	$ 2,920	$ 44.18
1942	34	$ 2,920	$ 42.71
1943	34	$ 2,920	$ 44.17
1944	34	$ 2,920	$ 50.01
1945	34	$ 5,600	$120.40
1946	34	$ 5,600	$143.92
1947	34	$ 5,600	$161.84
1948	34	$ 5,600	$165.84
1949	34	$ 5,600	$170.80
1950	34	$ 5,600	$169.12
1951	34	$ 4,200	$126.84
1952	34	$ 4,800	$156.96
1953	34	$ 4,800	$151.68
1954	34	$ 4,800	$182.40
1955	34	$ 4,800	$181.44
1956	34	$24,500 (Revaluation)	$556.15
1957	34	$23,000	$558.90
1958	34	$18,600 (Freeze)	$463.14
1959	34	$18,000	$448.20
1960	34	$18,000	$532.80
1961	34	$11,000 (Water damage)	$388.36
1962	34	$11,490	$405.59
1963	34	$11,170	$394.29
1964	34	$11,170	$441.22
1965	34	$22,140	$571.00
1966	34	$21,569	$552.96
1967	34	$19,249	$511.52
1968	34	$19,250	$431.24
1969	34	$16,502	$376.49

YEAR	ACREAGE	VALUATION	AGGREGATE TAX
1970	34	$16,502	$369.17
1971	34	$16,502	$355.27
1972	34	$16,502	$366.84
1973	34	$16,502	$358.09
1974	34	$16,502	$269.64

Perhaps the best indicator of "WHAT HAPPENED" during this period is the increase in the county population during those years. A look at the changes that occurred reflects the pressure for land, for living space, retail sales and service areas, streets and highways, etc. The statisticians tell us that theoretically the land requirements per 10,000 new residents are as follows:

Retail and Service Land	109 Acres
Parks and Other Public Land	580 Acres
Residential Land	1,000 Acres
Public Streets	400 Acres
Industrial Land	98 Acres
	2,187 Acres

This means that for each 10,000 new residents, some 2,187 acres of land is converted to urban use! It also tells us what "triggers" the land speculation which results in agricultural land being converted to urban use.

The following table demonstrates graphically the population changes in Orange County that stimulated all of the urban growth:

ORANGE COUNTY POPULATION

YEAR	POPULATION	YEAR	POPULATION
1910	19,000	1940	70,174
*1913	Reduction	1950	114,950
1920	19,890	1960	263,500
1925	38,325	1970	344,311
1930	49,737	1974	419,500
1935	58,184	1975	462,246 (Est.)

These figures corroborate the author's belief that August, 1940, was the curtain rising date for the countdown of agriculture in Orange County, and that the military-industrial complex was the major factor that brought this about! Looking back these facts seem quite evident. As for the future, the 1974 Kiplinger Forecast of Florida growth tells us that Orange County will gain 230,000 new residents by 1984. SO — the "countdown" continues!

*Seminole County Carved off Orange County

26

CHAPTER II
Countdown

For historical accuracy it must be noted that the "COUNT-DOWN" for the county territory preceded the "COUNTDOWN" for Orange County agriculture. At one time Orange County was one of Florida's largest counties and comprised over two million acres. Over a period of 68 years it was "carved up" into several counties. The present acreage places the county 21st in the state as to size. This unfortunate series of events is summarized on a plaque in the Orange County Court House Lobby which reads as follows:

"ORANGE COUNTY, PRECEDING STATEHOOD WAS A VAST UNORGANIZED SECTION SOUTH OF MATANZAS INLET, KNOWN AS MOSQUITO COUNTY. IT WAS CREATED BY THE LEGISLATIVE COUNCIL IN 1824, AND FOR THE SUCCEEDING TWENTY YEARS WAS VARIOUSLY DIVIDED TO FORM OTHER COUNTIES. FLORIDA WAS ADMITTED TO THE UNION IN MARCH 1845: AND THE PRECEDING JANUARY 30th MOSQUITO COUNTY WAS CHANGED IN NAME TO ORANGE. ORANGE COUNTY PASSED THROUGH NUMEROUS TERRITORIAL CHANGES BEFORE BEING REDUCED TO ITS PRESENT AREA OF 955 SQUARE MILES. PUTNAM COUNTY OBTAINED A PORTION OF ITS TERRITORY IN 1849, AND IN 1850 A PORTION WAS GIVEN TO SUMTER COUNTY. VOLUSIA COUNTY WAS FORMED FROM ORANGE IN 1854, AND IN 1872 A PART OF SUMTER COUNTY WAS GIVEN TO ORANGE. IN 1873 THE BOUNDARY BETWEEN BREVARD AND ORANGE COUNTIES WAS CHANGED, AND IN 1879 THE BOUNDARIES OF ORANGE WITH POLK AND SUMTER COUNTIES WERE REARRANGED. IN 1887 IT RELINQUISHED PART OF ITS TERRITORY TO LAKE AND OSCEOLA COUNTIES, AND FINALLY, IN 1913 SEMINOLE COUNTY WAS TAKEN FROM ORANGE, REDUCING THE LATTER TO ITS PRESENT AREA."

In 1913 Orange County's boundary was finalized in their present location. Future agricultural growth would be determined by the land resources of the county, an area of 916 square miles or 586,240 acres.

Many soil types occur within this area and the drainage patterns vary from excessively drained to very poorly drained. The soil types within the county, and the number of acres of each type as shown by the 1960 Soil Survey of Orange County are as follows:

SOIL	ACRES	PERCENT
Adamsville fine sand	3,751	0.6
Dark colored surface phase	1,379	.2
Shallow phase	454	.1
Alluvial land	7,084	1.2
Blanton fine sand:		
Level high phase	14,369	2.5

SOIL	ACRES	PERCENT
Very gently sloping high phase	18,950	3.2
Gently sloping high phase	4,326	.7
Sloping high phase	2,118	.4
Level low phase	16,169	2.8
Very gently sloping low phase	1,783	.3
Level shallow low phase	447	.1
Blanton and Esto fine sands, gently sloping and sloping phases	320	.1
Borrow pits	588	.1
Brighton mucky peat:		
Shallow phase	1,210	.2
Moderately deep phase	598	.1
Deep phase	422	.1
Very deep phase	965	.2
Charlotte fine sand	599	.1
Delray fine sand	3,891	.7
Shallow phase	1,353	.2
Delray mucky fine sand	380	.1
Eustis fine sand:		
Level phase	366	.1
Very gently sloping phase	565	.1
Everglades mucky peat:		
Shallow phase	904	.2
Moderately deep phase	1,618	.3
Deep phase	4,578	.8
Very deep phase	4,183	.7
Felda fine sand	532	.1
Fresh water swamp	31,327	5.3
Immokalee fine sand	21,687	3.7
Keri and Parkwood fine sand	21,687	3.7
Lakeland fine sand:	410	0.1
Level phase	5,502	.9
Very gently sloping phase	26,507	4.5
Gently sloping phase	10,617	1.8
Sloping phase	2,874	.5
Strongly sloping phase	258	(1)
Leon fine sand	166,783	28.4
Level heavy substratum phase	1,071	.2
Very gently sloping heavy substratum phase	628	.1
Made land	288	(1)
Manatee fine sandy laom	967	.2
Manatee fine sandy clay loam	1,317	.2
Manatee and Delray soils, overflow phases	23,561	4.0
Ona fine sand	6,401	1.1
Orlando fine sand:		
Level phase	1,235	.2
Very gently sloping phase	655	.1
Pamlico muck	3,632	.6
Plummer fine sand	22,711	3.9
Pomello fine sand	26,521	4.5
Pompano fine sand	16,416	2.8
Shallow phase	1.968	.3
Overflow phase	1,279	.2

SOIL	ACRES	PERCENT
Rutlege fine sand	30,292	5.2
Shallow phase	247	(1)
Rutlege mucky fine sand	26,898	4.6
St. Johns fine sand	5,432	.9
St. Luicie fine sand	9,827	1.7
Scranton fine sand	1,071	.2
Urban areas	43,956	7.5
Total	(2)586,240	100.0

1 — Less than 0.1 percent.
2 — In addition to the total land acreage, a total of 55,680 acreas consists of lakes.

Along with these historical and statistical aspects of the county's land resources, a review of its population growth is in order to put things in perspective. Although the size of the county decreased with time, the population increased tremendously, as follows:

YEAR	SIZE	POPULATION
1910	791,680 acres	19,107
1915*	586,240 acres	15,397
1920	586,240 acres	19,890
1930	586,240 acres	49,737
1940	586,240 acres	70,074
1950	586,240 acres	114,074
1960	586,240 acres	263,540
1970	586,240 acres	344,311
1974** (April 1st Estimate)	586,240 acres	420,230

*In 1913 when some 205,440 acres was "carved" from Orange County to create Seminole County, the county lost in population.
**East Central Florida Regional Planning Council estimate.

Between 1930 and 1969 eight Florida Counties acquired the distinction of making the state's "top six" list for value of agricultural products produced, according to the Census of Agriculture reports. Two counties — Seminole and Broward, made the "top six list" once each! Four counties, Polk, Hillsborough, Dade, and Orange, made the "top six" list every census year after 1930! A comparison of the six and population of these six counties shows the following interesting facts:

COUNTY	TOTAL LAND AREA	SIZE RANK IN STATE
DADE	1,306,816	1st
PALM BEACH	1,294,720	2nd
POLK	1,189,120	4th
BROWARD	779,968	7th
HILLSBOROUGH	664,192	13th
LAKE	614,784	17th
ORANGE	586,240	21st
SEMINOLE	195,136	64th

The 1970 census reveals these population comparisons:

COUNTY	1970 POPULATION	COUNTY POPULATION RANK
DADE	1,267,792	1st
BROWARD	620,100	2nd
HILLSBOROUGH	490,265	5th
PALM BEACH	348,753	6th
ORANGE	344,311	7th
POLK	227,222	9th
SEMINOLE	83,692	18th
LAKE	69,305	21st

These data show that Orange County was next to the smallest on the top six list until Seminole County was "bumped" off after the 1930 census and it seems noteworthy that Orange County has consistently been among the top three leading agricultural counties in the state. This was achieved with a small land area and a snowballing population.

Agriculturally these several counties ranked as follows according to the census taken every 5 years:

1930 AGRICULTURAL CENSUS RANKING

RANK	COUNTY	VALUE OF AGRICULTURAL PRODUCTS
1st	Polk	$9,984,571
2nd	Hillsborough	4,871,335
3rd	Dade	3,556,161
4th	Seminole	3,475,938
5th	Orange	3,375,742
6th	Lake	3,247,528

1940 AGRICULTURAL CENSUS RANKING

RANK	COUNTY	VALUE OF AGRICULTURAL PRODUCTS
1st	Polk	$10,372,349
2nd	Palm Beach	$ 7,203,531
3rd	Dade	$ 5,582,607
4th	Hillsborough	$ 4,116,541
5th	Orange	$ 3,838,427
6th	Broward	$ 3,410,922

1945 AGRICULTURAL CENSUS RANKING

RANK	COUNTY	VALUE OF AGRICULTURAL PRODUCTS
1st	Polk	$43,214,340
2nd	Orange	$17,434,138
3rd	Palm Beach	$15,540,669
4th	Dade	$12,139,560
5th	Hillsborough	$11,157,670
6th	Lake	$10,955,280

1950 AGRICULTURAL CENSUS RANKING

RANK	COUNTY	VALUE OF AGRICULTURAL PRODUCTS
1st	Polk	$51,178,252
2nd	Orange	$26,072,891
3rd	Palm Beach	$21,003,231
4th	Dade	$19,197,516
5th	Lake	$17,744,044
6th	Hillsborough	$16,436,167

1954 AGRICULTURAL CENSUS RANKING

RANK	COUNTY	VALUE OF AGRICULTURAL PRODUCTS
1st	Polk	$64,468,494
2nd	Orange	$37,906,720
3rd	Palm Beach	$34,614,947
4th	Lake	$32,041,842
5th	Dade	$31,672,905
6th	Hillsborough	$22,956,467

1959 AGRICULTURAL CENSUS RANKING

RANK	COUNTY	VALUE OF AGRICULTURAL PRODUCTS
1st	Polk	$ 98,430,403
2nd	Orange	$ 74,431,564
3rd	Lake	$ 53,919,328
4th	Palm Beach	$ 50,487,325
5th	Hillsborough	$ 43,679,774
6th	Dade	$ 36,673,267

1964 AGRICULTURAL CENSUS RANKING

RANK	COUNTY	VALUE OF AGRICULTURAL PRODUCTS
1st	Polk	$130,779,202
2nd	Orange	$ 98,606,406
3rd	Palm Beach	$ 96,568,109
4th	Dade	$ 48,242,137
5th	Lake	$ 47,599,144
6th	Hillsborough	$ 43,476,718

1969 AGRICULTURAL CENSUS RANKING

RANK	COUNTY	VALUE OF AGRICULTURAL PRODUCTS
1st	Palm Beach	$129,483,050
2nd	Polk	$ 95,031,373
3rd	Orange	$ 77,335,913
4th	Lake	$ 67,581,060
5th	Hillsborough	$ 56,932,418
6th	Dade	$ 51,428,352

It is obvious from these rankings that agriculturally Orange County reached its peak production in the year 1964. By 1969 the dollar value and rank had both decreased.

At this stage a comparison of how Orange County fared in the national agricultural ranking is in order to put its accomplishments in better perspective. A list of the top 100 agricultural counties in the nation is prepared every Agricultural Census year and is based on the total sales of all agricultural products. Florida's two leading agricultural counties (Polk and Orange) have placed nationally as follows during these countdown periods:

NATIONAL AGRICULTURAL RANKING

YEAR	1950	1954	1959	1964	1969
COUNTY					
Polk	21st	19th	12th	12th	28th
Orange	64th	44th	21st	20th	37th

Marketing conditions change from year to year, a problem faced by all counties in the nation. However, in Florida, counties depend on a limited number of crops such as citrus, winter vegetables, cattle, and ornamental plants and the value of these commodities can change drastically from one year to the next. After comparing Orange County's agricultural rank with other counties about the state as well as the nation, perhaps a more detailed analysis of the various aspects of its agricultural industry is in order. In fact, future generations may be interested to know when agriculture began its exodus from Orange County. Pinpointing the agricultural trends as a whole and by commodities should be helpful in that regard as follows:

CENSUS YEAR	VALUE OF PRODUCTS	STATE RANK
1940	$ 3,838,427	5th
1945	$17,434,138	2nd
1950	$26,072,891	2nd
1954	$37,906,720	2nd
1959	$74,431,564	2nd
1964	$98,606,406	2nd
1969	$77,335,913	3rd

Before examining the various agricultural commodities in detail, a summary of the number of farms in the county by census year might be of interest. In most census years, three acres or more and the sale of agricultural products in the amount of $250 per year, classified the operation as a farm. In recent census years, however, sales had to be at least $250.00 if the acreage was less than 10, but operations exceeding 10 acres could qualify with sales of only $50.00 a year.

On the basis of these guidelines we can see the point at which countdown for Orange County farm units commenced:

YEAR	NUMBER OF FARMS
1930	1,608
1935	3,280
1940	2,399
1945	1,919
1950	1,780
1954	2,726
1959	2,600
1964	1,853
1969	1,224

Knowing what transpired in the total agricultural picture, it is obvious that some agricultural commodities failed to expand or hold their own in the face of urbanization. What happened in each of the six agricultural fields requires individual analysis.

CATTLE COUNTDOWN

To develop any reliable statistics as to the size and importance of the Orange County cattle industry down through the years seems next to impossible. First of all, there are many people each owning a few head of cattle. Some are registered stock, some are range cattle and some are "cull" dairy animals. Does ownership of a few animals make that person a cattleman? If so, how many cattle does it take? Cattle are assessed for tax purposes, and it is understandable that many cattlemen are uncertain as to how many cattle they have roaming the woods!

Those who recognize this situation appreciate fully the difficulty of getting meaningful statistics about the cattle industry. While livestock market sales might be used as an index to the size of the this industry, this suggestion also has some shortcomings. For example, should cull dairy animals sold through livestock markets be credited to the dairy industry or to the beef cattle industry?

The cattle industry probably reached its peak during the early 1950's in Orange County, in both numbers of people involved and total cattle numbers. At that time land values were such that cattlemen could obtain long term leases from owners of large tracts of land. However, after the Martin Company land purchase announcement in 1956, speculation soon changed that situation and as land values went up, so did taxes. Furthermore, owners no longer wanted their land tied up in long term leases, and they asked higher rents to off-set higher taxes.

This trend grew more rapidly through the 1960's until land values became so high as to convince the largest cattle operation in

Orange County (Magnolia Ranch) to sell out in the summer of 1973. In the fall of 1973, the Mid-Florida Livestock Market on South Orange Avenue closed its doors.

These two bombshells signaled the end of an era. At the peak of the industry there were probably 32,000 head of cattle in the county whereas today the count is about 12,000. Individuals making over 50% of their income from the raising of cattle probably number less than a half dozen today.

The Orange County cattle industry has been knocked down. It is probably at the eight count and soon will be declared a technical knockout at the hands of changing times and economic conditions. A partial insight in some of the livestock sales by census years might be helpful in telling the peak reached prior to the big sell out of cattle operations.

VALUE OF LIVESTOCK PRODUCTS SOLD
(Other than poultry and dairy)

YEAR	SALES
1930	$ 28,294
1940	$ 54,489
1945	$ 181,701
1950	$ 641,564
1954	$ 870,224
1959	$1,627,457
1964	$2,030,548
1969	$4,750,007

CITRUS COUNTDOWN

Better bookkeeping and more statistics are available concerning the citrus industry than any other field of agriculture in Orange County and reviewing in detail the statistics of value, acreage, production by seasons, and by census years is most revealing. Fluctuations in value almost always follow the law of supply and demand. Because the census is taken every five years, freezes, hurricanes and such factors sometimes exert an exaggerated influence on the value of the citrus crop. Consequently, the number of citrus farms for a particular census year is more meaningful than the value of the crop.

YEAR	NUMBER OF FARMS	VALUE OF CROP
1930	954	$ 2,438,768
1940	1,422	$ 2,914,638
1945	1,349	$14,484,437
1950	1,440	$19,527,596
1954	1,496	$29,139,983
1959	1,030	$57,416,621
1964	726	$76,341,515
1969	549	$37,828,694

We are indebted to Dr. Paul Shuler, Director of Research and Statistics of the Florida Crop and Livestock Reporting Service for early reports of Orange County's citrus production, its value, and number of citrus trees (this latter figure was converted to approximate acreage). Shuler developed these statistics from a report of the Florida Department of Agriculture entitled — "Report of Commissioner of Agriculture of Florida" (annual report).

Unfortunately units of measurements for various fruits were quite variable in the early period — barrels, crates, and boxes and the records prior to 1913 were derived from an area much larger than the present county size. Orange County boundaries were finalized when Seminole County was "carved" from Orange County in 1913.

SEASON	ACREAGE	PRODUCTION	VALUE
1889-'90	16,181	390,157 Boxes	$ 333,498
1891-'92	21,767	759,815 Boxes	$ 755,200
1895-'96	21,872	None (Big Freeze)	
1897-'98	16,115	8,257 Boxes & 8 Barrels	$ 19,510
1899-1900	12,146	2,448 Boxes & 10 Barrels	$ 5,230
1901-'02	6,487	47,099 Boxes & 309 Crates	$ 64,574
1903-'04	9,611	80,143 Boxes & 2,637 Crates	$ 132,709
1905-'06	7,859	319,910 Boxes & 14,225 Crates	$ 376,890
1907-'08	9,003	686,400 Boxes & 42,400 Crates	$ 827,565
1909-'10	7,726	868,894 Crates	$ 787,121
1911-'12	11,081	798,630 Crates	$ 950,865
1913-'14	8,078	692,787 Crates	$ 749,899
1915-'16	13,442	510,662 Crates	$ 936,533
1917-'18	13,481	686,571 Crates	$1,221,655
1919-'20	17,931	1,396,448 Crates	$6,936,690
1921-'22	11,701	1,570,040 Crates	$1,299,850
1923-'24	24,708	1,945,575 Crates	$2,407,305

These records provide some interesting information on the size 'of the citrus industry in the early days of Orange County. Before the turn of the century a grove was generally five acres or less. Land clearing was done by hand, which may be why there were very few groves of large size in those "pioneer days". The hard freeze of February 1917 gave the industry a scare, but it was not of the magnitude of the '94-'95 freeze, so the industry was given a reprieve in which to grow and expand.

Another indication of the size of the Orange County citrus industry was given by the report of the Grove Inspection Department of the State Plant Board of Florida, December 31, 1931. This report showed citrus acreage of 33,782 acres, an increase of 9,000 acres over the 1923-24 estimate. However, a freeze in 1934 destroyed considerable acreage. According to the citrus tree survey of the USDA Bureau of Agricultural Economics — Division of Crop and Livestock Estimate of July 1935, Orange County's citrus production amounted to 3,300,016 boxes of citrus and citrus acreage had risen to 37,532 acres. In October 1941 the Florida State Plant Board survey showed Orange County's total citrus acreage to be 41,457 acres.

The thousands of newcomers that poured into the county in the post World War II period were the factor that really started the countdown for Orange County citrus. Raw land suitable for citrus was quickly used up for housing developments. The severe freeze of '57-'58 and the real block buster of '62 confirmed the belief that all "good" citrus land had been long since planted as well as a lot that shouldn't have been. Consequently, the county was "locked in" as to total acres of citrus. Only by increasing the yield per acre could the county keep ahead of counties with expanding new citrus plantings. As Orange County's production lead began to be "whittled" away by new acreage coming into bearing in Lake and St. Lucie Counties, it was just a question of time before Orange County production would be outdistanced.

The following summary of Orange County citrus production for 26 seasons shows that in 1956-'57 the county dropped from second to third place in the state. Then in 1971-'72 season Orange County dropped to fourth place for citrus fruit production. The production of 19,258,000 boxes in 1966-'67 was the peak and from this point on production declined.

The Florida Crop & Livestock Reporting Service figures for citrus production 1948 through 1973 are as follows:

ORANGE COUNTY TOTAL
CITRUS PRODUCTION BY SEASONS

SEASON	TOTAL ALL CITRUS (BOXES)	PRO- DUCTION RANK	SEASON	TOTAL ALL CITRUS (BOXES)	PRO- DUCTION RANK
1948-'49	10,753,000	2	1961-'62	15,112,000	3
1949-'50	11,940,000	2	1962-'63*	9,833,000	3
1950-'51	13,667,000	2	1963-'64	7,053,000	4
1951-'52	16,109,000	2	1964-'65	12,058,000	3
1952-'53	13,738,000	2	1965-'66	12,779,000	3
1953-'54	18,251,000	2	1966-'67	19,258,000	3
1954-'55	18,065,000	2	1967-'68	10,410,000	3
1955-'56	17,410,000	3	1968-'69**	16,985,000	3
1956-'57	17,211,000	3	1969-'70**	15,833,000	3
1957-'58*	13,650,000	3	1970-'71	16,088,000	3
1948-'59	14,330,000	3	1971-'72	16,295,000	4
1959-'60	14,940,000	3	1972-'73	16,792,000	4
1960-'61	15,179,000	3	1973-'74	15,359,000	4

*Severe freezes occurred.
**Hurricane Gladys (October), Hurricane Donna (September).

The countdown showing how and when Orange County was challenged for its #3 position is revealed in these figures from the Florida Crop and Livestock Reporting Service.

Citrus production by crop years in the six leading counties.

For 1964-'64.

RANK	COUNTY	ALL CITRUS (BOXES)
1st	POLK	23,409,000
2nd	LAKE	13,198,000
3rd	ST. LUCIE	9,649,000
4th	ORANGE	8,549,000
5th	INDIAN RIVER	6,828,000
6th	HIGHLANDS	5,660,000

For 1964-'65.

1st	POLK	35,003,000
2nd	LAKE	20,476,900
3rd	ORANGE	12,058,000
4th	ST. LUCIE	7,519,000
5th	HIGHLANDS	7,089,000
6th	HARDEE	5,999,000

For 1965-'66.

1st	POLK	41,723,000
2nd	LAKE	20,731,000
3rd	ORANGE	12,779,000
4th	ST. LUCIE	9,315,000
5th	HIGHLANDS	8,193,000
6th	INDIAN RIVER	6,429,000

For 1966-'67.

1st	POLK	50,876,000
2nd	LAKE	32,432,000
3rd	ORANGE	19,544,000
4th	HILLSBOROUGH	11,328,000
5th	HIGHLANDS	10,433,000
6th	ST. LUCIE	9,532,000

For 1967-'68.

1st	POLK	41,174,000
2nd	LAKE	18,230,000
3rd	ORANGE	10,410,000
4th	ST. LUCIE	10,338,000
5th	HIGHLANDS	8,714,000
6th	HARDEE	8,302,000

For 1968-'69.

1st	POLK	43,583,000
2nd	LAKE	29,804,000
3rd	ORANGE	16,985,000
4th	HILLSBOROUGH	11,009,000
5th	ST. LUCIE	10,013,000
6th	HIGHLANDS	9,099,000

RANK	COUNTY	ALL CITRUS (BOXES)

For 1970-'71

1st	POLK	46,391,000
2nd	LAKE	29,538,000
3rd	ORANGE	16,088,000
4th	ST. LUCIE	13,386,000
5th	HILLSBOROUGH	10,694,000
6th	HIGHLANDS	10,331,000

For 1971-'72.

1st	POLK	46,539,000
2nd	LAKE	29,915,000
3rd	ST. LUCIE	16,862,000
4th	ORANGE	16,295,000
5th	HIGHLANDS	10,208,000
6th	HARDEE	9,195,000

For 1972-'73

1st	POLK	51,241,000
2nd	LAKE	33,302,000
3rd	ST. LUCIE	16,867,000
4th	ORANGE	16,792,000
5th	HARDEE	12,492,000
6th	HIGHLANDS	12,118,000

For 1973-'74

1st	POLK	47,883,000
2nd	LAKE	32,935,000
3rd	ST. LUCIE	18,622,000
4th	ORANGE	15,359,000
5th	INDIAN RIVER	13,471,000
6th	HARDEE	12,075,000

Summarizing the citrus production figures shows that once a county's raw land has been exhausted that county can remain competitive only as long as the remaining acreage continued to produce larger and larger crops. When the existing acreage gives way to urbanization, that county has entered the countdown phase.

The following census figures reflect this trend for Orange County:

CITRUS INVENTORY YEAR	ACREAGE
December, 1965	65,817
December, 1967	68,005
December, 1969	65,961
December, 1971	60,567
December, 1973	56,320

The county engineer calculates that the county lost approximately 2,400 acres of citrus to urbanization in 1974. Orange County, California, another Disney attraction site, lost 50% of its citrus acreage (from 68,000 down to 34,000 acres) in 10 years due to urbanization. Will Orange County, Florida, experience the same countdown in 10 years?

DAIRY COUNTDOWN

The change from the family dairy herd of a few cows to today's "milk factory" operations of several hundred cows or more resulted from basic economic laws.

The rate at which this trend occurred in Orange County is shown by the decrease in dairy farms by census years. However, the gross returns from the Orange County dairy industry continues to increase.

CENSUS YEAR	NUMBER OF DAIRY FARMS	VALUE OF PRODUCT
1940	93	$ 321,164
1945	51	$ 905,507
1950	61	$1,805,041
1954	42	$2,072,092
1959	41	$3,354,861
1964	23	$2,785,215
1969	13	$2,508,535
1974	6	$??

By 1974 the number of dairy farms had reached an all time low. One reason for this was that production costs had increased to the point where a reasonable profit could not be obtained unless the size of the herd was increased. Because of skyrocketing land prices the capital required to do this in Orange County was too great and led to further reduction in dairy farms. Pollution abatement problems, ad valorem taxation based on speculative land prices made the maintenance of these dairy sites precarious and expansion utterly impossible.

The "countdown" for the dairy industry of Orange County shows clearly in the following tabulations:

YEAR	DAIRY FARMS	COW NUMBERS
1884	1st dairy cow brought to Orange County	
1927	85	1,350 Cows
1945	51	4,301 Cows
1950	61	Over 5,000 Cows
1974	6	3,334 Cows
1984	0 (?)	0 (?)

Briefly, this adds up to fewer dairymen with fewer but more productive cows, producing more milk for more people for less profit.

39

POULTRY COUNTDOWN

Before World War II, the Orange County poultry industry consisted of small family-operated flocks of 300 to 1,000 birds on open range. After World War II, "bigness" took over and caged layers and the "egg factory" type of operation were ushered in. Under this type of operation a poultryman single handedly cares for more birds than the total poultry population of Orange County prior to World War II!

The decrease in poultry farm numbers and the resulting increase in value of poultry production is shown by the census countdown:

CENSUS YEAR	NUMBER OF FARMS	VALUE OF PRODUCT
1930	84	$ 145,468
1940	320	$ 117,743
1945	235	$ 295,012
1950	61	$ 456,861
1954	60	$ 448,009
1959	32	$ 581,856
1964	31	$2,776,889
1969	38	$5,801,070
1974	23	$???

The actual number of birds in the county in different periods is largely unknown. Only two reliable records could be found. In 1927 the county poultry population was reported at 103,658 birds. By 1974 there were only 23 farms with 1,076,000 hens.

ORNAMENTAL PLANT INDUSTRY COUNTUP

Whereas other agricultural commodities are experiencing a countdown in the production of units involved and the value of their products, the ornamental plant industry of Orange County is experiencing just the reverse. And despite the great urbanization pressure of — higher labor costs, higher land prices, higher ad valorem taxes and runaway vandalism, the marketing outlook for foliage plants, landscape plants, ferns, sod and other landscaping material has continued profitable. Old establishments are increasing their business volume and newcomers are constantly entering the business. Of the six agricultural commodity areas, the ornamental plant industry is the only one with a bright future in spite of the present urban growth.

Income from this agricultural commodity area was at the bottom of the list before 1945. After World War II the foliage plant business "caught on" and now produces the 2nd largest agricultural income in Orange County. With the importance of citrus continuing to decrease, the ornamental plant industry could become the major producer of agricultural income in a few years. Although the foliage plant industry is the principal segment, ferns, landscape plants and flowering plants are important also.

Ownership of production units is so diverse and the units are so loosely federated that it is difficult to assess the industry's growth in terms of production units. The most telling point in growth of this industry is the tremendous increase in the value of its production. Nevertheless, some contend the values reflected in census reports are too low.

CENSUS YEAR	NUMBER OF UNITS	VALUE OF PRODUCT
1940	86	$ 197,082
1945	55	$ 506,190
1950	183	$ 1,851,975
1954	221	$ 2,542,999
1959	263	$ 8,585,508
1964	293	$ 9,063,865
1969	133	$13,620,743

In 1974 an estimated 1,000 acres of land was devoted to the production of ornamental plants in Orange County.

VEGETABLE INDUSTRY COUNTDOWN

Prior to World War II, Orange County's vegetable farms were located on "patches" of tile drained flatwoods soils in the Oakland — Winter Garden — Ocoee areas of West Orange County. However, after World War II the industry moved to the mucky peat soils and the flatwoods sandy soils adjacent to Lake Apopka in the northwest section of the county.

To provide a total view of the industry's value over the years, all vegetable crops are "lumped" together. The decrease in number of farms and the increase in value of the crops provides a yardstick for "bigness" in this commodity field.

YEAR	NUMBER OF FARMS	VALUE OF PRODUCTS
1935	62	$ 292,370
1940	89	$ 199,793
1945	167	$ 899,992
1950	75	$ 1,715,864
1954	30	$ 2,751,515
1959	29	$ 2,837,098
1964	22	$ 5,495,382
1969	22	$11,676,267

The present day industry is confined to a limited area with little possibility of expansion through new acreage. The major problem facing the industry today is the annual loss of one to two inches of the peat soils through oxidation. If this loss isn't sharply reduced, the "strip mining" of these peat soils through intensive farming operations could bring an end to this area of production by the year 2000.

Pollution abatement is another serious problem. Whereas other commodity areas are fighting urban pressures to retain land for agricultural use, the vegetable industry is contending with an equally serious pollution abatement problem. Drainage water from the diked farming area has polluted Lake Apopka and ruined it as a recreational area. A solution to the problem must be found. And the "countdown" could become a "count out" if these two serious problems are not solved in the next few years.

A COUNTDOWN PERSONIFIED

Happenings over a period of time are termed "history". However, happenings are often rather meaningless except in terms of people. For example, as changes in land use occur what do they mean in terms of people? People have successes, failures, hopes and goals and what happens to people is what interests other people most of all.

Unless some "people history" is reported, the reader is left to form his own conclusions of what happened during the "agricultural countdown". For instance, a person engaged in an agricultural endeavor suddenly finds he can sell his land for an exorbitant price and so make far more money than would ever be possible through agriculture. If he has no children who desire to continue the family venture in agriculture, should he be classified as a failure if he sells out when he is too old to continue? Others may buy more agricultural units to increase their bargaining position or production efficiency. This process is as normal in agriculture as in other enterprises in today's highly competitive world.

Some economists and historians tell us that such a reduction in numbers and increase in efficiency is a sign of progress. However, when these trends are reported simply as statistics, the reader is unaware just what factors brought about the reduction — urbanization, marketing problems, family decisions or a combination of them.

A few case histories might shed some light on the Orange County countdown story.

One trend that appeared in the early stages of the countdown was that farmers' sons were forsaking the family enterprise.

During the 1950's many young men in the 21 — 35 age bracket qualified for the Jaycees' Young Farmer contest. In fact, candidates were numerous in the areas of dairy, cattle, citrus, vegetables, poultry, and ornamental plants. However, by the mid-1960's most of these commodity fields were unable to muster candidates in the 21 — 35 age bracket. This also illustrated the fact that young men found it virtually impossible to enter agriculture because of the large capital required. Some Veterans of World War II began farming on a "shoe string" during this immediate post war period (some with G.I. Bill of Rights help), but stampeding land prices, equipment needs, etc., made "shoe string" ventures an invitation to failure. Consequently, the young people entering agriculture were mostly limited to children of people already so engaged.

However, many young people were cured of whatever desire they may have had to follow in their parents' footsteps by watching their parents struggle with the adversities of agriculture. These trends resulted in the virtual absence of agriculturists in the 21 — 35 age group in Orange County by the end of the '60's.

Let's examine another example. A special activity involving six agriculturists in different commodity fields, spaced 15 years apart, provides an interesting human interest story during these changing times. In November 1958 outstanding agricultural producers from six agricultural commodity fields were "invited" to be special guests at a luncheon meeting of the Orlando Rotary Club. The occasion was a special Rural-Urban Program in connection with National Farm-City Week activities. This same group was invited back for a "reunion" meeting 15 years later, November 1973. To provide the Rotarians with the background of the agricultural guests' individual farm activities, large pictures of their farms were hung from the speaker's rostrum. Doyle Conner, former Speaker of the Florida House of Representatives, and then candidate for the post of Commissioner of Agriculture, was the feature speaker.

The agricultural guests invited to represent the various commodity fields were: A. J. RUSTERHOLTZ, dairyman — Apopka; H. S. MUSSELWHITE, JR., poultryman — Wekiwa Springs Road area; R. I. "BERT" WETHERBEE, pioneer citrus grower — Boggy Creek area; KEN JORGENSEN, co-owner of the Zellwin Farms, vegetable grower — Zellwood farm area; BOB SCOTT, Sales Manager of "John's", the largest foliage grower in the county — Apopka; KIRBY & AL SMITH, a father-son team representative of the cattle interests of Orange County — Orlando.

AGRICULTURAL GUESTS — ORLANDO ROTARY CLUB — NOVEMBER 26, 1958 — Left to Right: Dairyman A. J. Rusterholtz, Jr., Poultryman H. S. Musselwhite, Citrus Grower R. I. Wetherbee; Herb Haack, President Orlando Rotary Club; Doyle Conner, Commissioner of Agriculture — Elect; Vegetable Grower Ken Jorgensen, Foliage Grower Robert Scott, Cattlemen, Al and Kirby Smith.

Fifteen years later, November 21, 1973, the Orlando Rotary Club invited these agriculturists back for a "reunion" and to describe their experiences and operations during the intervening 15-year period. All the agricultural guests returned to participate in this program except Kirby Smith who died February 19, 1969.

REUNION OF AGRICULTURAL GUESTS — ORLANDO ROTARY CLUB — NOVEMBER 21, 1973 — Former Dairyman A. J. Rusterholtz, Poultryman H. S. Musselwhite, Citrus Grower R. I. Wetherbee, Past-President Herb Haack, Dr. Truett Frazier, President Orlando Rotary Club, Vegetable Grower Ken Jorgensen, Foliage Grower Robert Scott, Cattleman Al Smith.

44

Noteworthy events that occurred between November, 1958, and November, 1973, were the following:

WEATHER

Rain

1959 — 12.40 inches above normal rainfall
1960 — 17.37 inches above normal rainfall (25-year record)

Drought

1967 — 10.46 inches below normal
1971 — 11.28 inches below normal rainfall (25-year record)

Hurricane

1960 — September — Hurricane Donna passed through the area.

Cold

Major freezes damaged crops in 1957-'58, 1962 and 1970

BIG DEALS (New enterprises of major proportions)

U.S. Naval Training Center opened July, 1968
Florida Technological University opened October, 1968
Valencia Junior College opened September, 1971
Walt Disney World opened October, 1971
Sea World opened December, 1973

POPULATION CHANGES

1958 — approximately 137,600
1973 — approximately 415,000

Approximately 177,400 new residents (a 75% increase) came into the county during this 15-year period!! With these basic facts in mind let us see what happened to the agricultural industries these men represented and what happened to each, individually?

DAIRYING CATTLE

There were approximately 42 dairies in Orange County in 1958 and by 1973 the number had dropped to 6! Thirty-two dairymen left Orange County and one was Mr. A. J. "Rusty" Rusterholtz, a guest at the Orlando Rotary Club "reunion" luncheon. Mr. Rusterholtz came to Orange County from New England in 1950 with the intention of going into the cattle business. However, after examining Florida agricultural conditions and possibilities, Mr. Rusterholtz decided that he would be more successful with dairy cattle in Orange County than with beef cattle. In 1954 he commenced operations on the old McLeod property at the edge of the Zellwood farm area with top grade Holstein cattle. He sold the milk to T. G. Lee Dairies.

Mr. Rusterholtz practiced careful selective breeding of his cattle through the cooperation of the Orange County Artificial Breeding Service. With a rigid culling program based on Dairy Herd Improvement Association records, he developed one of the top producing dairies in the state. The State DHIA records for the 15-year period 1947-'48 through '61-'62, show that the Rusterholtz herd topped the state in three major categories!

1st in state — Butterfat Production
1st in state — Fat-Corrected Milk
1st in state — Actual milk produced.

Mr. Rusterholtz' records among the top 20 all time herd records placed as follows:

Rank	Name	Address	Year	No. Cows	Pounds Milk	Test %	Pounds Fat	Pounds 4% Fat-Corrected Milk
BUTTERFAT PRODUCTION — Record Production Per Cow								
1st	A. J. Rusterholtz	Apopka	1961-62	93	15,105	3.6	548	14,262
7th	A. J. Rusterholtz	Apopka	1960-61	169	13,774	3.6	497	12,965
FAT-CORRECTED MILK — Record Production								
1st	A. J. Rusterholtz	Apopka	1961-62	93	15,105	3.6	548	14,262
2nd	A. J. Rusterholtz	Apopka	1960-61	169	13,774	3.6	497	12,965
ACTUAL MILK TESTED — Record Production								
1st	A. J. Rusterholtz	Apopka	1961-62	93	15,105	3.6	548	14,262
2nd	A. J. Rusterholtz	Apopka	1960-61	169	13,744	3.6	497	12,965

Dan Webb, Assistant Extension Dairyman at the University of Florida, reports that all of Mr. Rusterholtz' dairy records, established in 1962, are still on the prestigious D.H.I.A. Honor Roll after 11 years! His herd's first place position in butterfat production now ranks 6th place; the fat-corrected milk production record established by the Rusterholtz' herd in 1962 is now in second place after 11 years time, and the herd's actual milk production record is fifth place. So the records established by the Rusterholtz herd 11 years ago have not been too seriously challenged by the passage of time.

However, after dairying in Orange County for eight years, Mr. Rusterholtz sold out in 1962. There were many reasons. A few were scarcity of dependable help, the problem of D.D.T. used nearby by vegetable growers (within five years a nearby dairy herd had to close down because of this problem), and then there was Mr. Rusterholtz' age.

RUSTERHOLTZ VANQUISHED HERD

For the eight years he was in business he was one of the county's most progressive dairymen. He predicted that Holstein dairy cattle would be the best breed of milk cow for the area, contrary to the belief of other dairymen. They told him the Holstein "hay burners" could not compete under Florida conditions. Rusterholtz replied — "The great white plague (Holstein dairy cattle) will soon engulf the state". He based his assumption on their capacity to produce large quantities of low butterfat milk. The increased demand for low butterfat milk marked a major change in market trends. His prediction has long since proved to be outstandingly correct! Rusty predicted also that local dairymen could no longer "afford" to hire drifters to milk cows. The responsibilities of a first class milker were such that a high wage must be paid to obtain and keep such an individual. This very unpopular prediction also proved correct.

Briefly, that story illustrates the dairying business and the experiences of the man who represented the local dairy industry at two Rotary luncheons sponsored 15 years apart. First a dairyman and 15 years later an investor in the stockmarket!

BEEF CATTLE

The number of people in the cattle business in Orange County, as well as the number of beef cattle, reached its all time high in the early 1950's. After that the Orange County cattlemen gradually lost the fight to the land speculators.

Land owners did not want to tie up their land in long term leases that might interfere with future sales. As land prices and taxes went up, the cost of leasing cattle land followed and the interplay of these economic forces virtually strangled cattle operations in the county. Also, the high cost of fencing land for short term leases made this practice prohibitive. Prior to the "no fence law", the cattlemen enjoyed the luxury of not having to fence their cattle.

Kirby Smith and his son, Al, native born second and third generation cattlemen, were selected to represent the cattle interests at the Rotary luncheon on November 26, 1958. The Kirby Smiths also owned several citrus groves.

During the 15-year period between the two Rural-Urban Programs (1958 to 1973), the Smith's cattle operations changed little. They owned the land on which they pastured their cattle and were not affected by any lease problems. However, the value of their pasture land increased during the 15-year period, as did the taxes on this tract. Kirby Smith died February 19, 1969, and his son took over the cattle operations and the groves.

During this period "Al" became a co-owner of the Mid-Florida Livestock Market at 3600 S. Orange Avenue, Under his supervision, this one day a week market (sales on Monday) developed into business of $3,500,000 in gross annual sales and a yearly payroll of $190,000. However, the market closed in the fall of 1973 as a result of several factors. Traffic and other businesses had built up around the market to the point that livestock operations in such urban surroundings became impossible. Increasing market regulations and the disappearance of the small cattleman from the Central Florida area added to the problems. One of the largest cattle feed lot operations in the state, George Terry's Magnolia Ranch, sold out and closed operations in the early 1970's. This accumulation of adverse factors caused the decline of the livestock industry in Orange County.

By the fall of 1973 the situation had deteriorated to such a point that Smith said — "Local cattlemen could make more money by selling sod or fill dirt from their pastures than by using the land to produce cattle". At least this was the mood of the local cattle industry at the time of the "reunion" meeting of the agriculturists on November 21, 1973. Smith, a third generation-born cattleman, went on to remark that the future looked so dismal that he was going to sell out soon.

CITRUS

The 15-year decline in citrus acreage and reduction in total yields caused Orange County to be "bumped" from third to fourth place in citrus fruit production in the state.

Urban pressures, plus the "wet" years of '59 and '60 and freezes, especially the one in 1970, had their effects on R.I. (Bert) Wetherbee's grove at Boggy Creek. In the fall of '73 Bert received a "Dear John" letter from the City "fathers" of Orlando informing him that McCoy Jetport expansion plans would take 150 acres of his land, including 20 acres of his citrus grove. Bert invested the money from the sale of this property in additional farm land in the black belt of Central Alabama. As soon as he sells the remaining acreage, Bert will move to Alabama.

Bert came to Orange County in 1907 and has lived on the old home site ever since. Now he feels that most agricultural operations in the county have just become a "holding operation" waiting until someone offers the right price.

In addition to his agricultural operations, Mr. Wetherbee served as Supervisor of the Orange Soil and Water Conservation Board for the past 12 years. When Bert Wetherbee leaves, the county will lose an enterprising pioneer settler and a respected long time agriculturist.

ORNAMENTAL PLANT INDUSTRY

During the 15-year period, 1958 to 1973, the value of the ornamental plants produced in Orange County increased about six million dollars! All other commodity fields registered some degree of decline during the 15-year period, either in number of persons involved, acreage, value of products produced, units of production, or a combination of these factors. Not so with the ornamental plant industry. Despite the pressures of urbanization, increased land values, zoning restrictions, increased taxes and labor problems, the ornamental plant industry grew by leaps and bounds during this period. For example, Bob Scott of John's (Dr. John Masek) Nursery, Apopka, reported that his company's activity and his responsibilities grew tremendously. Scott attended the first Rotary Rural-Urban Program representing the Ornamental Plant Industry in 1958 when he was Sales Manager for John's of Apopka. At that time there were just over 100 employees on the company's payroll, but by 1973 the company's payroll had expanded to over 300 employees! When Dr. Masek died in 1964, Scott became President of the largest ornamental plant nursery in Orange County and assumed additional responsibilities.

During this period the firm's two market outlets expanded to over 15 and the greenhouses, slat sheds, packing sheds were all modernized completely. Shipment procedures changed drastically during this period. Ornamental plants were shipped mainly by railway express in 1958 but by 1973, shipments also moved by trucks, United Parcel Service, Greyhound bus, and air freight.

Almost from the beginning the foliage plant industry enjoyed a boom economy. To keep abreast of the tremendous changes "John's" engaged a group of talented young people whose purpose was to do futuristic thinking to help management keep abreast of coming changes! A bold concept generally associated with manufacturing and related businesses, rather than agriculture!

The ornamental plant industry, comprising foliage plants, ferns, sod, landscape plants, roses, flowering plants, etc., have a total value that makes Orange County rank second in Florida and eighth in the nation for the value of these products according to the 1969 Census of Agriculture. The future for this industry appears bright and Scott intends to keep his company abreast of these many changes and make John's the "pacemaker" for local foliage plant nurseries.

POULTRY INDUSTRY

During the 15-year period between the two Rural-Urban Programs, the number of poultry farms remained more or less constant. However, the total number of birds in the county increased substantially. The "egg factory" concept became more mechanized by the use of conveyor belts to collect eggs and dispense feed and with similar innovations for increasing the overall efficiency of the individual operator.

H. S. Musselwhite, Jr., expanded his operations considerably during this 15-year period and became "Mr. Poultryman" of Central Florida. He added not only a hatchery to his operations but a huge feed mill complex. He bought out the old Central Florida Poultry Cooperative and expanded his marketing system to handle his eggs and those of several poultrymen he had under contract. Musselwhite also changed the housing facilities for his birds during this 15-year period. He abandoned mass housing for the caged layer concept with three birds to a cage. In addition to his production flocks, Musselwhite developed a breeder flock to produce fertilized eggs for the hatchery. By totally integrating all facets of his operations — feed mixing, hatchery, breeding flocks, production flocks with a highly organized egg merchancising and distribution setup, he could successfully oversee all aspects of his operation as a totally coordinated unit.

VEGETABLE INDUSTRY

In the period, 1958 — 1973, the land area devoted to vegetable production increased by several thousand new acres despite tremendous urban growth in the county. Several thousand acres of new sandland for growing vegetables were developed on the north side of Lake Apopka. Also several hundred acres of new peat soils were cleared and put into production. This new land was farmed by a tremendous system of cropping. This expanded the vegetable industry from a 2-3/4 million dollar business in 1958 to a 11-1/2 million dollar business in 1973.

Ken Jorgensen, co-owner of Zellwin Farms and business partner with Bob Stewart, was the vegetable industry representative at the two Rotary Rural-Urban Programs. Zellwin Farms owned approximately 1,230 acres of Everglades mucky peat soils in the Zellwood Drainage and Water Control District in 1958. By 1973 the company had expanded to 3,000 acres of peat soils and 1,400 acres of sandland, all devoted to vegetable production. In recent years Zellwin Farms has farmed between 6,500 and 7,000 acres of vegetables per year. A single season's production comprises over 2,800 carloads shipped to out-of-state markets.

The future of the Orange County vegetable industry depends upon two major factors. The first concerns the peat soils. Oxidation due to drainage and exposure to air and sun and the intensive farming operations have caused them to shrink at the rate from 1 to 2 inches a year. Flooding these soils during the non-farming periods could reduce this rate of loss significantly if done for at least 60 days or more. It is becoming evident that careful conservation practices must be maintained to prevent the destruction of this peat farm area within the next 25 years. Wind erosion is often bad, particularly so during the month of March. The young corn is small at that time of the year and the prevailing winds quickly dry the surface of the ground and remove the top soil. Pollution abatement is another problem of major magnitude that faces the peat land farm area. The industry is evidently polluting nearby Lake Apopka and corrective measures must soon be taken. If this situation becomes unduly restrictive, the local vegetable industry may be forced out of business.

Zellwin Farms, the largest and most progressive vegetable farming operation in the area, will doubtless continue operations for years, provided that the oxidation problems and pollution abatement situation do not get out of hand.

SUMMARY

Hopefully, this case-history review into the lives of seven agriculturists and their respective commodity fields has provided the

51

reader with a picture of what has transpired in these fields in a 15 year period.

The 1974 Agricultural Census, when available in '76, will doubtless show other aspects of the countdown in Orange County agriculture. In a not too distant future, another generation will possibly wonder why the county as well as the Main Street, Orlando, both were once called "Orange". This "countdown for agriculture" could provide the answers to these questions.

CHAPTER III

Agricultural Firsts

INTRODUCTION

Being "FIRST" with an idea, discovery or accomplishment, is what makes history and becomes a sort of landmark.

A "FIRST" that reflects a high degree of achievement allows us to see into the "spirit" of the people who made that industry.

These various Agricultural "Firsts" are presented under several categories — "Big Firsts", "Mini-Firsts" and "Undesirable Firsts". There is no attempt to rank them in order of importance or in a chronological sequence.

Judged by their record of accomplishments, the agricultural achievers of Orange County left quite a legacy. Several of their Agricultural "FIRSTS" were national and international firsts as well.

In the final analysis, history has meaning only in terms of people and their accomplishments. Orange County's achievers have contributed a whopping record of "FIRSTS" to Florida's agricultural history.

I.   "BIG   FIRSTS"

"MOTHER" OF ALL TEMPLE TREES

Perhaps the most unique citrus tree in Florida is the "Parent" Temple orange tree on the private estate of James Gamble Rogers, II, in Winter Park, from which the first commercial budwood of the Temple orange was taken. That fact makes it the parent of a mighty large family. Controversy as to its origin and the need to give it special protection also helped make this "Parent" tree unique in the Florida citrus family.

According to the Florida Crop and Livestock Reporting Service estimate, there were 2,026,500 Temple trees in 23,380 acres of commercial groves, as of December, 1971. This figure fails to account for the thousands of Temple trees in dooryard plantings or in commercial nurseries. Commercial plantings of Temples are spread over 28 counties with the leading acreage in St. Lucie — 4,372. Other counties are, Lake — 4,232; Orange — 2,764; Polk — 2,362; Highland — 1,657; and Indian River — 1,385 acres.

During 1971-72, the last season for which complete figures are available, 5,300,000 boxes of Temples were harvested with on-tree value to the grower of $9,805,000. This sizable contribution to the state's overall economy was produced by trees descended from the Winter Park "Parent" tree!

MOTHER OF ALL TEMPLE TREES — County Agent Swanson talks to James Gamble Rogers II of Winter Park about his famous Temple tree in background.

Experts on Citrus varieties agree that this mysterious tree resulted from a cross between a mandarin orange and a sweet orange. Such a hybrid is called a TANGOR — from the combination of a TANG(erine) and OR(ange). But, how this strange hybrid happened to be planted as a single tree in a row of orange trees along the driveway leading to the residence, no one is certain. In 1915, Mr. T. A. Hakes, then owner of the property, noticed the unusual characteristics of the fruit on this tree and called it to the attention of W. C. Temple, his neighbor. Mr. Temple, formerly the manager of the Florida Citrus Exchange, was much impressed with it also, and called it to the attention of M. E. Gillett of the Buckeye Nurseries of Tampa. From Mr. Hakes, the Buckeye Nurseries secured the exclusive right to propagate this variety in 1916. To prevent budwood thieves from stripping the tree of buds, Hakes had to protect it with a twelve-foot woven wire fence with a padlocked gate.

During the devastating freeze of February, 1917, Hakes covered the tree with a tent and placed a small kerosene heater inside. He stayed on "weather watch" all night to maintain these protective measures. His efforts proved worthwhile, whereas unprotected orange trees nearby were severely damaged. The Temple variety has since proved more tender to cold, so this severe freeze could have destroyed the tree in the absence of these special precautions.

When enough nursery trees were ready for release in May of 1919, the Buckeye Nursery publicly announced this new variety to the industry. It was named the Temple in honor of W. C. Temple, then deceased, who had recognized its value and had introduced the Buckeye Nursery officials to Mr. Hakes, owner of the "Parent" tree.

If all of the children of the "Temple" tree were to have a reunion with the "Parent" tree in Winter Park, this citrus family gathering would equal almost 1/3 of the 1974 population of Florida (6,950,000)!

First Rubber Tired Farm Tractor in the United States

According to the old adage — "Necessity is the mother of invention" . . . mothered the invention of a rubber tired farm tractor to do something about the "highway eater" tractors of the 1920's. The invention also had a father, Mr. Hoyle Pounds, native Orange Countian and West Orange County farm implement dealer.

At that time Orange County was experiencing quite a highway building boom and as more and more county roads were paved, tractor operators found themselves with a new problem. When operators moved their tractors from one farm to another, they necessarily traversed eliminate many of these newly paved roads. Where they crossed these paved roads, the metal cleats on these metal wheels "chewed up" the road severely and hence the name, "highway eaters".

In 1918 Mr. Pounds was Florida's first Ford Motor Company tractor dealer, so it was obvious that complaints were directed mainly against the tractors he sold. In 1919 the Pounds Agency sold eight tractors and by 1926 was selling more than forty tractors a year.

However, it was difficult to convince the farmer of those days that the mule was on the way out as a power source. So, when laws were passed against tractors crossing the highways, some one had to come to the rescue of the tractor.

Mr. Pounds' answer to the problem was to order from Oklahoma some large hard rubber tires such as were used on oil well drilling equipment. He also experimented with various kinds of rims so that these solid rubber tires might replace the old metal clog wheels of the Fordson tractors. He had special rims built for these airless tires and designed special lugs on them to prevent the tire from spinning around on the rim. In Pounds original design a triple set of tires was attached to each wheel.

FIRST RUBBER TIRED FARM TRACTOR — Farm Equipment Dealer and inventor, Hoyle Pounds explains to Agriculture Commissioner Doyle Conner the gear ratio he had to develop in order for the tractor speed to compensate for rubber tires. This was one of the early tractors with dual rims and rubber tires for which he received his patent in 1928.

After considerable work with the first rubber tired tractor Pounds realized that the gear ratio to the drive shaft would have to be changed to compensate for the increased wheel revolutions. With tires, the wheel was moving on top of the soil rather than through it. The old metal wheels dug into the sandy soil and turned at a slower rate. The tire increased not only the tractor's mobility, but its overall speed as well.

When all of these details had been perfected and tested for a five to six month period, a patent was applied for and on March 13, 1928, Patent No. 1662208 was granted to Mr. Pounds for his rim and lug design for airless tires. Later, when larger tires became available, the triple tired wheels were reduced to two tires. As more and more orders for rubber tired tractors came in, a special assembly shop was operated to provide these modifications. Pounds' invention "ushered in" the use of rubber tires on virtually all movable farm equipment and during the Mediterranean Fruit Fly campaign of 1929, the Federal Government ordered many of these tractor modifications to increase their mobility in this eradication program.

In 1936 Mr. Pounds acquired a case tractor dealership in addition to his Ford tractor dealership. A sales agency for two makes of tractors under the same roof was most unusual in those days.

Mr. Pounds has continued to modify farm equipment to meet the special needs of Florida citrus growers. This fact was attested to by Patent No. 2,871,804 that he received on February 3, 1959, for a combined citrus tree cultivator and fertilizer distributor. In 1974, Mr. Pounds was 80 and still active after 60 years in the farm implement business.

At one time the Pounds' case tractor dealership was the largest in Florida. In 1967, before urbanization tipped the scales against agriculture in Orange County, the Pounds Motor Company had a peak in sales of farm equipment of over a million dollars.

Several New Break-Throughs in Processing Single Strength Orange Juice

The relationship between men and events throughout history raises the question, "Do the men make the times or do times make the men?"

Such a question might well be raised regarding the discoveries that developed single strength orange juice into a commercially acceptable product and resulted in the tremendous expansion of citrus canning in Florida. These discoveries are credited to a team of Orange Countians. The 1929 "crash" and the arrival of the Mediterranean Fruit Fly in Florida dealt severe blows to the citrus industry and perhaps stimulated their discovery. The men involved — R. D. Robinson, Carol Floyd, D. M. Smalle, and T. J. Kew, were employees of Dr. P. Phillips. The desire of Dr. Phillips to expand into the citrus canning business was the catalyst that set this team into action.

In the early 1920's little canning of citrus was done and that consisted mainly of canned grapefruit sections. Three small canning plants were in operation, one at Lakeland, one at Haines City, and one at Coral Gables. In producing canned grapefruit sections, the juice that ran off sectionizing tables was considered a "by-product". Several attempts were made to utilize this "by-product" juice but failed largely because the juice was "cooked" in open copper steam-jacketed tanks.

These early attempts to can citrus juice ran into many difficulties. For example, pasteurization caused a "cooked" flavor. The juice also possessed a metallic off-flavor, probably caused by the copper kettles used in pasteurization.

The corrosive nature of the juice was evidenced by oxidation rings left inside the cans. Another problem was the settling of solids to the bottom of the can because the pectins and enzymes in the juice were not deactivated during pasteurization. These facts and the "off-flavors" convinced many potential customers that canned citrus juices was still experimental.

By the time of the 1929 "crash" these various problems had collectively given canned citrus juice a bad reputation. Dr. Phillips was aware of these problems and knew that before the industry could move into the processing field, major discoveries were required. Towards that end Dr. Phillips acquired a large building at the corner of Princeton and Orange Avenue in Orlando that previously housed a Dodge automobile agency, a casualty of the depression. Dr. Phillips viewed this location, next to the Atlantic Coast Line Railroad, as ideal for conversion to a plant for processing citrus products. Always a careful planner and excellent judge of men, he put together a team of hard working and resourceful men and gave them the freedom to innovate new concepts and techniques. His first move was to make R. D. Robinson, who joined the Auditing Department of the company in 1926, General Manager of the proposed canning plant. Carol Floyd was made Plant Engineer. Mr. Floyd joined the company in 1918 as a grove hand and worked his way up through the ranks to become packing house Equipment Engineer. D. M. Smalle, a retired canning research consultant, was hired to work under Mr. Floyd. Mr. T. J. Kew, a recent graduate of Rollins College, was hired later as a chemist to analyze products and to assist in quality control of the product. This task force assembled the equipment and expertese required to explore new concepts, and reviewed the techniques then in use for possible improvement.

At that time, pasteurization of citrus juice meant "cooking" citrus juice in open steam jacketed copper kettles at 168°F. Stainless steel equipment was not available and copper was the metal used in all canning equipment of that day. When Floyd analyzed the problems of "off-taste" and poor appearance of the canned juice, he realized that the pasteurization method and the equipment used, had to be improved. Between 1929 and 1931, he ran countless experiments and relied on Plant Chemist, T. J. Kew, to evaluate the quality of these experimental packs. In describing some of these tests Floyd remembered placing many experimental packs on the roof of the cannery to see how they responded to outdoor exposure and incubation!

A FIRST IN CANNED CITRUS PRODUCTS — All of Dr. P. Phillips canned citrus products between 1931-'49 had the AMA seal of approval issued by the committee on foods. Looking at a label with this seal are left to right: Howard Phillips, son of Dr. P. Phillips; Carol Floyd, former plant engineer; and R. D. Robinson, former General Manager of the canning plant. Plant was located at corner of Orange Avenue and Princeton.

In testing different kinds of equipment Floyd soon found that aluminum corroded badly when heated with caustic soda in the usual cleaning process. In the early 1930's, a new corrosion resistant copper-nickel alloy, monel metal, was tried. This proved to be the answer to many of their citrus cannery problems and was the mainstay until stainless steel equipment became available.

Floyd began to believe that the pasteurization process would have to be modified to minimize or eliminate, the "cooked" taste.

At this point Floyd came up with a "flash" pasteurization concept coupled with a post-pasteurization technique.

Flash pasteurization consisted of pumping the juice from hand reamed fruit through a one-inch monel pipe surrounded by a six-inch steam pipe. The juice was passed through this steam jacketed pipe at a temperature of 180°F for 30 seconds. Later it was discovered that the pectin and enzyme actions were completely inactivated at 192°F.

Immediately after "flash" pasteurization the juice was sealed into cans, and the cans were immersed in cold water for some 20 minutes. Quick cooling the juice to room temperature, approximately 75° − 80°F., greatly improved this canned product.

As methods of canning citrus became more mechanized, it became necessary also to mechanize the hand reaming process. In response to this new need, the successful rotary juice press was born at the Dr. P. Phillips' cannery. This piece of equipment soon became a standard piece of equipment in all citrus canneries as they geared their plant operations along the lines that Dr. Phillips pioneered.

By 1931, the Dr. Phillips cannery had perfected various methods and techniques that made it possible to produce an improved single strength orange juice at the rate of 1,000 cases of (24 #2 cans) every 24 hours.

With this production potential the Dr. Phillips Company needed to become a leader in sales and to develop new sales techniques. Dr. Phillips sent Floyd on a special sales tour in 1932 to contact some leading retail outlets in Nebraska, Texas, Kentucky, Oklahoma, and Arkansas to promote customer acceptance for these new improved canned citrus juices.

Mr. Floyd set up a demonstration group to pass out samples of cold citrus juice and special promotional leaflets to store visitors. This demonstration group went from store to store in major grocery outlets in these several states and went a long way towards securing new customers for canned citrus products and to overcome the bad image that still persisted from earlier canned citrus products. Other Florida canneries soon began to copy the progressive methods developed by Dr. Phillips and more and more of the Florida Citrus Crop began to go to the processing plant. Looking back, it seems safe to say that these important break-throughs in processing single-strength juice, helped establish the confidence in citrus juice products which later paved the way towards the acceptance of such products as concentrate and chilled juice.

Credit for the discoveries that made single strength juice commercially successful, goes to the team of processing researchers, R. D.

Robinson, Carol Floyd, D. M. Smalle and T. J. Kew of the Dr. P. Phillips Company. Special credit and recognition should go to Dr. Phillips as the force behind these break-throughs because he set up the research team and promoted the product after it was developed. Furthermore, customer acceptance means repeat purchases and Dr. Phillips was able to expand his canned citrus juice sales by aggressive advertising and promotional efforts. Processed citrus products began to find their way into homes all over the country in increasing volume. At this point the reader might ask the question, "Did these men make the times or did the times make the men?" If they had not done it, perhaps others would have done so later. However, the fact remains that Dr. Phillips and his team accomplished this agricultural "first" for the citrus industry.

AERIAL DUSTING OF CITRUS GROVES

The first aerial dusting of citrus groves in Florida occurred at the Dr. P. Phillips grove adjacent to Sand Lake in Southwest Orange County on May 10, 1934. The account of this historic event as reported in the Orlando Newspaper the following day reads as follows:

"Two thousand citrus trees dusted for the rust mite and red spider in half an hour.

That was the record established yesterday at Dr. P. Phillips, Inc., on Sand Lake by an airplane reinforced with deadly sulphur dust, which skimmed the tree tops at a speed of 100 miles an hour to demonstrate that an aerial attack against these two pests is the best way of cleaning citrus trees. It was the first time in the history of the citrus industry that a plane was used for dusting purposes and entomologists of the U.S. Department of Agriculture and others from the University of Florida were on hand at 8 a.m. for the demonstration.

There was much of the spectacular in the demonstration, for shortly after the plane had ceased operations, a truck equipped with the latest power duster, ambled through another portion of the great tangerine grove to compete with the plane. The truck moved at approximately 5 miles an hour".

Regarding the pilot credited with this historical first, the newspaper article had this to say — "The plane was piloted by Henry Elliott of Monroe, La., and he apparently had had long experience flying low as the wheels of the machine almost grazed the tops of the trees as the thick, cough-provoking mixture came pouring down from the air".

Walter Phillips, who instigated this new concept and was in charge of these operations, provided us with the following information on this agricultural first. The Dr. P. Phillips and Sons citrus groves arranged with an aerial dusting concern in Texas to apply the sulfur dust at a specified price per lb. of dust. The rate of application was to be ½ to ¾ lb. of dust per tree and the airplane used was a Waco biplane powered by a 300 h.p. Wright radial engine. Flagmen were stationed at both ends of the grove to help the pilot to line up his dusting runs. When the pilot made a "pass" he covered two rows of trees whereupon the flagmen moved over two rows to guide him on his return pass.

Walter pointed out that aerial dusting of cotton was a common practice in the early 1930's, but at that time no one in Florida had used this method for dusting tree crops. Although sulfur dust was regularly used to control rust mites, it was distributed by ground machines.

Distributing sulfur dust is somewhat hazardous because static electricity can ignite it. Also, flying at a low altitude over the trees is always hazardous. Because of the static electricity problem, dusting had to be confined to the period between sunrise and about 10 a.m. in the morning when dew was present in the air to minimize the static electricity problem.

The first crash resulting from this new dusting method occurred in a Dr. Phillips grove in the Turkey Lake area in the fall of 1937. It was caused in part by the pilot's hurrying to finish his contract so he could return to Texas. The pilot continued his dusting operation one afternoon and failed to adhere to the caution concerning the static electricity. A fire started aboard the plane and this resulted in a fatal crash.

Aerial dusting of citrus groves was a regular practice in the Dr. P. Phillips' groves from 1937 'til 1941. However, when better ground equipment was developed by the John Bean Company, Dr. Phillips returned to ground equipment for their citrus insect control program.

Nowadays one reads of aerial applications of sprays or dusts in citrus groves by the use of helicopter or fixed wing aircraft, and it sounds like a revolutionary new concept. However, this "Agricultural First" by the Dr. P. Phillips Company occurred in 1937!

FIRST "PLANNED" ORANGE
GROVE OF SELECTED SEEDLINGS

In the pioneer period of the citrus industry, before the turn of the century, many small orange groves were generally established by planting trees grown from seeds.

These orange groves could be called "unplanned" because the seeds were collected at random without regard to fruit characteristics or yields and many were distinctly off-type for the variety. This situation left a lot to be desired. The fruit from these trees were quite seedy and matured during the period from December through February, making them mid-season varieties.

In the "Big Freeze of '94-'95", most of these pioneer seedling orange groves were killed back to the ground. However, many of these "killed" trees later regrew new "tops" from root suckers. As a result second generation sweet orange tops developed from root systems that survived this great freeze.

After this great freeze, the industry turned to the use of "budded" trees, typically sweet orange trees budded on sour orange root systems. Budded trees offered several advantages over seedling trees. First of all, the "budded" tree came into commercial production five to 10 years earlier than seedling trees. Also, the budded trees were more true-to-type, more compact, smaller, and less thorny. These additional features made it easier to pick, prune and spray. Furthermore, different root systems grew better, were more disease and cold resistant on different soils.

With all of these advantages favoring the budded trees, groves of seedling trees soon went out of style. That was until Dr. Ausker E. "Ed" Hughes, a research chemist with the USDA Bureau of Plant Industry Laboratory in Orlando, decided to the contrary. Dr. Hughes saw considerable merit in a seedling orange grove, but decided that a "planned" concept was needed to overcome some of the disadvantages.

His reasoning was based on the facts then available. Therefore, an historical account of what occurred and when, is a necessity if one is to view these events in proper perspective. At that time Dr. Hughes did not realize that his "planned" seedling approach might have "unplanned" benefits for the entire citrus industry. These would not be discovered until some years later.

Dr. Hughes came to the USDA Bureau of Plant Industry Laboratory in Orlando as a research chemist in July of 1931. Soon after he married Miss Lena B. Smithers, who was to carry his "planned" seedling grove through to success. In December of 1934 a "tree killing" freeze hit the industry and thousands of citrus trees were killed to the ground. The 1934 freeze was quite a "shocker" to the newcomers to the industry. Seeing mature trees killed to the ground was a new experience.

Old timers, who had seen the '94-'95 freeze and the aftermath, considered freezes were just one of those hazards that could be expected periodically. A major difference between these freezes was in the kind of root suckers that emerged from the roots of killed trees.

After the '94-'95 freeze the root suckers were sweet orange in most cases and with the passage of time another "sweet orange top" was grown.

After the '94-'95 freeze growers had planted mainly budded trees on various kinds of rootstocks and this presented an entirely new problem. In some "killed" groves the sucker sprouts were sour orange, in others rough lemon and in others grapefruit, and so on.

These worthless root suckers proved of little use to the grower. A complete replanting program, including a new root system, was required.

These post-freeze observations were discussed at considerable length in numerous discussions between Dr. Hughes and fellow researchers, Dr. Hamilton P. Traub, Plant Physiologist, and Dr. Ralph L. Miller, Assoc. Entomologist. From these sessions with his colleagues Dr. Hughes reasoned that a "selected" sweet seedling orange tree still had considerable merit over the budded tree. Furthermore, the recent freeze demonstrated that the seedling orange trees had considerable "built-in" cold tolerance and if the trees were killed to the ground, the surviving root system could regenerate a new top like the original parent tree more quickly than could a newly planted budded tree. This fact was well demonstrated by sweet seedling groves that survived the "Big Freeze of '94-'95".

To overcome the lack of uniformity as to type, excessive seediness of fruit, maturity problems and other undesirable features associated with the "unplanned" seedling groves, Dr. Hughes proposed to select his seeds and seedlings very carefully. He obtained his seeds from a named variety that was true-to-type. Adherence to this concept required a thorough investigation of the history of the trees being considered as sources of seed.

After he found a promising true-to-type grove, Dr. Hughes next selected fruit individually from the most desirable looking trees.

Dr. Hughes also told Dr. Paul Harding of his "planned" selection concepts. Dr. Harding was then doing extensive fruit maturity testing of true-to-type named varieties. For this purpose Dr. Harding suggested the Arthur Butt grove on Holden Avenue in south Orlando as a possible candidate grove for the Parson Brown (an early maturity) sweet orange variety. The budwood for this grove had come from the original Carney grove of Parson Browns at Weirsdale, the original source of Parson Brown budwood.

As a site for his proposed grove, Dr. Hughes and his wife acquired a 75-acre tract of raw land in the Plymouth area adjacent to the Lester and Vick Roads. Forty acres of this tract was cleared for the purpose of planting 20 acres with an early variety of sweet orange and the remaining 20 acres to a late variety.

Upon finding the Arthur Butt grove to fulfill the various criteria he had set up for an early variety, Dr. Hughes collected "selected" fruit from the grove in December of 1937. Dr. and Mrs. Hughes extracted by hand some 2,000 seed from these selected Parson Brown oranges and planted them in the backyard of their 323 North Magnolia Avenue Home in Orlando.

The Parson Brown seeds germinated quickly and by the following December (1938), they were large enought to be transplatnted to the grove site at Plymouth. Approximately 1150 of the "selected" Parson Brown seedlings were planted at 25' x 30' spacing on the 20 acre site in Plymouth. The actual planting was done by the Plymouth Citrus Growers Association, a citrus cooperative that the Hughes contracted with for grove care. It is of interest to note that the cost of planting the 20 acres of Parson Brown seedlings was $500 in 1938.

Shortly after this planting was completed, Dr. Hughes resigned his position with the USDA to become a Research Director for the Wyandotte Chemical Company in Michigan. This move necessitated his leaving Orlando with only half of his "planned" seedling grove planted. Dr. Hughes retired USDA colleague, Dr. W. W. Yothers, entomologist, a retired U.S.D.A. colleague of Dr. Hughes and a nearby grower in the Plymouth area, assisted him to establish the "selected" late variety of sweet orange. The trees in Dr. Yothers' grove were true-to-type Valencia sweet orange and were the source of seed for the Valencia seedling planting. In fact, the fruits were so nearly seedless that approximately fifteen field boxes were required for the approximately 3,000 Valencia seed secured. Dr. Yothers. extracted the seed and planted them in the Hughes' backyard in Orlando and in 1941 the seedlings were transplanted to the Plymouth planting site and set out on a 25' x 30' spacing. However, Dr. and Mrs. Hughes were now out-of-state citrus growers, so care of their grove was handled by the Plymouth Citrus Growers Association.

On October 23, 1944, Dr. Hughes died suddenly and his untimely death left Mrs. Hughes with a "star boarder", non-paying citrus grove. Furthermore, seedling Valencia trees are notoriously slow to bear fruit, so it was a non-producing juvenile seedling grove of questionable value. A budded grove would have paid its room and board, whereas because of its juvenile condition, Mrs. Hughes now found she not only had to support herself, but the grove as well.

For the next thirteen years Mrs. Hughes lived out-of-state and supported herself and the grove. For two of those years she worked in the metallurgical department of the Great Lakes Steel Company in Michigan and for the next three years taught at Kent State University in Ohio. In 1957, she returned to Orlando to supervise her "star" grove. The "boarder" term had been dropped because it now produced enough fruit to pay its room and board.

At one time during her out-of-state status, Mrs. Hughes was so discouraged with the non-producing Valencia trees and the cost of maintenance that she almost had them bulldozed out for replacement with budded trees. In fact, she was frequently advised by "experts" to do just that. In her 1950 visit to the state, Mrs. Hughes consulted with Dr. Ralph L. Miller, then Director of Research for the Plymouth Citrus Growers Cooperative that cared for the grove. Dr. Miller, a friend and colleague of the late Dr. Hughes, advised Mrs. Hughes to be patient and ride out this trying financial period, if at all possible. Because of Dr. Miller's encouraging advice Mrs. Hughes returned to Michigan and authorized Plymouth C.G.A. to continue caring for the two seedling blocks.

Mrs. Hughes' decision to stay with her "star boarder" seedling grove proved momentous because the series of events that would unfold in the next five years was to make this grove an "Agricultural First" of international importance.

The chain-of-events started with the discovery of a new bud-transmitted virus disease (cachexia-xyloporsis) of the Orlando tangelo, by Dr. J. F. L. Childs, Plant Pathologist with the USDA Station in Orlando. At that time only two other virus diseases of citrus trees were known. However, this new virus was found to be widely distributed in Florida citrus trees, even in trees without any disease symptoms. As Dr. Childs accumulated more and more evidence of the importance of this and other virus diseases and how they were transmitted by infected citrus budwood, he was asked to present his findings to the 1951 Gulf Citrus Institute program at Brooksville. There he pointed out that citrus virus diseases such as psorosis, tristeza, xyloporosis, and exocortis could be controlled only by growing nursery trees from buds of virus-free parent trees. He also pointed out that California had begun a program for control of psorosis virus in 1939, and Texas had done likewise in 1948 but that Florida, the producer of more citrus than both California and Texas combined, had done nothing.

OFFICERS OF HUGHES MEMORIAL FOUNDATION, INC. — Dr. A. E. Willson (left), Director of Horticultural Research and Technical Services Coca-Cola Company, Foods Division and Chairman; Mrs. Lena B. Hughes (center), owner of the Hughes Nucellar Grove; Dr. J. F. L. Childs (right), Research Plant Pathologist, USDA Horticultural Field Station.

Fortunately, not all of his audience slept through these provocative statements. After the meeting, A. H. "Al" Whitmore, manager of the Florida Citrus Production Credit Association, and R. E. "Bob" Norris, Lake County Agricultural Agent, asked Dr. Childs to ride back to Orlando with them so they could discuss ways and means of setting up a virus control program in Florida. This trio agreed that the first strategy needed was publicity on the seriousness of virus diseases and to alert growers to the losses they were causing. This was

67

to be followed by setting up a control program designed for Florida conditions that would halt propagation of these virus diseases.

To kick-off an "awareness" program, a symposium on virus diseases of citrus was scheduled for the August 1951 Citrus Growers Institute at Camp McQuarrie, Drs. J.F.L. Childs, of the USDA Station, and R. Suit of the Lake Alfred Citrus Station, gave technical reports on bud transmitted virus diseases. W. F. Ward, pioneer citrus nurseryman of Avon Park, presented the nurserymen's viewpoint; W. W. Lawless of Winter Haven gave the growers' viewpoint; and A. C. Brown, Plant Commissioner, Florida State Plant Board, gave the regulatory viewpoint.

During the discussion period following the symposium, by pre-arrangement, a motion was made that the virus control problem be laid before the Chairman of the Florida State Horticultural Society for appropriate action. In anticipation of that action, a special meeting was held at the home of R. S. "Bob" Edsall, of Vero Beach, to line up an "awareness" program for the Florida State Horticultural Society meeting scheduled for October 30 — November 1, 1951, in West Palm Beach.

Researchers Dr. Jim Childs and Dr. Ted Grant of the USDA Station in Orlando, and Dr. Ernie DuCharme, of the Citrus Experiment Station, gave papers on various virus diseases of citrus.

The Florida Citrus Production Managers Association paid the expenses required to bring Carl Waibel, Assistant Chief, Plant Quarantine Division, Texas Department of Agriculture, to the FSHS meeting to present an invitational paper on the Texas psorosis virus control program.

This special awareness program paid off because during its business meeting, the Florida State Horticultural Society went on record as favoring the immediate initiation of a program for certifying citrus nursery stock for freedom from bud transmissible diseases and they set up a committee to accomplish that purpose, with Mr. R. S. "Bob" Edsall as chairman. Also, they requested the Florida State Plant Board, the Florida Agricultural Experiment Station, the USDA in Orlando, and the Florida Agricultural Extension Service to work together to formulate a plan suitable to the needs of the citrus industry of Florida as soon as possible.

Perhaps because Dr. Jim Childs had spearheaded the move to establish a citrus budwood certification program and the late A. H. "Al" Whitmore was an Orlando resident in on this original planning concept, Orlando became the "strategy center" for putting together the operating procedures for the proposed virus-free citrus budwood certification program. Beginning February 7, 1952, a total of four conferences were held in the offices of the United Growers & Shippers League at 14 E. Church Street, Orlando. There the operational details were spelled out for the Florida Citrus Budwood Certification Program. These procedures were finalized by the summer of 1952, but it was too late to implement the program except through special funds from the legislature.

However, the funding obstacle was overcome by appealing directly to the Florida Cabinet for an emergency grant of $12,000 to enable the State Plant Board to implement this program. Dr. Jim Childs was requested by Plant Board Commissioner Ed. L. Ayres to Make this appeal. On November 12, 1952, he went to Tallahassee with Mr. Ayres and addressed Governor Fuller Warren and the State Cabinet. The request was approved according to newspaper accounts "to meet the growing threat of tristeza". Thus a timely idea presented to a citrus meeting in Brooksville in April, 1951, seeded the development of a program that quickly gained industry-wide support and special funding by the Cabinet to implement it, all in 19 months' time.

With funds available the State Plant Board initiated the Citrus Budwood Certification Program on January 1, 1953 and Commissioner Ayers appointed Gerald G. Norman to operate the program. Dr. Jim Childs and Dr. Carl Knorr were appointed technical advisors.

When the Budwood Certification Program commenced operations, it was generally believed by virologists that most commercial citrus trees were virus-free and that selecting healthy appearing candidate trees for testing, would be no problem. However, as the weeks stretched into months and months into years, it became increasingly obvious to Norman and his technical advisors that screening old line citrus trees in search of virus-free specimens had become virtually a "Mission Impossible".

Those aware of the many complexities of the situation were by this time agreed that the only way around this situation was to grow the necessary trees from seed because for some unknown reason citrus viruses were not transmitted through seed.[1] This was the state of affairs when in 1955, Norman discovered, by chance, the Hughes selected seedling grove while on a field trip in the Plymouth area.

Norman's "trained eye" told him this was a potential gold mine of high quality budwood of the Parson Brown and Valencia varieties and for which he had searched the past two years. The only clue to the grove's ownership was a caretaking sign of the Plymouth C.G.A. on one of the trees. He immediately sought Mr. Lee Mathews, Pro-

---

[1]In 1965, Dr. J. F. L. Childs discovered the psorosis virus in seed transmitted under certain circumstances, but generally the rule holds.

duction Manager of Plymouth C.G.A. Not finding Mr. Mathews in his office, he went across the tracks to the Minute Maid offices to visit Dr. Al Willson, a Co-operator in the\Budwood Certification Program, to see if he might know of the grove.

FROM LITTLE SEEDS — These 37-year old "Selected Seedling" Parson Brown trees were started in Orlando and later transplanted to the Hughes grove at Plymouth.

Dr. Willson, then in charge of Horticultural Research for Minute Maid, was active in the Budwood Certification Program because his company was in the process of planting several thousand acres of new groves in the Ft. Pierce area.

Norman's inquiry of Dr. Willson about the unusual seedling grove he had just discovered brought to light an ironic set of circumstances, almost beyond comprehension.

At that time Dr. Al Willson's immediate supervisor was Dr. Wally Roy, Director of Research for Minute Maid. Dr. Roy had worked with Dr. Hughes at the USDA Laboratory during the mid 1930's! Dr. Roy had often discussed the planting of his selected seedling grove with Dr. Hughes, but never dreamed that he would be vitally interested in this same grove 18 years later! Almost as strange is the fact both Dr. Willson and Dr. Roy knew of the Hughes grove, as did several other individuals, but none had thought to call Mr. Norman's attention to it. Perhaps this was because they lacked the background knowledge that Norman brought to the situation. Most people who knew of the Hughes' grove considered it just another

70

planting of seedling orange trees. Norman deserves the credit for discovering the grove and getting Mrs. Hughes' permission to work with it. Furthermore, he spent four years (1955-'59) in screening, selecting, and appraising the over 3,000 individual seedling trees in this grove in order to select the best individuals as sources of budwood.

Dr. Hughes' decision to use only seed from "selected" trees in establishing his Parson Brown and Valencia seedling groves, unknowingly initiated two physiological procedures that later proved extremely important to the Citrus Budwood Program. One process consisted of nature's method of "filtering" out certain virus — as mentioned earlier, seeds from virus-infected citrus trees are almost virus-free, as are the trees that develop from those seeds. Whereas, trees produced from buds of virus-infected trees perpetuate the same virus generation after generation.

Also, through the seedling procedure, nature sometimes creates more productive as well as less productive strains through the process of hybridization. Extensive screening, selection and appraisal of every tree in the Parson Brown and Valencia blocks were required to find the outstanding trees and to avoid substandard ones and the work done by Norman and his co-workers was a tremendous undertaking. This activity was a considerable expense to the state in money and manpower and posed the problem of how these budwood selections could be made available equitably and at a fair price to all interested growers and nurserymen. In addition to resolving that problem, Mrs. Hughes also wanted the foresight and courage of her late husband in estalishing this selected seedling grove to be recognized. As an answer to both problems, it was decided to set up a non-profit organization to be called the Hughes Memorial Foundation which would receive a nominal fee from budwood from trees selected by the Division of Plant Industry.

Dr. Willson proposed to the Florida Citrus Nurseryman's Association that Minute Maid contribute $2,000 toward the establishment of a foundation named in honor of Dr. Hughes. The Minute Maid Corporation also offered to test in the Cloud grove at Ft. Pierce, 25 trees propagated with buds from each Valencia tree selected by the Division of Plant Industry. This rapidly increased the amount of budwood available to the Foundation for distribution to Florida growers and provided a production test of each budwood source tree.

The Citrus Nurserymen's Association was vitally interested in virus-free budwood, and they agreed to this proposal with the concurrence of the State Plant Board (now Division of Plant Industry). Mrs. Hughes, with the legal staff of the Minute Maid Corporation, drew up a charter for the Hughes Memorial Foundation. Mrs.

Hughes, Dr. Jim Childs, Gerald Norman, Orange County citrus nurseryman R. G. "Bob" Pitman, and Dr. A. E. Willson were original directors of the Hughes Memorial Foundation and are still active. Dr. A. E. Willson presently serves as President. Since 1955 hundreds of thousands of citrus trees have been propagated with Hughes certified budwood taken from these two varieties of oranges. In addition to the virus-free status of this budwood, the extensive screening process along with production testing resulted in-true-to-type budwood of a high production potential. This was a major break-through especially for the Valencia variety.

This non-profit Foundation presents incentive awards annually to several outstanding horticulture students, particularly citriculture students at Florida Southern College and the University of Florida.

In summary of this story within a story, Orange Countians spearheaded the budwood certification concept for the Florida citrus industry, and contributed high quality virus-free budwood of the variety most urgently needed, Valencia, through a project initiated by Dr. Hughes way back in 1937. Without doubt these "Agricultural Firsts" by Orange Countians will go down in history as major contributions to a better citrus industry.

HAVE GROVE WILL TRAVEL — Following techniques developed by Dr. Phillips but using modern day equipment, the Minute Maid Corporation in April 1960 moved 2,800 trees, 13 years old, in 11 days to a location on State Road 437 near Plymouth.

TRANSPLANTING A GROVE OF MATURE CITRUS TREES

Successfully transplanting one mature citrus tree is not an unusual accomplishment, but to transplant an entire grove successfully is another matter entirely. In 1938, the Dr. P. Phillips Company did just that. They successfully transplanted to a new site some four miles away a 25-acre grove of 10 year old trees! An operation of this scope certainly constitutes an "Agricultural First".

The decision which prompted this operation was unusual. By the mid-1920's Dr. Phillips had established the world's largest single planting of tangerines in the Sand Lake area of Southwest Orange County. However, the outlook for tangerines was not too bright by 1931, so Dr. Phillips inter-planted this block with several varieties of sweet oranges. The varieties used were — Parson Brown, Valencia, Enterprise and Jaffa. By 1937, these interplants were crowding each other to the point something had to be done. Either the oranges or the tangerines had to be moved, if a jungle condition was to be avoided. On a flip of a coin Dr. Phillips decided that the orange trees would be moved. He directed his grove manager to work out the plan of operations for this proposal. It was our good fortune to talk with Ben Houston, Assistant Grove Superintendent and a Dr. Phillips employee for over 40 years. He related to us the unique aspects of this first grove transplanting operation. They got underway in February and completed this operation in three weeks. The year was 1938, before bulldozers, fork lifts, automatic pruning equipment were standard grove equipment. Hand labor and plenty of it was required for an operation of this type then. Crews were organized to carry out certain phases of the operation. One crew pruned the trees back to the main limbs by hand pruning shears. Another group prepared the trees for digging by cutting the roots to a four foot radius around the "hatracked" trees. This established the ring area around each tree where the digging crew began their job. The digging crew shovelled the dirt away from the root pruned trees and to a deeper level on one side. The tree could then be pushed towards the low side so the tap root could be cut with an axe.

When the "hat-racked" tree was completely dug and the tap root severed, it was lifted out of the hole by hand and placed on a flat bed truck. From six to ten trees at a time were moved by truck to the new grove site four miles away. The operation was so organized that newly dug trees were not out of the ground more than an hour! Sufficient manpower and a well coordinated crew operation were the ingredients required to keep these freshly dug trees from dehydrating excessively and to insure success. Before the trees arrived at the planting site, the preparation crew had the property spaced and holes newly dug to receive them. The trees were lifted off the truck and quickly placed in the previously dug holes. Lastly, the crew shoveled in dirt around the roots and added water to help pack the dirt and eliminate air pockets.

73

Once these "hat-racked" trees were firmly in place, special white wash was applied to prevent sun burn to the bark. Twice a week, special tree watering crews watered the transplants until new leaves and shoots began to appear.

This transplanted grove of some 1750 trees was appropriately named by Dr. Phillips, the Aladdin Grove because one day the 25-acre cleared tract was bare and three weeks later there were hundreds of ten year-old trees waiting to regrow new tops!

According to Ben Houston, this transplanting operation was 95% successful. The high rate of survival indicates how well planned this "Agricultural First" operation was. Dr. Phillips later repeated this operation several times. In 1947, approximately 3,500 trees were moved 22 miles to another location. This time fork lift equipment was used and the crews were able to move almost 200 trees a day! An amazing 100% of these survived the first year and only some eight or ten died the following year!

OBSOLETE HAND SPRAY GUN — Ariel A. Wallace, left, reminisces with George W. Daughtery (in 1975) how his Speed Sprayer made this piece of spray equipment obsolete.

THE SPEED SPRAYER — A NEW CONCEPT IN SPRAY MACHINES

An idea was born in Hartford, Connecticut in 1929 that led to development of a revolutionary spray machine 10 years later in Orlando! This Agricultural "First" was of world-wide importance because it "ushered" in a whole new system of applying spray materials to plants.

Before the 1929 "crash", George W. Daugherty of Valdosta, Georgia, worked as an air-ventilation specialist in the New York City area. On one of these jobs a new "air blast" principle of delivering spray materials was revealed to him. At the time, Daugherty was installing an air-ventilation system for the Oyster Bar Restaurant of Hartford, Connecticut. He noticed that the exhaust fans used to dissipate the fumes and steam outside the building were dispensing a steady stream of water droplets. He remembers exclaiming, — "My God, wouldn't that make a beautiful spray pattern for peaches and citrus?" Because of his agricultural background, he immediately saw in this phenomenon the solution of an agricultural problem. However, Daugherty realized that to adopt this concept to agricultural practice, he needed to research it in an agriculturally oriented environment. The New York City area was not very conductive to "brain-storming" such a development.

The '29 crash resolved that problem and he found himself in Jacksonville, Florida, working on a crude spray machine in his brother-in-law's back yard. By 1930, Daugherty had roughed out his idea enough to apply for a patent based on his design concepts. To establish close contact with the citrus industry, he became a fertilizer salesman for the Armour Fertilizer Company in 1932. He worked in the Orlando area through 1935 where he became associated with the late "Cliff" Davis, an Orange County citrus grove caretaker. In 1936 patent #2,220,082 was issued to Daugherty for his design which employed the air blast from a centrifugal pump to carry droplets of spray material to the leaf surfaces. This system eliminated the need for high pressure pumps, hoses, and hand guns. It also multiplied many times the number of trees that could be sprayed in one day.

FIRST CUSTOM-MADE SPEED SPRAYER — Inventor George W. Daugherty stands proudly by the first speed sprayer turned out of his shop in 1939. This first model was sold to Southern Fruit Distributors.

In 1937 Daugherty rented from Dr. P. Phillips a building at the corner of Robinson Avenue and Kentucky (now Orange Blossom Trail) and established a machine shop to custom build his spray machines. In the fall of 1938, Ariel A. Wallace joined the crew that was assembling these machines. Mr. Wallace remained with the company for 35 years and retired in 1974. In 1948, he designed a stainless steel dilution nozzle for this machine which is still used today. The first custom made speed sprayer (so named because of the rapid rate at which trees could be sprayed compared to the old hand-gun sprayers) was completed in 1939 and sold to Southern Fruit Distributors. Chester C. Fosgate, Chase & Company, Dr. P. Phillips of Orange County and a Mr. Douglas of Weirsdale all purchased these early custom made sprayers. In 1940, the Speed Sprayer plant was moved to expanded facilities on the corner of Washington Avenue and Orange Blossom Trail. With an enlarged crew, mass-production of this new sprayer began to meet the growing demands of growers of citrus, peaches, apples and cherries.

In August of 1941, Paul Davies, President of Food Machinery Corporation of San Jose, California, Clarence Frazier, his assistant, and Jim Hart in charge of the amphibian tank division of FMC, came to Florida to visit their Lakeland plant. During this visit they and Courtney Campbell, head of the Florida Division of FMC, were taken on a tarpon fishing trip by Walter Phillips of the Dr. P. Phillips Company. On this trip, Walter suggested to Mr. Davies that his company should see the new speed sprayer that was revolutionizing the whole concept of pest control in citrus. In fact, the Dr. P. Phillips Company was abandoning its aerial dusting for this new concept.

Mr. Davies did look into the speed sprayer development and was so impressed that he convinced his Directors to purchase the manufacturing rights to this patented sprayer. In 1942 the Food Machinery Corporation did just that and by 1944 the company was turning out over 300 sprayers a year and had become one of the largest employers in the entire Orlando area! In 1953 the Food Machinery Corporation also bought Daughterty's patent rights and continued to manufacture and assemble these sprayers and related equipment at their bustling plant on Orange Blossom Trail. In 1966 FMC moved the plant from the busy Orange Blossom Trail site to Ocoee and housed it in an industrial plant site. This new facility turned out some 1,000 units of all kinds in a year's time. It now also manufactures toppers, hedgers, potato diggers, harvesting equipment, rakes, and related equipment.

Thus an idea conceived on the roof of the Oyster Bar Restaurant in Hartford, Connecticut, resulted in Orange County's becoming the site where equipment now used all around the world was developed.

FROZEN ORANGE JUICE CONCENTRATE

What event, or series of events, caused Orange County to be selected as the site of the pilot plant where the world's first commercial frozen orange juice concentrate would be made? This question goes back to the Boston area during World War II where a scientific group from Boston known as the National Research Corporation (referrred to by some as The M.I.T. and Harvard "whiz" kids), were developing a line of high-vacuum apparatus. Not satisfied with designing the equipment, this group had both the engineering ability and imagination to make several major breakthroughs in high-vacuum technology. For example, they engineered high-vacuum systems for processing dried blood plasma, evacuating retorts in the Pidgeon magnesium process, drying penicillin and for several new procedures in food dehydration. It was their food dehydration research that formed the basis for Orange County's becoming the birthplace of a new food processing industry.

Of the several products investigated by N.R.C. in their high-vacuum food dehydration work, the one that the Army found most interesting was orange juice powder. This high vitamin-C product could be reconstituted simply by the addition of water and promised to meet the needs of the Armed Services from both storage and convenience criteria. The idea was not new, however. Over the years numerous researchers and research groups had experimented with products of this nature. The important point was that the National Research Corporation development was a break-through that made it possible to move out of the laboratory with a marketable product.

It was at this stage of development that the dynamic talents of John M. Fox, Vice President of N.R.C. convinced potential buyers that the time was right for such a product and his company could do the job. Mr. Fox knew that Army officials had orders to purchase some 500,000 pounds of orange powder. He made it his mission to see this contract awarded to N.R.C. Mr. Fox had the Herculean task of convincing Army Quartermaster personnel that his company could manufacture the product in the quantity and quality required and at a reasonable price under the watchful eyes of Army inspectors.

In this undertaking, Mr. Fox encountered endless "Army red tape". A less dedicated person would have conceded the impossibility of the operation. However, the Army officials could, if they chose, award a contract for 500,000 pounds of orange powder, and he eventually aroused the Army's interest in his proposal.

At that stage of negotiations, there was only that, an interest. First, however, a pilot plant must be built, samples of the product must be produced under Army technical inspection and finally the product must meet Army requirements of quality and quantity at a reasonable price. After these criteria were met, a purchase order for 500,000 pounds might be forthcoming! It was a mighty expensive and risky undertaking on the basis of nothing more than "an interest" on the part of a potential customer! However, the "go ahead interest" by Army officials caused N.R.C. officials to look for a place to establish a pilot plant.

At this point the late Mr. Linton Allen of the First National Bank in Orlando was asked about the possibility of finding a pilot plant site in the Orlando area. After discussing plant sites and other points, Mr. Allen suggested that Holman R. Cloud, Vice President of Florida Public Service in Winter Park could be helpful as a possible co-ordinator of this project. After discussing this project with Mr. Fox, Mr. Cloud agreed to resign his position with Florida Public Service and become Vice President of Florida Foods, Inc., which organization would pioneer the pilot plant research. In 1945 this organization was formalized and Mr. Cloud began the local development activities. To that end he arranged with Bob Carlton, General Manager of Plymouth Citrus Products Cooperative at Plymouth, Florida, for a site on which to construct the proposed pilot plant. Since a supply of orange juice would be a requirement for the pilot plant, Mr. Carlton proposed a site just west of the Plymouth juice plant. He also suggested constructing a special pipe line from their juice plant, under the railroad tracks, to the proposed pilot plant. A special metering device would be incorporated and the pilot plant would be "billed" for the quantity of juice received via the pipe line.

A small band of engineers and scientists assembled at the pilot plant site in the winter of 1945. They were under the supervision of Mr. Holman Cloud, who was responsible to Mr. Fox, the President, in Boston. Other key personnel during this pioneer period were — Henry Cragg, Plant Superintendent; Frank Penn, Chief Engineer, Dr. Wally R. Roy, Senior Chemist; Hugh Schwarz, Administration; Dan Draper, Financial Affairs; and Jack Keller, Ken Arnett and Billy Meadowbrooks, Shift Foremen.

However, the problems were not ended when the pilot plant turned out a product meeting all the specifications set forth by the Army Quartermaster Corp. The Florida Foods organization faced another major production obstacle. **The Army contract specified that the capital to build a plant had to be raised by the company.** Thus the company's only bargaining tool was the original Army contract.

What transpired at this point has been vividly described by Auren Uris*, as follows:

"At this critical juncture, the new venture's problems began to multiply. In the spring of 1945, with the end of the war in sight, the Army suddenly canceled the contract. The securities underwriters promptly suspended their activities; unless the Army order was reinstated, there would be no basis for the offering.

This cancellation came shortly before the offering was scheduled. In a state of shock, Fox caught a plane for the Chicago headquarters of the Quartermaster Corps, determined to get a reinstatement of the contract. On arrival he found that he was just one of hundreds of frantic businessmen whose orders had been canceled.

'Forget it', he was advised, time and time again. But Fox was not the forgetting type. He would 'hang on'. Learning that the only man who could countermand the Chicago officer's order was a general in Washington, D.C., Fox flew there. He soon found himself treading a well-beaten path up and down the chain of command. He bounced from lieutenant to major to colonel and back down the line again, seeking a review hearing from the general. Turned down time and time again by the staff, including one particularly obdurate colonel, Fox's persistence finally wore the Army brass down. He obtained a hearing from the general in an atmosphere of reluctance and even antagonism. Fox presented his case. He argued that the company had spent tens of thousands of its own money developing the product at the request of the armed forces. He pointed out that the company had been promised that if it were successful in producing a satisfactory product the Quartermaster Corps would buy it in large quantities. He said that the company was not asking for funds to be used to construct the plant, but would accomplish capital formation for these purposes with private sources.

'We had the encouragement of the procurement officers in the Army to proceed with our plans right up to the arrangement for the financing which had been done at considerable expense to National Research,' Fox remembers telling the general,' and it was necessary for the Army order that was involved to be reinstated if the financing was to be consummated. Finally, I pointed out that the

*Uris, Auren — Executive Breakthrough, Pages 174-175, Published in 1967, Doubleday & Company, Inc., 277 Park Avenue, New York, N.Y.

79

quantities of orange juice powder in the initial order were relatively small in relation to the needs of the base hospitals where the product was destined to be used.' His final argument was that the orange juice powder was for use in base hospitals that would continue to care for the sick and injured after the armistice. The contract was reinstated and the Florida Foods stock issue was underwritten.

There was another close call for Fox. Under wartime regulations War Bond drives took precedence over all other types of security offerings. The company succeeded eventually in getting its securities sold only by placing them in between these drives, raising a total of $2,650,000.

The day that Fox received the check from the public underwriting, the A-bomb was dropped. This really signaled the end of the war, and the Army order for powder was again canceled. However, by that time the new company had its capital and, of even greater importance, it also had priorities for obtaining essential, but hard-to-get, materials and equipment to build the plant and get into production."

In the post-war period of early 1946, Florida Foods, Inc., found itself with a 2½ million dollar plant capable of dehydrating 20,000 gallons of fresh orange juice daily and no government contract or other means of selling this new product. In April of 1946 the first pack of frozen orange juice concentrate was put in quart (institutional) cans under the Minute Maid label. That same year some of the product was also put up in 6 oz. (5–3/8 oz.) cans for Snow Crop. The entire 1946 production consisted of 60,000 gallons of 42° Brix concentrate.

The summer of '46 also saw a change in name for the company. Mr. Fox explained the reasoning for this name change. Thus "we were contemplating setting up a sister operation in California, and it seemed to me that it would not be wise or politic to have the name Florida Foods Incorporated in a sign over such a plant." Mr. Fox went on to say — "Vacuum Foods sounded like a less controversial banner under which to fly when and if we did operate in the State of California, or possibly in Arizona and Texas."

The new change in name was a minor problem compared to the major ones now facing President Fox. Potential overseas markets for powdered orange juice had evaporated with the war's end. Furthermore, the cost of the powder was not competitive with ordinary canned juice, of which there seemed to be plenty in the stores. At this stage a new direction had to be taken in product manufacture that of a concentrated and frozen product. The door to this new development was opened by Dr. L. G. MacDowell, Research Director of the Florida Citrus Commission. Dr. MacDowell discovered that the concentrated product could be greatly improved in flavor by over-concentrating it and then diluting back to a standard fourfold concentrate by adding 6 to 25 per cent of fresh, single strength juice.

CITRUS HALL OF FAME INDUCTEE — Left, Jerry J. Chicone, Jr., President of Citrus Showcase and Orlando citrus grower, Lt. Governor Jim Williams and John M. Fox (right) appeared together prior to Fox's induction in the Citrus Hall of Fame.

Vacuum Foods found itself trying to merchandise this new product on a market plentifully supplied with a bumper crop of fresh oranges and warehouses stocked with single strength juice. One move made by the company at this time (1947) to get itself established in the market place was to change its company name to that of its product name — MINUTE MAID. The following year another big step was taken when Bing Crosby became affiliated with the Minute Maid Corporation and began to "plug" this new product. Sales soon began to soar, customers began to seek this product, and a new era began. Previously all kinds of give-aways were tried to get people to at least try the product but now sales were beginning to exceed supplies.

More and more oranges were diverted from fresh fruit channels to this new processed product; the industry had turned the corner on the marketing of citrus. Processed citrus products were soon taking the lion's share of the market and fresh fruit sales became the smallest segment of the citrus market. As a consequence of this situation citrus products could be marketed continuously 12 months of the year. Many peaks and valleys associated with fresh fruit sales leveled off, and a big boom in citrus tree planting took place to meet the demand for this new Cinderella product.

Now, as we look back upon that small pilot plant at Plymouth, Florida, and those bleak days of 1945, who would have realized that an historic milestone was in the making? Then too, who would have realized the name changes that would take place for this company that was beginning a new era in food technology? First, it was National Research Corporation, then Florida Foods, Inc., then Vacuum Foods Corporation, then Minute Maid Corporation, which would later be bought (1961) the the Coca-Cola Company? It operated as the Minute Maid Division of the Coca-Cola Company until 1968, when the M.M. Division and the Duncan Foods (coffee) Division were consolidated as the Foods Division of the Coca-Cola Company.

This latter consolidation led to a rather ironic twist of fate which history should record. The first operational plant to put up commercial packs of Frozen Orange Juice Concentrate and the one which "triggered" a rash of similar plants all over the citrus belt, was now converted to making frozen concentrated coffee!!

CITRUS CONCENTRATE PIONEERS — Holman R. Cloud (left), former Vice-President of Production Vacuum Foods and Dr. Wallace R. "Wally" Roy, former Chief Chemist who were members of the team that first developed a commercial pack of citrus concentrate at Plymouth, Florida, April 1946. The dried orange juice powder was the fore-runner of citrus concentrate.

Further mention should be made of two Orlandoans who played such important roles in this Agricultural "FIRST". Mr. Holman R. Cloud, Vice President of Florida Public Services in Winter Park, who resigned that position in 1945 to go with a pilot plant project when it was really no more than an idea backed up by the strong convictions of John M. Fox, was destined to do great things. Mr. Cloud caught this visionary concept when he became Vice President and guided the handful of dedicated scientists and engineers in the day to day operation of building this idea into a reality. He continued as Vice President until 1961. When Mr. Fox left the Company in 1961, Mr. Cloud agreed to serve as President for one year before retiring in 1962. When serving as President of the Foods Division of the Coca-Cola Company — a tremendous change had taken place in the personnel as well as the organizational setup since he became Vice President of Florida Foods back in 1945.

Another Orlando pioneer who should also be recognized for his contributions in this historic milestone was Dr. Wallace "Wally" R. Roy. Dr. Roy had come to Orlando in 1935 as a research chemist with the USDA Bureau of Plant Industry's Research Laboratory on Parramore Street. He entered the military service in 1942 and returned to Orlando in the summer of 1945. On December 1, 1945, he joined the ranks of this pioneer concentrate research group as senior chemist. Later he became Vice President of Quality Control Research and Development for Minute Maid Corporation. Dr. "Wally" Roy, in effect, wrote the first manual on quality control for the manufacture of Frozen Orange Juice Concentrate.

So Orange County not only furnished the site for the birth of this new food processing technique but two citizens who helped in its development. A major contribution to a major Agricultural "FIRST".

FIRST LARGE SCALE FIELD TEST
OF DDT FOR CONTROL OF CATTLE PESTS

August of 1945 ranks as one of the most memorable dates in the history of mankind. For, in this historic month the first atomic bomb was exploded and a new era began to unfold. The atomic age brought both good and bad omens for mankind. Another new era began to unfold for mankind in August of 1945, but on a lesser scale. It too had both good and bad omens for mankind. For, on this date DDT, the new wonder insecticide, was first tested on a large scale. The tests took place here in Orange County and were for the control of horn flies of cattle. One might ask why Orange County was "chosen" as the test site for this historic Agricultural "FIRST" out of the several thousand possible counties in the U.S.

The question was partially answered in the Orlando Reporter-Star of Thursday, August 16, 1945. Under the caption — "Bruce Brought DDT Tests to Orange County," the editorial had this to say:

"Some may wonder why Orange County, of all the counties in the U.S., was selected by the Bureau of Entomology as the place to try out on a large scale, the new wonder insecticide DDT for control of the bothersome horn fly that infests cattle herds.

The answer is simple, Orange County had a friend in the department, a friend who was won through the ordinary courtesies of Orlando and the Orange County public. There was no wire pulling, no politics, no high pressure in bringing this test that has meant so much to the cattlemen of the county. Because Orlandoans are friendly and because the cattlemen of this section are modern in their methods, when the bureau chiefs asked W. G. Bruce of the Savannah, Ga., District to choose a location for the tests, Bruce, without hesitation replied 'Orange County, Florida'."

Why Mr. Bruce selected the Orlando area, goes back to a personal experience in 1935. In that year Mr. Bruce came to Orange County to work with the Bureau of Entomology's Division Laboratory — "Insects that Affect Man and Animal". This Bureau Laboratory was established in the Orlando area in 1932 to conduct research in the Central Florida area on the biology and control of mosquitos. Bruce later transferred to another division but returned to the Orlando laboratory for some special work in 1942. After this latter assignment he went to another section of the Insects Affecting Man and Animal Research Branch in the Savannah laboratory.

Because of his knowledge of the facilities provided by the Orlando staff and of County Agent Moore's rapport with local cattlemen and dairymen, it seems only natural that Bruce would give the nod to Orange County as the logical place to conduct this large scale test demonstration. An additional plus item was the Orlando laboratory's pioneer research on the merits of DDT. Dr. E. F. Knipling and other staff members had several years experience with the "wonder" insecticide prior to its use on cattle.

The main purpose behind this test-demonstration was to determine in a large area (approximately 360 square miles) whether horn flies could be eliminated in the center of the test area and how long it would take for the flies outside to reinfest the treated area.

In a period of 9½ days 53 dairy barns and 14,192 animals were sprayed with DDT in the 360 square mile area, and about 1,000 head of cattle dipped in a 0.1 per cent mixture. Outside the demonstration area two large herds of range cattle and two herds of dairy cattle, plus their barns, were treated.

In summarizing this massive experiment Bruce said — "It was the most extensive demonstration and experiment in control of insects of livestock that had ever been conducted up to that time and covered a larger territory. It was also the most successful control of flies, mosquitos and cockroaches. It was the most convincing demonstration of which I have knowledge."

Because of this historic research accomplishment and other work, the Orlando Investigation Laboratory for Insects of Man and Animals, soon gained a world-wide reputation for its outstanding research contributions. The laboratory staff gained the esteem of entomologists around the world.

One of their most revolutionary research findings came in 1948 when the research staff announced the discovery that house flies could develop a resistance to insecticides. There were those who accused the researchers of trying to perpetuate their jobs, but time has since substantiated the accuracy and significance of that important discovery. This historical "First", by the Orlando research staff, brought the wonder insecticide DDT again into the spotlight, but this time with bad implications for those who previously hailed it as the answer to all the world's insect problems. Orlando and Orange County shared national and international publicity because of the outstanding research conducted by this laboratory.

Moreover, these facilities would in a few short years become the site of another major agricultural "First" of international magnitude!

ORLANDOAN KNIGHTED — Alfred H. Baumhover (left), entomologist with the U.S. Agriculture Department, yesterday received the insignia of knighthood in the Order of Orange-Nassau from the Netherlands Government in recognition of his work of ridding the Dutch Island of Curacao of the screw-worm fly. The medal was presented by T. Van Eyck, Tampa vice consul of the Netherlands, in a ceremony at the T. G. Lee Dairy yesterday on behalf of Queen Juliana. The insect elimination resulted in a yearly savings of $110,000. *Sentinel-Star Photo, Oct. 28, 1955.*

PILOT-PLANT SITE FOR
MASS-REARING OF STERILIZED SCREWWORM FLIES

In 1954 Orlando became the site of the first pilot-plant for mass-rearing of sterilized screwworm flies. The first phase of this program began at the former USDA Entomology Research Division Laboratory (Insects Affecting Man and Animals) in Orlando. During 1955, additional rearing facilities were constructed near Bithlo, Florida, in a relatively uninhabited area 20 miles east of Orlando. Later in July of 1958 Florida's Screwworm Eradication Program moved into full scale operations at the old Sebring Air Force Base facilities.

This historic chain-of-events had its beginning in 1933 when a shipment of infested cattle from drought areas in Texas, resulted in the screwworm being introduced into Georgia. Shortly thereafter, it spread into Florida. County Agent Moore reported the first screwworm cases appeared in Orange County in 1935.

Trying to limit the screwworm population in those days consisted of treating wounds on cattle with a protective coating of pine tar oil. Also, the navels of new-born calves had to be treated in the same manner to discourage female flies from laying eggs in these exposed areas. If infections were found then benzol-pine tar oil combination became necessary. This costly and time-consuming practice did not reduce the fly population because wildlife provided a constant reservoir for new infestations as well as stray cats and dogs. The mild winters in Florida afforded the screwworm an opportunity to "carry over" during the winter months and build up to high populations during the warmer months.

The first major new concept to come along that could possibly lead to the eradication of the pest was proposed in 1937 by Dr. E. F. Knipling, a research Entomologist, noting the female screwworm fly mated only once in a life time, Dr. Knipling proposed the release of sterile male flies as a means of eradicating this serious pest of the livestock industry. However, this concept could not be employed until a method could be developed to successfully sterilize the flies. Once this technical break-through had been accomplished, then mass-rearing techniques along with release procedures would also have to be forth-coming.

Initial laboratory studies for developing a sterilization process was conducted at the Livestock Insects Laboratory at Kerrville, Texas, during 1949 to 1951 by Doctors R. C. Bushland and D. E. Hopkins. In 1951, these USDA research scientists found that radiant energy from cobalt-60 could be used to successfully sterilize 5-day-old pupae. This made it possible to use laboratory-reared sterile flies to reduce the population of screwworms in infested areas and eventually to eliminate the pest.

Late in 1951 Dr. Bushland assigned Dr. A. H. Baumhover and A. J. Graham to the sub-laboratory at the Orlando USDA Entomology Research Division Laboratory (Insects Affecting Man and Animals), to conduct research under Dr. G. W. Eddy who spent part time on insects affecting man and part time on screwworm.

The first field test conducted by Orlando personnel was on Sanibel Island off the coast of Florida near Ft. Myers. According to Dr. A. H. Baumhover, the first demonstration that screwworms could be eradicated using the sterile male technique was conducted by Orlando personnel on Curaccao, Netherlands Antilles, using flies reared and sterilized in Orlando.

Since Sanibel Island was only a few miles from the mainland, an attempt to effect eradication was impractical. However, field tests gave scientists promising results so an isolated area with a long record of screwworm infestation was required to demonstrate this concept.

The island of Curacao, 40 miles north of Venezuela in the Netherlands Antilles, was chosen for the initial eradication effort. This 170-square mile island had a large population of screwworms and a large number of goats that served as hosts for this pest. According to Dr. Baumhover, once the program got underway, the screwworm was eradicated in a five-month period in 1954 by releasing of 400 sterile males per square mile per week. These sterilized screwworm flies were sterilized in Orlando and air-shipped to Curacao.

This significant and historic demonstration which proved that screwworms could be eradicated, and increased interest in this approach for the southeastern United States. As a result, a special campaign was designed for field evaluation techniques needed to efficiently combat the screwworm in a 50,000 square-mile area.

In 1955, additional rearing facilities were constructed near Bithlo, Florida. Goals set forth for these research endeavors were those of — establishing a vigorous Florida strain of screwworms, improve mass-production techniques, decrease operation costs and solve the odor problem. A production goal of one million flies per week was scheduled.

Beginning on May 1, 1957, Orlando personnel conducted the first large-scale field test in a 2,000 square-mile area southeast of Orlando using flies reared at the Bithlo facilities.

The northern boundary of this 2,000 square-mile field test area extended westward 30 miles from a point four miles north of Cocoa, and southern boundary extended 46 miles westward from Vero Beach. On the west the boundary extended 35 miles south from the northwest corner through Ashton to the mideastern shore of Lake Kissimmee, and then followed the Kissimmee River to a point of intersection with the southern boundary paralleling Highway 60. The Atlantic Ocean provided a natural barrier on the east.

Orange County cattleman W. A. "Al" Smith, whose pasture was located in this field trial area, recalled that weekly aerial drops were made in his pasture. Regardless of the weather conditions, Smith said he could almost "set his watch" according to the pattern established and the pattern of the dropped empty cartons in his pasture was also consistent. Smith also watched the researchers monitor the fly "catches" they made in special monitoring traps nearby.

After this successful field trial in 1957 in this 2,000 square-mile area, the Florida Legislature appropriated three million dollars to share the cost of a joint state-federal program to blanket 50,000 square miles of Florida with sufficient sterile flies to eliminate in time the entire wild fly population. This state campaign got under way in January of 1958 and finally was transferred to the Sebring facilities in July of 1958 when these facilities were completed.

Releases were discontinued on 10,000 square miles in southern Florida in late July 1959 and in the entire southeast on November 14, 1959. Summarizing this two year campaign Dr. Baumhover wrote — "3.7 billion screwworm pupae were produced, and 6.3 million lb. of horsemeat and whale meat were used. Twenty light aircraft were used to release flies over a maximum area of 85,000 square miles, and peak employment, including plant personnel, fly distributors. field inspectors, and clerical and administrative help, totaled 500. However, for a research cost of only $250,000 and an eradication-program cost of $10 million, ranchers in the southeast have experienced $140 million in savings since inception of the program in 1958."

In recognition of his work of ridding the Dutch Island of Curacao of the screwworm fly, Dr. A. H. Baumhover was knighted by the Netherlands Government with the order of Orange-Nassau on Oct. 28, 1955. This knighthood honor brought another agricultural "First" to Orange County.

Today, Sir Alfred H. Baumhover is Research Leader for Tobacco Insects at the Southern Region Tobacco Research Laboratory at Oxford, North Carolina.

KEY PERSONNEL IN SCREWWORM ERADICATION PROGRAM — Photo of recipients of the "Unit Award for Distinguished Service" from Secretary of Agriculture, May 1961. Front Row, Left to Right — C. C. Skipper, F. H. Dudley, A. J. Graham, W. D. New, A. H. Baumhover, and C. L. Smith. Second Row — J. Diamont, S. C. Gartman, V. H. Blackwelder, W. H. Cross, C. N. Husman, O. Krause.

In August of 1945 the Orlando laboratory and its personnel were responsible for the first large scale field test of DDT for cattle pests, in the United States. Not satisfied with one historical landmark accomplishment for the record books, the laboratory provided the necessary springboard for another landmark demonstration within a space of nine years! In reflecting on the world-wide magnitude of the two agricultural "first", DDT field demonstration work (1945) and the sterilization of screwworms (1954-'58) at the USDA Research Division Laboratory in Orlando, one wonders what was the reaction by the hometown folks?

Although the entire staff of the Insects Affecting Man and Animal Laboratory were not directly involved in the pilot-plat operation for mass-rearing of sterilized screwworm flies, the facilities were responsible for attracting fellow researchers from the Kerrville, Texas, Station. The unpretentious quarters of these researchers were in a group of abandoned army barracks adjacent to the newly opened Colonial Plaza Shopping Center. Although their accomplishments were known world-wide in entomology circles, local civic leaders were too engrossed in making the "Action Center" the envy of the state in securing new industries to be unnecessarily concerned about the needs of a home-based group. The researchers found themselves with the old adage — "A prophet is without honor in his own country."

89

THE RESEARCH LABORATORY THAT LEFT US — For over 30 years the Insects Affecting Man and Animals Research Laboratory was located in Orange County. Today, this million dollar complex is located on the University of Florida Campus.

As the Bureau of Entomology put out "feelers" for new quarters, local promoters were too busy working on other projects to be "concerned" about the physical facility needs of this research group. They had been located in Orange County for over 30 years, so why make a fuss over something you already have nailed down, seemed to be their attitude.

By the time the Chamber of Commerce got around to calling a special luncheon to discuss the needs of the entomology group, the decision had already been made to transfer the staff to Gainesville.

The Gainesville "rustlers" had previously moved the State Farm Bureau Headquarters from Winter Park to Gainesville in 1956. Now, the Gainesville promoters had come back to get this highly respected research group to move to the University campus in 1963. So while the Orlando promoters were about the country promoting new industries to come to Orange County, others were playing the same game in their back door!

Today, the Insects that Affect Man and Animal Laboratory is housed in a million dollar research center in Gainesville and has a staff of some 65 permanent employees of whom 24 are scientists.

ASSOCIATION FOR ARTIFICIAL INSEMINATION OF DAIRY CATTLE

Orange County dairymen have been as progressive and as receptive to new ideas as their counterparts in other fields of agriculture.

90

For example, the Orange County Artificial Breeding Association was formed in September of 1948. It proved to be a major Agricultural "FIRST" in the state. This "FIRST" led automatically to another, the "FIRST" Florida dairy calf born as the result of artificial insemination.

FIRST "TEST TUBE" DAIRY CALF – "Pansy" grade Jersey calf born July 28, 1949 to a grade Jersey cow in the dairy herd of the Forest Lake Academy. Robert Mathis, student at the Academy proudly displays first dairy calf born as result of artificial insemination through Orange ABA. Sire was Sir Brampton Wonderful X #401669.

Progressive dairymen in Orange County were aware of the need for proven sires to increase milk production even before this Artificial Breeding Association (Orange County A.B.A.) was formed. Furthermore, most progressive dairymen were aware that judging a dairy bull on "show ring awards" left much to be desired. Breeding records scientifically correlated with extensive production testing over the years had proven again that "beauty is only skin deep". A dairyman makes his living by selling milk and if each new generation of cows doesn't meet or surpass the production record of the previous generation, he is losing ground and probably going bankrupt as well!

Accordingly, production testing comparisons between daughters and their mothers (dams) gave rise to the value of bulls (sires) in transmitting hereditary capabilities for higher milk production. This

91

new production information focused attention on the vital role the bull played in upgrading the milk production records within a dairy herd.

These "findings" ushered in the bull farm and the techniques of collecting, diluting, storing and air freighting the semen of proven sires to dairymen all over the country. This technique gave dairymen access to the best bulls in the country at a reasonable service fee. However, to bring this about required the formation of a local dairy breeding association which could in turn affiliate with an organization that provided semen from proven sires.

Under the leadership of County Agenty F. E. Baetzman, Orange County dairymen — B. W. Judge, Sr., Howard Kellie, Glen Nelson, Gordon Eunice, Carroll Ward, Sr., T. G. Lee, O. D. Thompkins, and J. T. Raper — Met on September 15, 1948, to elect officers and sign articles for Incorporation. T. G. Lee was elected President; Carroll Ward, Vice-President; Agent Baetzman, Secretary; and J. T. Raper, Treasurer. At this organizational meeting Elbert Cammack of Gainesville submitted an application for the technician's position and Mr. Maury Gaston, Fieldman of the Southeastern Artificial Breeding Association of Asheville, N.C., summarized the services of his association. In October (1948) Cammack was officially hired as the technician and a contract was signed with the Southeastern Artificial Breeding Association for one year. The breeding fees agreed upon amounted to paying the technician $4.00 for each "new" cow except cows in excess of two artificially inseminated per farm visit, which shall be at $3.00 per cow.

The first cow artificially inseminated by Technician Cammack was in the herd of the How-Ann Dairy (Owned by Howard & Ann Kellie) located on Highway #441 across from the Ben White race track. Although this herd was the first to use this service of the Orange Co. A.B.A., the Forest Lake Academy herd at Forest City reported the first calf born (July 28, 1949) through artificial insemination unfortunately, it was a premature birth.

Other dairies among the early producers of "test tube calves" were — the Twin Gates Dairy, How-Ann Dairy, T. G. Lee Dairy, Carroll Ward (Lakemont Dairy), C. W. Baker Dairy, and J. C. Trice Dairy. However, Technician Elbert Cammack's activities in a local milk producers' association had stirred up a controversy and in July of 1950 several local dairymen asked for his resignation. At a special Director's meeting called on July 18, 1950, to decide the matter four of the seven Directors present voted "Yes" to continue Technician Cammack's services and three voted "No".

Because of this the dissatisfied dairymen created a second Artificial Breeding Association in the county (giving Orange County another "FIRST"), the only county to have two such organizations at the same time! However, the differences between local dairymen were soon resolved and on Jan. 21, 1952, the Orange A.B.A. and the Central Florida A.B.A. were consolidated. Within a few years, a second technician was required, but this lasted only a short while. After a few years the herds declined to the point where only one technician was required.

By 1967 the few herds left could not afford to continue the organization and on September 1st of that year the Orange County A.B.A. was officially dissolved. A farm hand was taught the work of the technician, obtained the necessary equipment and embarked on a direct service basis with the few remaining herds in the county.

A most interesting and stormy series of events brought about two Artificial Breeding Associations which later went back to one and enabled Orange County dairymen to make some of the highest individual cow and herd milk production records in the state!

"SIX OF A KIND"

When Robert A. McGregor became the Statistician-in-charge of the Florida Crop and Livestock Reporting Service office in Orlando, on May 1, 1973, Orange County acquired a unique "FIRST" among USDA employees. On this date the administrators of four different USDA agencies within the county found themselves all members of a rather exclusive USDA club. Each administrator was the recipient of the USDA's second highest award for meritorious service. In addition to these four active USDA employees, the county could also point to two "retired" recipients of this Superior Service Award. Having six USDA Superior Service Award winners residing in one county is most unusual.

The fact which makes this distinction so unique and impressive is the mathematical improbability involved for such an occurrence. First of all, there are over 3,000 counties in the United States and the possibility of the USDA having four or more different agencies within one county is greatly limited. Then considering the number of employees within a USDA agency or department that might be selected for this award, the odds are statistically reduced to an extremely small percentage level. For example, in the 22 year period, only five county agents in the entire Florida Cooperative Extension Service have been recipients . . . Only five employees out of several hundred in the 22-year period!!! Thus, the probability of having a

Superior Service Award winner in four different branches of the USDA in the same county, makes the odds against this rare combination astronomical.

FOUR RECIPIENTS OF USDA SUPERIOR SERVICE AWARD — Silver Medal Winners — Left to Right, Seated: H. F. Swanson (1970) — County Agent; Dr. William C. Cooper (1968) — Director of the USDA Horticultural Field Station. Standing: Robert A. McGregor (1966) — Statistician-in-Charge, Florida Crop and Livestock Reporting Service; Fred Merrill (1969) — District Conservatist with the Orange Soil and Water Conservation District. — *Sentinel Star Photo.*

Orange County's six USDA Superior Service Award winners and the year of their individual citation are as follows:

1.   J. R. WINSTON — (Retired) Awarded Superior Service Award in 1954 for his outstanding research with the local USDA Horticultural Field Laboratory in the field of decay control on citrus fruits in transit and in storage.

2.   DR. PAUL L. HARDING — (Retired) Awarded Superior Service Award in 1957 for his outstanding research at the local USDA Horticultural Field Laboratory which led to the establishment of maturity standards for Florida Citrus fruits.

3.   ROBERT A. McGREGOR — Statistician-in-Charge of the Florida Crop and Livestock Reporting Service, received his Superior Service Award in 1966 for developing a monitoring system for California agricultural production.

94

4. DR. WILLIAM C. COOPER — Director of the USDA Horticultural Field Laboratory, received his Award in 1968 for his research studies with cycloheximide in loosening fruit so it can be harvested mechanically.

5. FRED S. MERRILL — District Conservationist with the Orange County Soil and Water Conservation District, received his Award in 1969 in Ohio for his application of soil and water conservation techniques to urban situations, stopping erosion in subdivision instead of farm land.

6. HENRY F. SWANSON — County Extension Director, received his Award in 1970 for "Imaginative and dynamic leadership in developing educational programs that achieve public understanding, economic betterment, and vital improvements for farming in one of the nation's leading agricultural areas".

PLANT PATENT CHAMPIONS

Orange County has the distinction of having two commerical foliage growers who have amassed a string of plant patents unequaled by any other two commercial foliage growers in the state. What makes their accomplishments even more impressive is the fact that neither man had formal training or extensive agricultural background to motivate him in this direction. Both were self-made individuals with driving desires to improve their plant products.

Also, the fact that their livelihoods depend upon their successfully selling plants does not afford them the time and financial resources of plant breeders who can pursue such a course in a carefree manner. Hence, both growers had to gear their nursery operations to a commercial venture and at the same time devote their research and development of new varieties in a systematic and business-like manner. However, before describing these growers and their activities and accomplishments, a quick insight into plant patents is in order.

The Plant Patent Act of May 23, 1930 (now denominated in the U.S. Code as 35 U.S.C. 161), reads as follows as the basis for the issuance of plant patents:

"35 U.S.C. 161 Patents for plants. Whoever invents or discovers and asexually reproduces any distinct and new variety of plant, in-

95

cluding cultivated sports, mutants, hybrids and newly found seedlings other than a tuber propagated plant or a plant found in an uncultivated state, may obtain a patent therefor subject to the conditions and requirements of this title".

Patents are issued consecutively and so numbered regardless whether they be foliage plants, roses, citrus or what-have-you.

The first plant patent issued, Plant Patent #1, was issued Aug. 18, 1931, for a climbing or trailing rose. As of Oct. 15, 1974, there had been 3,643 plant patents issued. In that a plant patent is good for 17 years, the first 1,655 plant patents issued had expired by Oct. 15, 1974.

As of Oct. 15, 1974, there were some 2,000 plant patents in force with some 20 to 25 plant patents being issued monthly.

For this background information on Plant Patents we are indebted to Frank B. Robb, attorney-at-law, Patent & Trademark Law of Willoughby, Ohio. Attorney Robb has had a long professional career in this field in that his uncle, Harry C. Robb, Sr., was instrumental in shepherding the plant patent act through Congress and assisted the committee in drawing up the Act.

The foliage growers who became "plant patent champions" under the provisions of this Act, are Robert H. "Bob" McColley of the Bamboo Nurseries of Orlando and B. L. "Larry" Cobia of B. L. Cobia, Inc. of Winter Garden.

McColley came to Orange County in 1949 from Indiana and started his plant nursery near the present Hollieanna Shopping Center in Winter Park. In 1950 he moved to his present location just off Highway #441 on Clarcona Road.

PLANT PATENT CHAMPIONS — Left — Larry Cobia holds one of his patented *Hoyeas* (left) and a patented *Zygocatus* while Robert McColley holds patented *Philodendron X* "Prince Dubonnet".

96

In 1951 McColley began his Philodendron hybridization in hopes of obtaining plants with increased beauty, good keeping qualities in transit and hopefully some resistance to some troublesome diseases. His first hybridization experiments were with *Philodendron squamiferum* and *P. laciniatum*. McColley's desire was to create a hybrid that would have the good qualities of both parents and therefore be a plant with greater commercial value than either of the two parent plants. The *P. squamiferum* was a slow grower and would not stand winter shipment. As a result, northern buyers frequently complained about the poor condition of these plants when shipped to them during the winter months. Since a strain of *P. laciniatum* was found to resist temperatures of approximately 27°F., this was a desireable trait both growers and buyers would like to have in a new hybrid. However, the *P. laciniatum* had very little else in its favor since its foliage characteristics were not outstanding. Since *P. squamiferum* had these desirable features, McColley hoped he could create a hybrid having the "plus" features of both parents.

At this point we should recognize those traits both McColley and Cobia possessed that helped them succeed in a specialized field that was completely foreign to both men. The fact that neither man had mental barriers to keep them from dashing in "where angels fear to tread" was no doubt their key to success. They both had a natural curiosity to accept trial and error approaches regardless of frustrations and uncertainties. Had they been pre-conditioned as to why it couldn't be done, maybe they would become victims of the easy method of letting someone else come along with new varieties and we will just grow and sell them. Besides, we have to make a living and we don't have the patience or time to fool around in such a hazaradous area.

McColley experienced these difficulties first. He found the flowering habits of philodendrons were quite variable between species. Some flower in the spring while others flower in the fall. Forcing flowering or delaying flowering were just the tip of the iceberg in this complex field. There were the mechanics of pollination, methods of handling and storing of pollen, fruit as well as seeds. Then there was the final challenge of all — successfully growing to maturity the seedlings to come up with new varieties the trade wanted.

Time and space do not allow us to share with the reader the countless trial and error frustrations McColley encountered as he began his pioneering experiments in the hybridization of Philodendrons. It should be pointed out whereas extensive hybridization work done with orchids, grains, and fruit crops, his was an entirely new field and he literally had to write the book as he went along.

97

McColley's first successful hybrid was P. x "Florida". Because of many desirable features, cold hardiness, foliage, etc., it was quickly accepted in the commercial trade. A few years later two more hybrids created by McColley, P "Emerald Queen" and P. x "Burgandry" also became popular new plants in the commercial trade.

With these successful accomplishments under his belt, McColley felt the time had come for him to patent his next successful hybrids. Through hundreds of crosses and growing of millions of seedlings, he was able to produce eight hybrids for which he has plant patents. In addition, as of late 1974, he has another four new hybrids for which he has applied for patents. His patented plant hybrids are as follows:

NAME	PATENT #	DATE PATENTED
Philodendron x "Red Princess"	3034	March 10, 1969
Philodendron x "Emerald King"	3081	March 10, 1969
Philodendron x "Prince Dubonnet"	3398	September 18, 1973
Aglaonema x "Snow Queen"	3399	September 18, 1973
Philodendron x "Royal Queen"	3396	September 18, 1973
Philodendron x "Emerald Duke"	3397	September 18, 1973
Philodendron x "Majesty"	3535	April 2, 1974
Philodendron x "Red Duchess"	3502	March 5, 1974

As of October 1974 McColley has submitted the following hybrids for patents: P. x "Royal King", P. x "Pincushion", P. x "King of Spades", and P. x "Painted Lady". Because of his outstanding hybridization work with tropical plants, McColley was selected to serve on the Prestigious Plant Breeders Committee of the Society of American Florists. He is the only foliage plant hybridizer on this nationwide committee; all other members are associated with flowering plants.

The other plant patent champion member of this agricultural "First" team is Larry Cobia of Winter Garden.

Cobia, a native Orange Countian, came into the nursery business through an interning program. By working for other nurserymen for 10 years of learning the basics before venturing out on his own. Prior to going into the military service he worked for the Winter Garden Ornamental Nurseries for approximately 2½ years. After he got out of the service in 1952, he worked for the Wallace T. Champneys Nursery in Apopka as a day laborer for 85 cents an hour and eventually worked himself up to greenhouse manager for Mr. Champneys. He resigned in July of 1960 to go into the nursery business on his own in the Winter Garden area.

Cobia believed that if he specialized in the production of zygocactus species and species of Hoya, he could become a leader in that plant field. At the time he began his nursery (July 1960), the exotic Hoya and Christmas Cactus plants accounted for perhaps less than $5,000 annually in the entire U.S. By specializing with these two plants, and producing high quality ones, Cobia increased the annual business of his nursery until today he is one of the largest independent growers in Orange County.

Cobia followed both the "discovery" as well as the "Invention" process in securing his many plant Patents. However, his seven Hoya variety patents were all issued on the basis of discovery. Horticulturally, such new "finds" are referred to as mutations. To protect such new plant specimens, the grower must carry out a rigid selection and vegetative propagation process to insure the purity of his plant material.

Working with the zygocactus plants (referred to as Christmas or Thanksgiving cacti because of their bloom season), Cobia has used hybridization to develop a patented variety. In addition to this patented variety of zygocactus created as a result of hybridization, he has patents pending on three new varieties. Cobia's Plant Patents are as follows:

PATENT #	ISSUED	TITLE OR NAME
2950	12-9-69	Hoya carnosa Tri-color
3054	8-10-71	Hoya carnosa Compacta Mauna Loa
3008	12-8-70	Hoya carnosa Krinkle "8"
3105	4-11-72	Hoya carnosa Rubra
3310	2-27-73	Hoya carnosa Marginalis
3306	2-20-73	Hoya carnosa Compacta Regalis
3307	2-20-73	Hoya carnosa Argentea Picta
3574	6-18-74	Zygocatus truncatus Alba

Cobia also has patents pending on a plant in the Bromiliad family, *Cryptanthus Bwittatus Minor,* 'Pink Starlite', and three *Zygocactus truncatus* varieties — "Kris Kringle", "Peach Parfait", and "Lavendar Doll".

An indication of how committed Cobia is to developing new varieties and improved strains of these plants is shown by the 11,000 sq. ft. of his greenhouse devoted to extensive research and plant breeding purposes. He has a full time researcher and two aides working with him.

The 3600 cacti plants under selective study, will be "culled" to 100 plants. At this ratio one out of 36 plants is retained on the basis of — habit of growth, rate of growth, disease resistance, time of blooming, size of bloom, life of bloom, bloom color, number of blooms and overall plant appearance. By constantly selecting in this manner, Cobia will have at the end of two years a new and improved strain of stock plants.

In addition to his plant patents, Cobia has a patent pending on a planter device that accommodates three 3 inch pots and has an automatic water system (by capillary action) built in to adjust a uniform water level for each of the three pots. All of these accomplishments, plus building up a nursery business employing over 100 people in 14 years is evidence of the progressive nature of this particular individual.

II.   "MINI-FIRSTS"

Of the many Orange County Agricultural "FIRSTS," the "Mini", group require only modest documentation. However, this does not lessen their historical importance. The following Agricultural "FIRSTS" of this class are claimed by Orange Countians:

LARGEST TANGERINE BLOCK

In 1925-26 Dr. P. Phillips established a planting of over 600 acres of Dancy tangerine trees on rough lemon rootstock near Sand Lake in Southwest Orange County. For many years this was hailed as "The World's largest solid block of Dancy Tangerines."

AMA ENDORSEMENT

Based upon research conducted by the Massachusetts State College at Amherst on the vitamin C potency of canned citrus products, the American Medical Association's Council on Foods in 1930 or '31 issued its Seal of Acceptance on all of Dr. Phillips' canned products. After that, all of Dr. Phillips' canned product labels bore the seal — "Accepted American Medical Ass'n. Committee on Foods." This coveted AMA endorsement effectively promoted the nutritional value of canned citrus products when the Florida citrus canning industry was young.

BUDDED SOUR ORANGE GROVE

In 1938 Dr. Tayloe Gwathmey, M.D., planted a 10-acre grove of sour orange trees budded on sour orange rootstock southwest of

Apopka. He established this grove for the purpose of selling the sour orange fruit to the Cross & Blackwell Company of Baltimore, Maryland, for making English-type bitter orange marmalade. Budded trees were used instead of sour orange seedlings to reduce the time required to bring these trees into production. Some 10 to 12 years later marketing problems developed, and Dr. Gwathmey had the grove "top-worked" to Temple oranges. However, the 1955 freeze severely damaged the budded trees and so the entire grove was bulldozed. This is believed to be the first "budded" sour orange grove established in the state for a special sour orange market.

FIRST HOME – FLORIDA FARM BUREAU FEDERATION

The Florida Farm Bureau Federation came into being in 1941 and chose Orange County as the headquarters for the new state-wide organization. At first the Florida Farm Bureau office was located in the old Washington Street Arcade office building in downtown Orlando but after World War II (1947) the office was moved to the old Aloma County Club Building at the corner of Lakemont and Aloma Avenues in Winter Park where it remained until 1956. At that time the headquarters office was moved to Gainesville and has since remained there and in the fall of 1973, the Federation moved into its new 3½ million dollar office complex on Highway #75 south of Gainesville. The slogan of the Florida Farm Bureau Federation is "Voice of Florida Agriculture" and Orange County played a vital role in the early history of this statewide farm organization.

CITRUS PATENTS

Orange County has the distinction of having plant patents covering new citrus varieties issued to two former residents (now both deceased). The patents cover the following discoveries:

Donald John Nicholson, who established the Royal Purple Citrus Research Nursery in 1930, was ever on the watch for superior varieties. He found two naval orange trees that produced what he considered outstanding fruits, on which he was issued plant patents. The U.S. Plant Patent office granted patent #548 for his "Paradise" naval orange on October 13, 1942, and granted Patent #625 for his "Dream" naval orange that he found near Sanford on April 25, 1944.

R. G. Pitman, Sr., who came to Orange County in the early 1920's, was principal of the Ocoee High School for many years. He also operated a citrus grove and in the early 1940's secured some Ponkan seedlings from a party in Marion County. When these trees fruited, one was found to be a "sport" and superior to the standard variety. On the basis of these characteristics, the U.S. Patent office granted Patent .#863 covering this Ponkan "sport" on August 9, 1949. R. G. Pitman, Sr., died in 1951, but his son, R. G. Pitman, Jr., continued to operate the Florida Ponkan Corporation and has made it one of the largest and most progressive citrus nurseries in the state. The excellent quality of this fine fruit was acknowledged by all but its shy bearing and inability to withstand handling in shipping greatly reduced the once extensive plantings of this variety.

ORNAMENTAL PLANT ENTERPRISES

Through the years several Orange Countians have grown ornamental plants on a commercial scale. These were the first commercially grown ornamental plants in the state. Dr. Henry Nehrling of Gotha is believed to have introduced the commercial growing of fancy-leaved caladiums to Florida. Prior to the disastrous freeze of 1917, he had about two thousand plants of named varieties in his plant houses.

Commercial culture of the Boston fern was introduced to Florida by W. P. Newell and Frank Ustler. They started a small fernery in a slat shed next to Lake Eola in 1912. The culture of Boston ferns later moved to the Apopka area where many ferneries took up the practice.

Frederick W. Fletcher, an Orlando florist and orchid grower, seems to have been the first to grow leatherleaf fern. His operation was on West Jackson Street in Orlando around 1923. The late E. S. Marsell bought out Mr. Fletcher's leatherleaf fern and started a commercial fernery in Zellwood in 1925. Prior to selling his entire stock to Marsell, Mr. Fletcher sold some stock plants in 1924 to John Springer, a nursery inspector for the Florida State Plant Board. Springer started a commercial leatherleaf fernery in the Conway area. Later he moved his operations to his home place at Holden Avenue in South Orlando.

Whereas Fletcher was first to grow it in Orange County followed by Springer, it was E. S. Marsell who became "Dean" of the leatherleaf fern growers. Mr. Marsell grew this fern over 50 years and was active in the business up to the time of his death, January 16, 1975.

ORNAMENTAL PLANT PIONEERS —
John Rice Springer (left), first nursery inspector of Orange County and second
person to grow leatherleaf fern commercially in Orange County. Robert D.
Mitchell first to grow commercially *P.
cordatum* and Chinese Evergreen.

Of all the various foliage plants grown in Florida, *Philodendron cordatum* exceeds all others in total value. The distinction of being the first to grow it must be divided between two individuals. About 1928 W. W. (Wade) Walters of Apopka made a test planting of this foliage plant next to his Boston ferns and let it grow like a grape vine. No one was impressed with its potential so after a couple of years he discarded it. In the early 1930's, Robert D. Mitchell of Orlando started the first commercial production of *Philodendron cordatum*. Mitchell had a friend who talked about this plant in land-scape workshops all over the country. When people became in-terested in this foliage plant, he referred them to Bob Mitchell, his Florida friend. As a result of such demands, local fern growers started converting more of their operations to the growing of this foliage plant.

Gloriosa rothschildiana is another ornamental plant that is be-lieved to have been grown commercially first in Orange County. During World War II, Julian Nally of Gotha grew bulbs of this variety extensively on the old Nehrling estate. (These bulbs were originally introduced into Florida by Dr. Nehrling in 1905.) Mr. Nally air shipped the gloriosa flowers to florists all over the country. However, by 1955 a virus disease so devasted his planting that all his plants had to be destroyed. Air shipment of cut gloriosa flowers was considered an unusual florist "FIRST" for the state.

CITRUS INSECTICIDE MANUFACTURER

Orange County claims the distinction of having the "FIRST" insecticide manufacturing plant in the state. The John Schnarr In-secticide Company was originally located on Church Street in Orlando adjacent to the railroad in the early teens. Mr. John Springer, former nursery inspector, worked for this company when he first came to Orlando in 1915. Among other products this company made "red oil" which was fish oil treated with caustic soda to make a soap. This was the material used by citrus growers of that period to control white fly and scale insects on citrus trees.

COST-SHARING, A NEW FEDERAL CONCEPT

When battling for a cause the Orange County agriculturists, like their urban counterparts, have long been recognized for their tenacity to principles. For example, the Supervisors of the Orange County Soil and Water Conservation District struggled four years to secure a Federal cost-sharing program "tailored" to meet a special conservation need peculiar to the peat soils of the Zellwood Drainage and Water Control District.

For over 25 years the Federal Government was involved in a nation-wide cost-sharing conservation program to assist the nation's farmers and ranchers to carry out needed soil and water conservation practices under the Agricultural Conservation Program. This program was begun in the 1930's when poor farming practices were brought to national attention by the ravages of the dust bowl. The Federal cost-sharing program gave financial assistance to farmers to induce them to practice much needed conservation measures.

As the nation recovered from the depression and the effects of poor farming practices into the post World War II period, many believed that this program should be terminated. Those who thought so said that a good farmer would take care of his land without expecting the taxpayer's help for so doing.

Although the program continued, many farmers refused to qualify for Federal cost-sharing help because they believed the program had out-lived its usefulness. Some others maintained that as long as the program continues, "I will apply for the benefit because if I don't, others will!" The merits and demerits of the program's usefulness for Orange County interests were much debated into the late 1950's.

From this background, Supervisors of the Orange Soil and Water Conservation District reasoned that if this program was used to help provide the conservation needed in Orange County, then it should provide some cost-sharing assistance for the peat soil areas of the Zellwood District. Because of intensive farming and the consequent oxidation, these valuable peat soils were shrinking at the rate of one to two inches a year. In some Everglades farming areas, shrinkage of up to five feet occurred over a 50-year period and farmers wondered whether the same fate could be expected for the peat soils in northwest Orange County. All agreed that "flooding" of the organic soils during non-farming periods would greatly reduce the annual loss of one to two inches. Many of the farmers were flooding their land without any subsidy from the federal government. The cost of banking and flooding for a six-week period was estimated to be about $7.50 per acre.

Since funds were available in Orange County for less deserving conservation practices, the Supervisors of the Orange Soil and Water Conservation District reasoned that a special program should be written to make federal cost-sharing available to these farmers, should they wish to participate.

The proposal seemed quite reasonable but breaking through the bureaucratic "red tape" to bring this program into being required four years of letter writing to agency officials, letters to a U.S. Senator, and special resolutions from Orange County Farm Bureau and State Farm Bureau in support of this proposal.

Finally, on February 1963, the Chairman of the Florida Agricultural Stabilization and Conservation State Committee received a letter from Donald L. Gillis, Director, Southeast Area, concerning County Conservation Practice F-2, Flooding of Organic Land in the Zellwood Drainage Distric, 1963 ACP for Orange County, your memorandum of December 14, 1962. This letter stated:

> "It is recognized that some conservation would result from the flooding of organic land in the Zellwood Drainage District of Orange County through a reduction in the soil loss due to oxidation. However, as indicated in correspondence regarding your proposal to use the practice under the 1962 Program, the cost of measures which would be eligible for cost-sharing. While these specific items of cost are not eligible for cost-sharing, it is felt that the estimated cost of $.25 per acre for installation of dikes may be too low.
>
> From our interpretation of the manner in which the practice will be performed and the measures each farmer will need to take, we feel, that a cost-share rate of approximately $.50 per acre for the practice can be justified. We therefore are approving the practice for use in the Zellwood Drainage District of Orange County at a cost-share rate of $.50 per acre, provided the county wishes to use the practice at that rate of cost-sharing."

This correspondence is so typical of the bureaucratic way of seeming to say something without really doing so that the reader might well ask — "What did it say?" Essentially it says, you proved your point after "dogging" us for four years. Will $.50 an acre do? All farmers eligible for this new practice, except one, said that to drive the 34-mile round trip to fill out the necessary papers was too much — so forget it! Supervisors had fought for a principle and won a moral victory although the cost-share help was much less than in any other program. Nevertheless, the practice was eventually adopted by other Florida Counties having peat soils with similar problems and later, the cost-sharing help was increased. With all that bureaucratic "run around", a less determined group would have thrown in the towel!

CITRUS INDUSTRY FILM

It is believed that Orange County has claim to another and most unusual "FIRST". It is the first county to produce a movie film in color of citrus production and processing. The honor for accomplishing this goes to Dr. P. Phillips Company.

Dr. Phillips' son, Walter, originated this idea in 1937 and arranged for the Wurtele Film Company, of Orlando, to make a series of films. The first film entitled "Let's Visit Dr. Phillips" covered such industry activities as propagating young trees, planting a grove, fertilizing, spraying, cultivating and harvesting. The washing, sizing and packing of fruit and canning procedures were also covered.

Certain sequences were re-made annually to update the various activities for the years 1938, '39, '40, and '41 and sound was added in 1940. These films were shown to audiences all over the country. They publicized the Dr. P. Phillips Company but actually benefitted the whole Florida citrus industry.

PORTABLE IRRIGATION SYSTEM FOR CITRUS

Horace S. Hull, Sr., of Oakland, shared with us his childhood experience of assisting his father, S. B. Hull, in what he believes to have been the "FIRST" use of a portable irrigation system for citrus in Florida. This unusual management "FIRST" took place in his grandfather's seedling orange grove just went of Winter Garden, during the severe drought of 1907.

At the time Mr. Hull was seven years old and he vividly remembers the cool water on his feet as he worked to keep the basins of soil around the trees from breaking loose as they were filled with water. He also remembers his father telling in later years how this portable system saved the trees and the crop during that severe drought. He described the system as consisting of a perforated well with a pump driven by a large one cylinder Hagen gasoline engine of the make-and-break magneto type of ignition.

The well was located across the dirt public road from the grove, and the water was conveyed to the grove through an iron pipe. The water was distributed through a canvas hose attached to the pipe and pumped into earth basins about 10 feet in diameter around each tree.

Water was hauled in barrels to fill the basin around these trees that the hose would not reach.

According to Mr. Hull, his mother constructed the hose of white canvas or duck sailcloth material, obtained from Sears, Roebuck and Company. The price for the material in the 1897 catalogue was 42 cents a yard for the 18-ounce — 48 inches wide material. The 1902 catalogue listed the material for 41 cents per yard. As he remembers, she made the four inch diameter hose from strips sewed into a tube on her Singer Sewing Machine. The finished tubes were boiled in linseed oil in a huge old iron wash pot.

The pump kept the hose only one-fourth to one-third full so handling it while filling the basins was not a difficult task. Although this make-shift arrangement is a far cry from today's highly automatic irrigation systems, the concept of transporting water by means of a portable pipe was the forerunner of the numerous portable aluminum pipe irrigation systems used so many years by the citrus industry.

CITRUS PELLETS

Contrary to general opinion, the making of citrus pulp is not new. Many people think that the process of making citrus pulp is a by-product of the citrus concentrate industry. As a matter of fact, making citrus pulp goes back to the days of citrus canning in the late twenties. However, making citrus pulp into pellets for feeding livestock is new and this development is associated with the concentrate industry.

In the opinion of Dr. Ralph L. Miller, formerly Director of Research for Plymouth Citrus Products Cooperative, Florida, this company was the "FIRST" to undertake commercial manufacture of pellets from citrus pulp. This was commenced when Hugh Young, plant engineer, installed pellet making equipment in the Plymouth feed plant in 1948. Dr. Miller remembers carrying a pocket full of pellets in his travels about the state to introduce this new concept of marketing citrus pulp. Pressing citrus pulp into pellets allowed manufacturers to utilize the fine dust-like material along with the larger particles. It also facilitated transport of pulp to the range where the cattle could consume it.

TWO DAIRY INDUSTRY FIRSTS

Orange County is believed to have established two "FIRSTS" in the history of the Florida dairy industry in November of 1973 and in April, 1975.

In November of 1973, the Jersey Jug Dairy sold their dairy herd, and brought to a close 50 continuous years of dairy operations at one location. This is believed to be the first time that a dairy operated 50 years continuously on the same parcel of land in Florida. This 85-acre tract is located across from the Ben White Race track north of Orlando.

The first dairy farm was established on this particular site in the early 1920's by James Carder. Howard and Ann Kellie bought the dairy from Carder in 1938 and re-named it the How-Ann Dairy. In 1952, George and Jerry Baumeister and Bill Cammack bought the How-Ann Dairy business and leased the land from the Kellie's to continue the operation. In 1956, the Baumeister's changed the dairy's name to Jersey Jug Dairy. The 85-acre site was later sold to an investment group, but the Baumeister's continued leasing the land for their dairy operations until November of 1973 when the lease was terminated. The new owners converted the site to a warehouse facility to keep up with the surrounding urbanization pressures. At this point the Baumeisters decided to sell their herd altogether and terminate their business. This ended what is believed to be a state record for continuous operation of a dairy on the same site.

In April of 1975, Mr. T. G. Lee, Dean of Florida dairymen, began his 50th year of active dairy farming and this is probably another "FIRST" in the dairy field. No doubt others have established similar records on a family business basis or other members of the same family have continued the business in their name, but Mr. Lee is still actively running his own farm and business on a daily basis and looking forward to continue dairying well past the ½ century mark.

ORNAMENTAL PLANT RESEARCH FACILITY

When the Ridge Ornamental Horticultural Laboratory near Apopka was formally dedicated on November 24, 1969, Orange County became the "FIRST" Florida County with a University research facility devoted solely to research on ornamental plants.

The fact that Orange County ranked 7th in the U.S. for the value of horticultural specialities in the 1969 Census of Agriculture did not automatically guarantee such research facilities for the industry. Actually, it was quite an "uphill struggle" for the foliage industry to get the research facility established and then only after everyone else had agreed to the need for such research.

When a prominent foliage grower approached the Director of Agricultural Experiment Stations in the 1950's with a request to establish a research facility to work on problems of the foliage industry, the request was turned down rather bluntly. It was stated that there were already sufficient research facilities in the state and regardless of land donations or other gifts to support such a request, new research facilities were a No-No. However, when a new Director of Research arrived several years later, the request for an ornamental research facility was "revived".

The industry chose Professor Alex Laurie, a foliage plant grower, to approach Dr. J. R. Beckenbach, Director of Florida Agricultural Experiment Stations, regarding establishment of an ornamental plant research facility. Professor Laurie was selected for this mission because he had taught Horticulture at Ohio State University, and Dr. Beckenbach had been one of his students. Also, the fact that Professor Laurie was then a grower of foliage plants in Lake County gave him a legitimate interest in the proposal and hopefully would earn him a sympathetic ear for the foliage research request.

Dr. Beckenbach told Professor Laurie in October of 1962 that he would neither block or "push" for such a request. The Director stated he intended to remain neutral and that the foliage industry would have to pursue the matter independently of the University. This seemed to mean that donations of sufficient land to meet the physical needs of the laboratory and of some $150,000 would be required to get the project going.

FOLIAGE RESEARCH STATION DEDICATED — NOV. 24, 1969 — Left to Right: Former County Commissioner John Talton, Former Representative Henry W. Land, Jim Griffin Executive Secretary FNGA, Dr. E. T. York, Jr. Vice President Agriculture Affairs IFAS — University of Florida, Late former Senator Beth Johnson, Henry Swanson County Extension Director, Dr. John Sites, Dean of Research IFAS University of Florida, Dr. Will Waters Director of Station, Jack Christmas Past President Central Florida Chapter of FNGA.

On October 26, 1962, John Talton, Orange County Commissioner and foliage grower, called a strategy meeting to discuss the "don't ask for my help" response of the Director of Agricultural Experiment Stations. Present at this meeting were: Commissioner Talton; Representative Henry Land (Orange County); Representative Bill Reedy (Lake County); Senator Welborn Daniel (Lake County); Professor Alex Laurie; Jim Griffin, Executive Secretary of the Florida Nurserymen and Growers Association; Charles Chaplin, President of the Florida Nurserymen and Growers Association; John Payne, Secretary-Treasurer, Central Florida Production Credit Association; Wayne Hawkins, Fieldman, Florida Fruit and Vegetable Association; and Orange County Agent Swanson.

The meeting convened on November 11, 1962, and Jim Griffin, FNGA Executive Secretary and member of the Florida Agricultural Council, opened the meeting with a discussion of research needs. The Ag Council took the position that the University's refusal to budget the project was final, and if the foliage industry wished to pursue the matter in the upcoming legislative session, the request would have to be a separate item, totally independent of the agricultural budget.

At a second strategy meeeting in January, 1963, it was agreed that Representative Henry Land (Orange County), would introduce the foliage research need request in the House, and Senator Beth Johnson (Orange County) would introduce a companion bill in the Senate. No appropriations were to be sought, only the legislature's recognition of the industry's need. It was believed that if local legislators could get their colleagues to endorse this need publicly, this legislative endorsement would head off any future opposition that might develop.

The bills of the two Orange County legislators were acted upon favorably by the 1963 legislature. This action provided the necessary springboard for the University to request funds in the next fund request and have the blessing of the Ag Council.

Before this formal request for funds was submitted, a site had to be secured for the proposed facilities. In order to have the research facility located in Orange County, County Commissioner Talton secured the Board's approval of the purchase of 18 acres of cold damaged grove land north of the county's Magnolia Park adjacent to State Road #437. The purchase was made on September 20, 1965. Once the deed to this 18-acre tract was turned over to the University of Florida, the Ornamental Plant Research facility was virtually assured. Several other obstacles appeared, but these were successfully overcome, and in November of 1969 the facilities were formally dedicated. The name of the station was officially changed to the Agricultural Research Center in 1971. This change resulted from an administrative directive to eliminate all reference to the type of research in an Experiment Station's name.

YOUNG FARMER AWARDS

In 1954 the National Jaycee (Junior Chamber of Commerce) organization began a program to recognize Outstanding Young Farmers all over America. At the community level, local Jaycee Chapters conducted surveys to find outstanding farmers between the ages of 21 and 35 who derived 2/3rds or more of their income from farming. Candidates meeting these requirements were judged on three additional criteria — (1) their progress in their agricultural career, (2) the extent to which good soil and natural resource conservation is practiced in their farming operation, and (3) their individual contribution to the well-being of the community, state and nation.

The records of winners at the community level were sent to state elimination contests where a state winner was selected. Winners of state contests were sent to the National Awards Banquet. At the national level four contestants were chosen as the nation's Top Four Young Farmers.

In 1956, the second year of this contest, Jack Dodd, Dairyman at Goldenrod, was selected as Orange County's Outstanding Young Farmer. Dodd was later selected the Outstanding Young Farmer of Florida and represented the state at the National Awards Program in

JAYCEE OUTSTANDING YOUNG FARMER AWARD — Chester Karst (left), President of Orange County Farm Bureau, William D. "Billy" Long (center), vegetable grower, and County Agent Swanson (right) admire trophy Long won for being selected one of the nation's top four young farmers by the National Jaycees at Ft. Collins, Colorado, April 1965.

111

Pittsburg, Pennsylvania. Orange County had another state winner in 1960, Dairyman B. W. Judge, Jr., of Conway.

In the years 1960, '61, and '62 the Jaycees were unable to secure a sponsor for Orange County participation in the National Awards Program. However, in 1964, William "Billy" D. Long, vegetable grower at Zellwood, was selected as Orange County's Outstanding Young Farmer. Long later won in state competition and represented Florida in the National Awards Program at Ft. Collins, Colorado, where he was selected as one of the Top Four Young Farmers in America.

Thus, within eight years Orange County had placed three state winners and one national winner in this Outstanding Young Farmer Contest. This is a "FIRST" of its kind in the state that is definitely noteworthy.

LADYBIRD BEETLE LABORATORY

Orange County has the unique distinction of being the "FIRST" commercial producer of ladybird beetles and the man credited with this unusual undertaking is Dr. L. W. Ziegler, currently Professor of Fruit Crops in the College of Agriculture, University of Florida, Gainesville.

Dr. Ziegler has another Orange County "FIRST" to his credit. In 1925 he was the "FIRST" winner of the Board of County Commissioners' Agricultural Scholarship. This scholarship helped him enter the College of Agriculture of the University of Florida, Gainesville. He received his BSA degree there in 1930 and accepted the position of Assistant Entomologist with the Florida Agricultural Experiment Station, working jointly in Gainesville and Lake Alfred. In that posi-

Dr. L. W. Ziegler

tion Dr. Ziegler worked with organisms beneficial in the control of various pests of citrus. Nowadays this is called biological control.

The Cryptolaemus ladybird beetle, a predator of the citrus mealybug was introduced into the state for investigative studies at that time. At that same time, Dr. E. W. Berger of the State Plant Board (now Division of Plant Industry) was distributing vedalia ladybird beetles for the control of the cottony cushion scale on citrus. (This species was introduced from Australia to California in 1889). Dr. Berger and his colleagues also worked with various so-called

112

friendly fungi which at that time were believed to control certain citrus insects and mites. So, biological control of agricultural pests was a funded and functioning operation in the early 1930's. However, when the "Big Depression" struck Florida, funds were severely cut back in this important field and young Ziegler's position was eliminated. His colleagues suggested that he try his hand at commercially producing beneficial insects for control of citrus pests.

Dr. Ziegler rented a vacant store in the Fairvilla section of Orlando across from the old Walker Fertilizer Company. There he undertook the rearing of Cryptolaemus ladybird beetles. However, this site proved undesirable and he moved his operations to a building on Holden Avenue in south Orlando.

Dr. Ziegler patterned his insect rearing operation after insectaries in California that pioneered the methods of producing insect parasites and predators of citrus pests. He planned to do likewise for Florida citrus growers at his "Crypt Laboratories" on Holden Avenue.

Operations progressed well during 1931. A small group of growers from various sections of the state contracted for delivery of ladybird beetles yet to be hatched, and made down payments which supplied the "cash" to buy potatoes. The potatoes sprouted in trays in the darkened rooms of the laboratory. Mealybugs were fed on the white potato sprouts and when the mealybug infestations were well established, a few of the Cryptolaemus ladybird beetles recently introduced into the state were liberated on them. Exceeding Ziegler's most optimistic expectations, the laboratory rooms were soon filled with the small white beetle larvae that grew rapidly, pupated, and then emerged as adult beetles.

Adult ladybird beetles are attracted to light, so a window in each room was screened with a muslin sheeting. Early each morning the recently emerged adults were scraped off the sheeting into medicinal capsules, ten per capsule, and placed in a refrigerator before shipment. When sufficient beetles had been collected to fill an order, the capsules were taken to citrus groves in the cool morning hours. There they were released over limited areas in sufficient numbers to insure breeding. During that year, production of ladybird beetles was adequate to satisfy their entire list of customers. The operation proved most successful in every respect thanks to the providence of nature and the cooperativeness of growers.

George Oakley, the son of a nearby citrus grower, became interested in Ziegler's operation. Together they talked about grandiose plans of what should be done. However, without financial backing for their plans and ideas, the operation remained quite limited. The hard times that growers were experiencing lead to economies which virtually ended the ladybird beetle business. Consequently when the California Spray-Chemical Corporation (now Chevron Chemical Company) offered Ziegler a position as a Research Entomologist in 1931, he accepted and the Crypt Laboratory closed its doors forever. One wonders, with tongue in check, of course, if the California Spray-Chemical Corporation thought that the best way to eliminate biological-control competition was — "If you can't beat them, have them join you?!" However, times change and today's concern about air pollution, insecticides, insect resistance and related problems, has renewed interest in biological control. Evidently Dr. Ziegler's pioneer enterprise in biological control was some forty years before its time.

III. "UNDESIRABLE FIRSTS" — AGRICULTURAL PESTS

If we are counting our coups, it is only fair that we recognize some undesirable first too and Orange County has the questionable distinction of five such undesirable "FIRSTS". Two of these were insect pests — the Mediterranean Fruit Fly and the West Indian Sugarcane Root Borer Weevil, two were virus diseases — Cachexia (Xyploporosis — Orlando Tangelo Disease) and Tresteza, and lastly the Milkweed, a new vine pest of citrus.

MEDITERRANEAN FRUIT FLY

The "FIRST" Mediterranean Fruit Fly infestation in Florida was found in the Hamlin grove on Mills Street just off Marks Street in Orlando, April 6, 1929. The grove has long since succumbed to urbanization, but the distinction remains. However, a person intimately familiar with this "FIRST" Mediterranean Fruit Fly infestation told me that "Technically the fly was found first in Gainesville, Florida." According to this account, a State Plant Board inspector visiting the Orlando area, had taken some fruit home to Gainesville for use. Several days later several pretty little flies appeared on the screened porch where this fruit was stored and these were sent off for identification. Upon learning that they were Mediterranean Fruit Flies, a survey team was immediately sent to the Orlando area. So, technically the first Mediterranean flies were found in Gainesville, Alaucha County, but the first infestation was found in Orange County. However, further field inspections revealed that the infestation was widespread throughout the state. A campaign to eradicate the Mediterranean Fruit Fly was set up and over 10 million acres were treated at a cost of over seven million dollars of federal and state funds.

114

A second infestation of the Mediterranean Fly was found near the Miami International Airport in 1956, and State Plant Board inspectors found that the infestation extended as far north as Central Florida. Another extensive campaign was undertaken using new insecticides and World War II bombers, converted for aerial spraying. With these improved methods, the fly was soon eradicated. In 1962 another localized infestation was found in the Miami area and successfully eradicated.

Whereas, Orange County was credited with the first "find" of the Mediterranean Fruit Fly in 1929, the 1956 and '62 first "finds" were credited to Dade County. Because of their proximity to the Miami International Airport experts believe the 1956 and '62 infestations were brought into Dade County by international air traffic. No one was ever certain as to why and how the 1929 infestation got started in the Orange County area.

SUGARCANE ROOT BORER WEEVIL

In 1964, a single adult weevil of the West Indian Sugarcane Root Borer Weevil — *Diaprepes abbreviata,* a new pest of citrus, was found in a citrus nursery north of the Apopka city limits. No further "finds" were made until September of 1968 when this pest was found in several new locations near Apopka. In the 6-year period following 1968, this weevil was found repeatedly in an area between Apopka and north to the Lake County line.

Adults of the sugarcane root borer weevil feed on the foliage of citrus trees, but the primary damage is caused by the feeding of the larva stage on the roots, where the damage can be extensive.

This pest is native to the West Indian and Puerto Rico area of the Caribbean, so there has been considerable speculation as to how it "happened" to appear "FIRST" in Orange County. Some authorities believe that it came in with some foliage plants shipped to Apopka from the Caribbean area.

CACHEXIA (XYLOPOROSIS — ORLANDO TANGELO DISEASE

In 1950, after several years of research, Dr. J. F. L. Childs, Plant Pathologist with the USDA Horticultural Laboratory in Orlando, announced that a new bud-transmitted virus disease of citrus trees had been found in Orange County. At that time this was only the third virus disease of citrus ever discovered.

The virus was "FIRST" found affecting Orlando Tangelo trees on the Bill Story property south of Winter Garden. Using methods worked out by Dr. Childs, the State Plant Board subsequently found the virus in 72 percent of the citrus trees examined throughout the state. The disease, Xyloporosis, was not new. It was first described in Palestine in 1931. But that it was caused by a virus and it was present in Florida were both "FIRSTS". The name Cachexia was coined because the USDA officials objected to anyone's saying that Xyloporosis had been found here without a comparison study which was obviously impossible. Because of the international rules of nomenclature, the "FIRST" descriptive name Cachexia is the correct one, but Xyloporosis is the one generally used. Since the disease was first found affecting the Orlando Tangelo, another common name has been Orlando Tangelo Disease.

TRISTEZA

Tristeza, called Quick Decline in California, is a virus disease of citrus trees budded on sour orange rootstock. It was first discovered in South Africa and later South America and California. Florida was thought to be free of the disease until February 20, 1952, when Dr. T. J. Grant of the USDA Laboratory in Orlando, announced discovery of the virus in Florida. The infected material came from trees in the Winter Garden, Ocoee, and the Avon Park areas. Thus, Orange and Highland Counties share the dubious distinction of being "FIRST" with this new citrus virus disease.

The "FIRST" commercial grove with an extensive spread of the disease was found in the Winter Garden area, and was used as a demonstration grove for State Inspectors, Extension workers, and researchers to familiarize themselves with the symptoms of this new disease.

MILKWEED VINE

The milkweed vine, *Morrenia odorata* Lindl., is another unwelcome "FIRST".

CITRUS PEST – MILKWEED VINE – Eve Lenchuk observes habit of growth of the milk weed vine found growing on a cattle chute.

Several events, with supporting correspondence, pretty well document the fact that Orange County can claim the exclusive honor of being "FIRST" with this vine pest. In 1957 the late Donald J. Nicholson, citrus grower and nurseryman, wrote State Plant Board officials of having "FIRST" observed this new vine pest in his 5-acre orange grove on Grand Avenue, just off the Orange Blossom Trail. He paid it scant attention at that time, because he thought it was — "merely some common ornamental gone wild".

By December of 1959, however, Nicholson found a number of his orange trees almost totally covered with this new vine pest. The rapid spread of this perennial vine, and its ability to survive extremely cold weather during the freeze of 1957, and the winters of 1958, and 1959, prompted Nicholson to write a detailed report to State Plant Board officials. In January of 1960, in which he pointed out the seriousness of this new pest to the Florida citrus industry, another "find" of the milkweed vine in Orange County was made in June of 1959 by G. W. Hammett, local fertilizer salesman. This second find was not associated with the Nicholson problem, because of the lack of positive identification due to insufficient plant material.

Mr. G. W. Hammett had found some white fleecy material covering the ground in a Conway grove and brought a handfull to County Agent Swanson's office. This fluffy material was so thick that it appeared as though someone "plucked" several chickens and left the fine chicken-down all over the place.

Closer examination of this mass of white filamentous material revealed many small black seeds. Each small black seed had some of the fine white filaments attached to it. Since the origin of the seed was uncertain, Mr. Hammett suggested sending them off for identification. These seeds were packaged and sent to the late Erdman West, Mycologist and Botanist with the University of Florida Agricultural Experiment Station in Gainesville.

On June 30, 1959, Mr. West wrote County Agent Swanson:

> "It is an interesting coincidence, that I received a pod containing the same kind of seeds which was located in an orange grove in Lake County last summer. The vine is in the milkweed family. The Botanical name is *Cyanchium cubense* (Griseb) Woodson. I would have been completely stumped had it not been for last year's experience.
>
> Now, I want to gripe a little bit, although it possibly is not your fault that I want to complain. Even after receiving your seeds, I still have no specimen of the plant. Do you suppose that your fertilizer salesman could be prevailed upon to collect a specimen of the vine, including a piece of stem with the leaves attached? Of course, I should like to have a pod or two, and flowers as they are available.

> It is exasperating to know that a plant is growing in the state,
> and I do not have a permanent specimen in our herbarium."

Since Mr. Hammett did not know from what plant the seeds had come, Botanist West's exasperation continued for another six months. However, in January of 1960, Mr. Nicholson brought into Agent Swanson's office a strange looking seed pod with a portion of the vine pest from his Grand Avenue citrus grove. At about the same time, C. D. Wilder brought in some of the same pods from his Maitland grove. These pods and vines were sent to Botanist West. He identified them as *Cyanchium cubense* (Griseb) Woodson. He said the pods contained seeds like those received from Mr. Hammette the previous June. Also, they matched the pods sent to him from Lake County in 1958. Since Mr. Nicholson had first observed this vine in his grove in the summer of 1957, and was familiar with it and its potential danger to the citrus industry, he deserves the credit for first finding this pest.

To focus attention on this newly found pest, Agent Swanson prepared a backup story with pictures that appeared in the Orlando Sentinel of March 6, 1960. Some 20 people responded to this story by reporting this new pest in their neighborhood. The greatest number lived in the Conway area of Orange County. One report each made from each of four locations, Goldenrod, Winter Park, and Apopka, and Leesburg, in Lake County.

This plant was referred to as *Cyanchium cubense* until February, 1961, when Erdman West informed H. Swanson as follows:

> "We have just received a letter from a specialist giving us the correct name for the (milkweed) vine that has caused so much commotion among the citrus growers in yours and adjacent counties. Instead of *Cynanchium cubense*, it should be *Morrenia odorata* Lindl. It is a native of Argentina and has never been collected in this area before. The name I gave you before was the best we could do under the circumstances. Now, you may have the fun of giving the correct name to your constituents."

By February 1961, the industry not only knew the correct name of this vine pest but was aware that the pest was rapidly getting out of hand. Like many new introductions it spread like wild fire and was soon reported in groves all over the Central Florida Ridge area. Growers pressed the researchers to find herbicide experiments that might rid them of this pest. The years rolled by and discovering a practical control proved far more difficult than anyone had anticipated. All herbicide trials continued to be unproductive from an eradication point-of-view and growers began to believe that they were going to have to learn to live with this pest.

However, on October 5, 1972, John Carpenter asked Agent Swanson out to see something unusual in his Turkey Lake grove.

118

Carpenter showed him sick and dying milkweed vines all over his grove. Not a healthy vine was to be seen anywhere! Carpenter said, "If we were trying to grow the darn stuff we would be concerned!" and then added, "What do you suppose is causing those vines to die?" Questioning revealed that no herbicide or other sprays had been used. Obviously some pathogen was attacking the vines.

This story of the sick and dying milkweed vine was reported in the County Agent's monthly newsletter and this news item turned up another grove with "sick" milkweed vines in the Winter Garden area.

In October of that year, Dr. Dave Tucker, Associate Extension Horticulturist at the Research Center at Lake Alfred, secured diseased specimens of milkweed for cultural studies from both groves.

Research Plant Pathologist, Dr. Harry Burnett, Division of Plant Industry in Winter Haven, found that the fungus *Phytopthora citrophthora* was the agent responsible for killing these vines. This fungus is now being cultured on artificial media for use in experiments on biological control of this major vine pest of citrus groves.

Thus, this milkweed vine pest was "FIRST" reported in Orange County in 1957 and some 16 years later, the "FIRST" suggestion of a method of control was also found in Orange County.

These two Orange County "FIRSTS" are unique in several ways. The Nicholson grove where this pest was first reported, is about four miles (as the crow flies) directly East of the Carpenter grove, where the "sick" milkweed vines were first found. The fact Agent Swanson became involved in the original identification of the pest as well as the "find" of a possible biological control for it, adds a rather unusual twist.

CHAPTER IV

History of the Citrus Industry

Orange County was at one time destined to become the state's largest producer of citrus fruits due to the tremendous size of the county. Perhaps the founding fathers recognized this potential and for that reason changed the name from "Mosquito County" to "Orange County" before the new state was a year old.

At that time the county consisted of over two million acres and extended from south of Matanzas Inlet near St. Augustine south through the center of the state to a point below Kissimmee then eastward to the coast near Melbourne. With the passage of time, Orange County's size was reduced. Large areas were carved off to create new counties or parts of other counties. The size reduction continued until about 1890 when the county consisted of the land area comprising today's Orange and Seminole Counties. Then in 1913, Seminole County was "carved off" leaving the area which is Orange County today.

Had this once vast area remained as Orange County, it would without doubt have become the state's "orange" county. The acreage suited for growing citrus within this big Orange County territory could have become the citrus kingdom of the world! However, even with the reduced land area, the county by the time of the "Big Freeze of 1894-'95", was still probably the leading citrus county in the state.

ONE OF THE OLDEST AND LARGEST GRAPEFRUIT TREES — Mrs. Robert A. Awtrey (Left) and County Agent H. F. Swanson stand in front of this tree with 12 foot pole (notice white card) to demonstrate the height and size of this tree. Tree spread is 52 feet and trunk circumference 18" above ground level is nine feet 1 inch.

The Orange County area in the early 1890's had a population of approximately 7,000. Some 12 to 14 settlements accounted for most of this early population. As for the county's citrus acreage at this period, a Commissioner of Agriculture's report for the 1889-'90 season indicated the county had 16,181 acres of citrus. By the time of the 1894-'95 freeze Orange County's acreage was estimated to be 21,872.

Because of space limitations, we cannot provide a complete and detailed account of all events as they unfolded, nor can we mention more than a few growers' activities for various periods. Hopefully, the reader will accept our limitations and recognize that a "complete" history of the industry is not within our financial ability to provide.

Hopefully, a record of the major "happenings" and activities of the local industry during the several 10-year intervals will enable the reader to better picture the historical developments as they unfolded. Citrus history prior to the "Big Freeze of 1894-'95" is rather nebulous and more descriptive than factual.

BEFORE THE BIG FREEZE OF 1894-'95

The individuals who came to Orange County to grow citrus prior to the "Big Freeze" were truly the "citrus pioneers". Those who came on the scene after a transportation system of railroads and highways began to open up the area, were really early citrus growers. It is true these early growers of the teens, twenties and thirties truly had their hardships but by those times, trial and error had worked out the answers to many early problems.

Water transportation from Jacksonville "up" the St. Johns River to Mellonville (Sanford) was the principal access route of the earliest citrus pioneers prior to 1880, other than by horse over unblazed trails. In the 1880's railroad connections between Orlando and Sanford and on to Jacksonville and Tampa was the major stimulation to opening up Orange County to a "population explosion". Railroad expansion to areas in the county such as Winter Garden — Ocoee — Oakland, and Apopka between 1885 and 1890 stimulated some 15 towns and settlements on or near the railroad and was a major factor in fostering a citrus boom.

Some of the "citrus pioneers" of this pre-freeze period established citrus families that persist to this day. Many of their descendants helped rebuild the industry after the freeze. Some pioneer citrus growers of this early period, by location, were:

122

MAITLAND AREA

James E. Hill and his fourteen year old son S. B. Hill came to Jacksonville by train from Eufaula, Alabama. They then traveled by boat to Mellonville (Sanford) and by horse back to the Maitland area. After looking over this area of the county they decided an ideal site for a grove would be adjacent to Lake Faith. For Alabama cotton farmers this was a totally new agricultural endeavor but after obtaining two wagon loads of citrus fruit from someone near Kissimmee, they obtained the necessary seed to establish, in 1874, a 10-acre seedling grove near Lake Faith in the Maitland area.

Before many years they had one of the first citrus nurseries in the area and were selling trees to California growers prior to the 1894-'95 freeze. After the big freeze the old home grove was re-planted, S. B. Hill's two sons were born in Maitland, J. Harold Hill (1897) and S. B. Hill, Jr. (1899). J. Harold Hill said his father S. B. Hill, Sr. traveled to Spain and brought back some of the first bud-wood of Jaffa, Mediterranean Sweet, Valencia and Maltese Oval varieties of citrus. He was also active in the organization of the Florida Citrus Exchange in the period right after the turn of the century.

For years he had his own packing house in Maitland but later he was associated with Plymouth Citrus Growers Association as well as Orlando Citrus Growers Association. S. B. Hill, Sr. as well as his son J. Harold Hill each served as Mayor of Maitland.

The family still owns a grove in Maitland today (1975) although the proposed New Maitland Highway Interchange is scheduled to cut through this pioneer grove. The trees in this old grove were spaced 15X15 giving a tree count of some 216 trees per acre. The Hills have devoted some 100 years to the local citrus industry, as growers.

PLYMOUTH AREA

Just north of Plymouth, and adjacent to Highway #441 is an early settlement referred to as McDonald. This settlement was named after Civil War Veteran, Colonel Andrew McDonald who settled in this locality in early 1880. Colonel McDonald planted considerable citrus acreage and left acreage to his various sons — Fitz, Percy, George, John, and Matthew Gey. His daughter, Margaret, married Charles G. Lee who was a prominent citrus grower from before the 1894-'95 freeze until 1926. Both of their sons M. Donald and T. G. Lee are native Orange Countians and T. G. Lee is one of Orange County's pioneer dairymen.

A grandson of Colonel McDonald, Marion F. McDonald is still active in the citrus industry at the old home place. His father was Fitz McDonald.

WINTER GARDEN AREA

L. Frank Roper's grandfather, William C. Roper, came to Winter Garden from Woodbury, Georgia in 1857. In 1958, he moved his family there and proceeded to establish a farm as well as a small planting of citrus. His small seedling grove was one of the first in west Orange County. Through the years, his various descendants have continued to grow citrus. The Roper family today own several hundred acres of citrus in several counties.

Another pioneer citrus family in the Winter Garden area whose descendants have long been connected with the industry, was John Wenkelman. According to Horace S. Hull, Sr., his maternal grandfather, John Wenkelman, acquired some 159 acres in his original homestead from President Grover Cleveland on December 19, 1885.

Wenkelman established a small planting of seedling orange trees just west of the Winter Garden city limits in 1885. These orange trees were raised from seed taken from the fruit from the Luther F. Tilden grove was located on the south side of Lake Apopka. Hull's maternal grandfather, Wenkelman helped clear and plant the Tilden grove.

H. S. Hull, Sr's father, S. B. Hull, was born in Orlando (1867). He lived on the Wenkelman property for six years before moving to the west side of Oakland in 1912. He purchased the "Burdette Island" grove in 1909. This grove located on an island near the south shore of Lake Apopka and west of Oakland was said to be one of the oldest in the state.

It was claimed the Indians planted seed for the original trees since there were no rows or equal spacing of the trees. Some of these trees were quite large by the time of the "Big Freeze of 1894-'95". Today, (1975) there are only two battle scarred survivors left. Footrot, fluctuation of the lake level, freezes, neglect, etc. have taken their toll. Hull said at one time they had to use 36 to 40 foot ladders to get some 15 to 20 boxes of fruit from these old seedling trees in this "Burdette Island" grove. Of the Hull descendants the following are still actively engaged in the growing of citrus — H. S. Hull, Sr., Mrs. Marion Board, Herman Hull, W. B. Hull, Mrs. Hilda Bradley and Cecil Hull.

BEULAH AREA

The John E. Nicholson and Sidney Emmett Roper families were pioneer citrus growers in the Beulah area of west Orange County and their descendants continued in citrus after the "Big Freeze" and are still operating the home groves today. Nicholson came to Beulah from Canada around the period of 1882-84. He bought a small grove and proceeded to raise his family at this location. His son Donald J. Nicholson was born at the home place in 1890. His other son, Wray was born in Orlando in 1911.

Wray continues to operate the old home grove and has some of his brother's "patented" Dream Navel orange trees planted in the old grove. He also has a collection of Navel grapefruit trees on the old home place.

Sidney Emmett Roper was above five years old when his father William C. Roper moved to Winter Garden in 1858. After teaching school for a short while at Chuluota (then Orange County) he moved to Beulah in the late 1870's. His sons — Bert House, Emmett Oscar, William Fred, and L. Frank Roper have been associated with the citrus industry all of their adult lives.

Today, (1975) L. Frank the last living son of Sidney Emmett Roper and his son Bert Edward direct the activities of Roper Growers Cooperative. Their citrus operations cover several hundred acres in several counties.

PIEDMONT AREA

On Highway #441, about midway between Lockhart and Apopka, is an old Swedish settlement named "Piedmont". One of the earliest settlers there was Olaf Larson. His sons Jonas and Lars and their families later added to the growth of the community. In addition to the Larson family there was John J. Anderson, O. F. Johnson, Gust Jackson and Peter Olson were other pioneer settlers. Charles Fox an out-of-state property owner, and the Larsons, and Jacksons all had small citrus plantings in the area before the 1894-'95 freeze and through the years their descendants have continued with citrus right up to today. Charles Fox seems to have been Orange County's original absentee citrus producer.

Page McKinney obtained a 40-acre tract in the community as a land-grant from President Arthur. In 1884, William Burwell and Charles Fox bought it for $400.00 and planted several acres of seedling orange trees there, prior to the 1894-'95 freeze. In 1895 Charles Fox bought out Burwell's interest.

BEFORE THE 1894-95 FREEZE — A portion of the Charles Fox grove located in the Piedmont section of Orange County prior to the 1894-95 freeze.

New seedling sprouts re-grew from the roots of these killed back trees. Since Mr. Fox lived in New London, Connecticut his neighbor Gust Jackson cared for his grove. After Charles Fox's death in 1927, his son Edgar became the owner of the property and in 1932 he put the grove under the care of Plymouth Citrus Growers Association. Edgar lived in New London, Connecticut and continued to operate it under absentee ownership. His widow, Mrs. Julia Oddo still operates the property of some 13 acres.

CONWAY AREA

According to George D. Livingston, his grandfather, George Livingston, had an unusual set of credentials. He was a Civil War Veteran from Tennessee who had served with the Union forces! Livingston said he believed that during his grandfather's tour of duty he visited Florida and that visit motivated him to come here to live. He arrived in the Conway area around 1885 and purchased some 20 acres on the north side of Lake George. There he established a small planting of seedling orange trees prior to the 1894-'95 freeze. He also established another seedling grove where the Conway Methodist Church is presently located.

Grandfather Livingston died about the turn of the century and the property remained untended until 1924 when George, his father and brother took over the old homestead. Around the five seedling orange tree "survivors" of the 94-95 freeze, the Livingstons planted

126

six acres of Pineapple oranges budded on grapefruit rootstock. They obtained these trees from Daetwyler Nursery. In 1929 they added another four acres of oranges and in 1933-'34 they planted 10 acres of grapefruit. This old home site has been in the Livingston family since before the big freeze and is certainly a pioneer grove site.

ONE OF THE ORIGINAL TREES — George D. Livingston stands beside one of the original five seedling orange trees in his grove off Lake Margaret Drive in the Conway area his grandfather George Livingston planted in early 1890. Around these five seedling trees, George, his father and brother planted their grove of pineapple oranges budded on grapefruit rootstock in the middle 1920's. Sept. 3, 1971.

APOPKA AREA

Long time Apopka resident George McClure, a present member of the Florida Citrus Commission, said his grandfather Hugh Hungry McClure killed a carpet bagger in Georgia and headed south. He arrived in the Apopka area around 1868. There he planted several acres of seedling trees on the east side of Lake Apopka near State Road #437 in the late 1870's or 1880's. His son, Gillen, was born in Apopka in 1889 and followed in the family tradition by planting citrus groves. He planted several groves in the Apopka area and among them was the first Hamlin grove planted in the area (1925) the year George was born. George McClure, a third generation of citrus growers, worked in the industry as a Production Manager for Libby, McNeill & Libby and as a private citrus caretaker in addition to carying for his own groves.

WEST SIDE OF LAKE BUTLER

Stanley H. Scott's father, Stanley Scott graduated from Edinburgh University, Scotland, as a medical doctor. In 1885 he came to the west Orange area and established his home site in nine acres of seedling grove on the west side of Lake Butler. His son Stanley was born at the home place in 1896. After the "Big Freeze" several acres of old seedling orange trees survived from root suckers. Around these old trees son Stanley replanted new trees and expanded the family grove and has continued the citrus business until the present time.

CHRISTMAS AREA

J. R. A. Tucker came to the Christmas area in early 1866 from the Laker Butler area. He established a small citrus grove in the Christmas community. His son, John H. Tucker was born in Christmas and he too had established a small grove in the community prior to the 1894-'95 "big freeze."

John H. Tucker moved to Chuluota (then in Orange County) where his son, Richard T. "Dick" Tucker was born in February 1899. Today, two of J. R. A. Tucker's descendants, great granddaughter Mrs. W. B. Llewellyn of Christmas and Ricahard T. "Dick" Tucker of Orlando, are still associated with the citrus industry.

SANFORD AREA

Before 1913 this area was a part of Orange County. Several pioneer citrus growers were active in the Sanford area of Orange County prior to the "Big Freeze". Later they started groves in other parts of Orange County both before and after the "Big Freeze". Two such growers were Sidney O. Chase and James Bailey Magruder. Sidney O. Chase's activities are discussed under the Windermere area of pioneer growers.

James Bailey Magruder had several seedling groves in the Sanford area prior to the 1894-'95 freeze. When these trees were killed to the ground he moved to the Orlando area to start life anew. He established a livery stable in Orlando and bought a grove in the Spring Lake section of Orlando near the present Orlando Country Club. His son, Ches G. Magruder, took over the family business and groves in 1923 and his father died in 1925. Mr. Ches Magruder was the first to plant a grove in the Lake Hickory Nut section of southwest Orange County in the late 1920's.

ISLEWORTH GROVE – NEAR WINDERMERE

According to Frank Chase some 700 large seedling orange trees and several acres of young lemon trees were growing at this grove site when his father Sidney O. Chase and his Uncle Joshua Chase "happened" upon the grove one day around 1888. The Chases were riding horses in the area in search of orange trees to buy fruit. The freeze of 1886 had reduced the crop considerably around the Sanford area so the Chases thought they would survey that area of Orange County.

As to the history of this early planting, Frank Chase said his father believed these seedlings had been planted around the time of the Civil War. Upon finding the owner the Chase Brothers bought the property in 1892. They harvested 25,000 boxes of oranges in the 1893-'94 season just prior to the "Big Freeze". A narrow gauge railroad was adjacent to the grove at that time so the Chases had transportation connections from the packinghouse in their grove to northern markets.

As a result of the 1894-'95 freeze many seedling trees were killed back to the ground but after a few years many grew root suckers and were soon back into production. Through the years additional acreage was set out 'til today some 700 acres of grove have been planted in the area.

It is interesting to reflect on the events that prompted pioneer citrus growers to come to Florida before the "Big Freeze". In Sidney Chase's case he was a resident of Philadelphia when in 1878 he read a glamour article about the citrus industry in Harper's magazine. It impressed him so much that at the young age of 18 he decided to become a part of this glamour industry. He worked for Gen. Sanford for a while and in 1884 he encouraged his brother Joshua to join him to form Chase and Company.

After purchasing the grove near Windermere his future father-in-law asked him if the island was worth something. This prompted him to name the grove "Isleworth". His son, Frank W. Chase, was born in Sanford in 1908 and in 1933 he moved to Isleworth to care for the grove. Today, Frank and Frank W., Jr., supervise their beautiful citrus acreage which is located in one of the warmest areas in Orange County.

Oakland Communnity

An early settler and pioneer grower in the Oakland Community was James H. Sadler. Around 1870 Sadler came from South Carolina to the Oakland area as a young boy to live with his grandfather, James Gamble Speer. He married Matilda Minerva Tilden in 1887 and was a citrus grower prior to the 1894-'95 freeze.

In 1909 Sadler, along with L. W. Tilden, G. R. Croft, D. L. Pierson, S. B. Hull and A. W. Hurley, organized the South Lake Apopka Citrus Growers Association. This is the largest citrus growers' association in that area and its members have several thousand acres of citrus groves.

Several of J. H. Sadler's descendants are still actively involved in growing citrus. Among these are: sons R. T. Sadler, Oakland; Luke Sadler, Jacksonville; daughters — Mrs. Katherine E. Ross, Oakland; Mrs. Edith Stanford, Oakland; Mrs. Floy Maier, Winter Park; and Mrs. Myra Bowen, Eustis. There are also a good many grandchildren.

SOUTH OF WINTER GARDEN

Shortly after the Civil War Mr. Al Thomas, a Union soldier with the Eighth Regiment of Connecticut, homesteaded 160 acres in west Orange County. Here he started an orange grove which he named Almyra, for himself and his wife, Myra. In 1894 Mr. Thomas brought his young nephew, Harold E. Fowler, of Westfield, Massachussetts to Florida to help him with his grove. In 1909 Mr. Fowler married and brought his bride to Almyra Groves. Eventually, Mr. Fowler inherited the property, added additional acreage to it, and left it to his son, Harold E. Fowler, Jr. who has also added more acreage. The groves continued under the name of Almyra Groves until recent years when it was changed to Fowler Groves in order to avoid some business confusion. The original homesteaded property has been in the same family for more than 100 years.

HISTORIC FREEZES

With these various biographical sketches of pioneer citrus families behind us, let us now re-examine that catastrophic event which their descendants still talk about today.

Because the freeze of 1894-'95 touched the lives of so many people and reduced the industry to almost zero, many consider this as the greatest freeze ever in terms of low temperatures. This was not the case. Other freezes have had lower temperatures and others equaled it but in terms of combination of factors including havoc created, it no doubt will be remembered as the most damaging of all the major freezes.

Meteorologists who have researched the records thoroughly feel the freeze of 1835 was the most severe in terms of minimum lows. Records of ice forming over large bodies of water indicate that the low temperatures over a considerable period and this makes the 1835 freeze perhaps the record breaker of all times. However, since the state was sparsely settled and there was no citrus industry, this freeze frequently goes unmentioned as one of the "biggies".

The big freezes of January 1886, January 1898 and February 1899 should rate as major freezes in the citrus history books. However, the fact there was little citrus left to "freeze" in 1898 and 1899 probably accounts for the little mention given these two severe freezes. Since the industry really hadn't started by 1886 probably accounts for the little publicity that this particular freeze has been able to generate through the years.

It is interesting to note that the minimum temperatures at selected stations were recorded for the freezes of 1886, '94, '95, '98, and '99 that they are available to us from regular Weather Bureau and Climatological Station Records:

MINIMUM TEMPERATURES

Station	January 1886	December 1894	February 1895	January 1898	February 1899
Archer	14	13	15	17	10
Avon Park	--	21	23	--	--
Bartow	–	20	22	18	22
Brooksville	–	17	16	23	18
Clermont	--	20	18	26	20
Eustis	--	16	16	25	17
Merrit Island	26	22	22	28	24
Orlando	--	18	19	23	20
St. Augustine	17	16	16	25	13
Titusville	--	18	19	22*	16*

*New Smyrna

What separates the 1894-'95 freeze phenomenon from most other severe freezes, was its double-barreled nature. On December 29, 1894 the first freeze severely damaged the trees. This was followed by warm rainy weather in January. The "shocked and defoliated" trees responded to these two stimulants. The sap began to flow and the trees started to "push" out new growth and then on February 7, 1895 the second freeze "hit" with temperatures around 18°F. Old timers said the trees literally "popped" like pistol shots as the freezing sap "busted" the bark on these defoliated trees. As a result many trees were killed to the ground. Large trees, whose root systems survived, were able to regenerate new tops from root suckers. It is these groves that so many of us recognize as the "seedling survivors" of that great 94-95 freeze.

There are not too many old timers around today who can recall their impressions of this great freeze but we were fortunate to record two such interviews. F. O. "Oscar" Journigan, who was born in the southern part of Polk County, May 22, 1885 told us of his boyhood remembrances of the freeze, as follows: Journigan, who was nine at the time, said they were living a few miles west of Frostproof. He was told that down the road someone had a recording thermometer and that it went to 7°F. and stayed there for several hours. Journigan said a small lake near their place had been frozen over for several feet from shore and he played on the ice. For this he got a "paddling" from his father.

He remembers the citrus trees and how bare they appeared with bark split and fruit all over the ground.

Donald A. Cheney, prominent Orlandoan who was born here January 23, 1889, also has vivid memories of the big freeze. On February 7, 1895 he remembers in chasing around the house he fell down and got a severe cut above his eye so that date had special meaning in his life. He too remembers how stark the citrus trees looked with all their leaves gone and the bark split and peeling off with fruit lying all over the ground.

The magnitude of the damage done is probably best reflected in the orange production figures reported for Orange County during post-freeze years in various Commissioner of Agriculture reports.

SEASON	ACREAGE	PRODUCTION	VALUE
1895-'96	21,737	None	0
1897-'98	16,093	8,257 Boxes	$ 19,510
1899-1900	12,107	2,448 Boxes	$ 5,230
1901-1902	6,363	47,099 Boxes	$ 63,492
1903-1904	9,332	80,143 Boxes	$123,306
1905-1906	7,594	319,910 Boxes	$350,255
1907-1908	8,478	646,400 Boxes	$747,987
1909-1910	7,334	799,164 Boxes	$675,416

The pioneer citrus growers of the pre-freeze period began the rebuilding process, but were joined periodically by newcomers although, the influx of newcomers remained slow through the turn of the century and during the "teens." However the Florida "boom" of the 1920's saw a big influx of new citrus growers. After noting of what transpired up to the turn of the century let us now record various industry "happenings" during different time periods.

MARKETING BECOMES A PROBLEM

1900 - 1909

Probably the biggest industry move that occurred during this 10-year period was the creation of the Florida Citrus Exchange and the uniting of local growers to market their fruit cooperatively. J. Harold Hill of Maitland, says his father S. B. Hill, Sr. was one of the "sparkplugs" in creation of the Florida Citrus Exchange and he remembers as a young boy going to Tampa to attend some of the organization meetings.

The creation of the Florida Citrus Exchange evidentally catalyzed for the creation of a number of local cooperatives in 1909. That year Winter Garden Citrus Growers Association, the South Lake Apopka Citrus Growers Association, and the Plymouth Citrus Growers Association came into being. About this same time or later the Orlando Citrus Growers Association was also formed.

132

TRAVELING PACKINGHOUSE — Before the turn of the century and during the early teens, a packinghouse operation was set up in a tent in some isolated groves. Scene of such operation at Boggy Creek around 1914. Fruit was hauled by ox cart — twenty-five boxes to the load — to railroad at Kissimmee.

Prior to the turn of the century and shortly thereafter, the packinghouse crew operated in the grove under a tent. Once the fruit was packed in the grove then it was hauled by a team of horses or mules in a wagon to the nearest railroad station for transportation to northern markets. With the advent of packinghouses, the industry took on a different image.

DO-IT-YOURSELF OF YESTERYEAR — W. L. Wetherbee of Boggy Creek delivers a wagon load of his packed citrus fruit to a railroad siding near Kissimmee. Picture taken 1914.

133

When Henry S. Symonds arrived with his parents in the Conway section of Orange County (age 17) in December of 1908 he said there were few shippers of citrus in the Orlando area. As he remembered that in addition to the Symonds' packinghouse, Dr. P. Phillips and Walker Brothers were about the only other shippers in Orlando. Shortly thereafter, he believes Gentile got into the business. Symonds said they first washed fruit by hand in a tub and they shipped a car or two of fruit in a week. Later, they expanded their packing facilities so they could handle a car load of fruit a day. They reached a peak of some 300 to 400 cars a year before a fire destroyed their packinghouse in 1938. According to Symonds a team with a wagon load of fruit (25 boxes) made about two trips a day from the McCoy Airport area to their packinghouse at Peel and Kaley streets.

Another severe weather hazard hit the industry during this post-freeze period. It was the prolonged drought of 1906-'07. According to records this severe and protracted drought lasted for nearly a year in which very little rain fell. It was so bad "that from 10 to 50% of the pine trees were estimated to have died except those that were growing on lower and moister lands".

It was during this severe drought that S. B. Hull and his son Horace S. Hull, Sr. probably instigated one of the first portable citrus irrigation systems in the state at the John Wenkelman grove in the Winter Garden area.

According to H. S. Hull, Sr., the irrigation system consisted of a pitted well, pump, and one cylinder large Hagen engine. The engine used gasoline and make-and-break magneto ignition. The well was located across the public dirt road from the grove, and the water was brought to the property through an iron pipe. The distribution to the trees was through a canvas hose attached to the pipe, filling basins constructed around each tree. Where the hose would not reach the

50 YEAR CLUB — Native-born Orange Countian Ches G. Magruder (left), a 50 year citrus grower welcomes his life long friend T. G. Lee, another native-born Orange Countian, into the 50 year club. Lee's activities were in dairying.

134

tree the water was hauled in barrels to fill the basins. Young Hull's responsibility was to keep the basins repaired and this proved to be an exciting responsibility for a boy because it involved water and dirt that soon turned to mud!

Several citrus pioneers began activities during this rebuilding period (1900-1910) and they should be mentioned because of the contributions they would make in the years ahead.

James Bailey Magruder and his son Ches G. Magruder moved from the Sanford area of Orange County to Orlando in 1900. His father acquired some groves in the Spring Lake area of Orlando in addition to operating a livery stable and other businesses in Orlando. He was also instrumental in helping the U.S.D.A. in locating a building for the staff in downtown Orlando around 1904-'05. White fly had become quite a serious problem for citrus growers and the government was beginning a research project on this pest. Dr. W. W. Yothers joined the staff in 1906. In 1920, these research workers moved to facilities on Parramore Street and conducted research there 'til 1952 when they moved to 2120 Camden Road.

Another citrus pioneer who came on the local scene was Dr. P. Phillips. He had a grove in the Satsuma area but it had been killed by the 1894-'95 freeze. In 1904 he acquired a grove at Lake Silver and a grove at Altamonte Springs in 1907. In 1909 he established his first packinghouse at Robinson Avenue in Orlando.

GROVE MECHANIZATION BEGINS

Years 1910 — 1919

Three unusual events recorded during this period indicated the industry was beginning to respond to changing times. One trend was the hiring of professional care for groves and there were two moves towards mechanization of certain grove operations.

Trying to find out what the industry looked-like during this period we interviewed 89 year old Reasley Vincent who came to Zellwood in 1911. Vincent said there were "scattered" small citrus groves in various locations around the county and these were just beginning to come back into production after the 1895 freeze. Newcomers were coming to the county in "droves" during this period, and a new confidence in growing citrus was evidenced by the greatly increased acreage being planted. However, changes in county boundaries caused some re-alignment of both citrus acreage and population. In 1913, the state legislature created Seminole County from the northeast third of Orange County. After the '94-'95 freeze the

YESTERYEAR CITRUS DUSTER — William "Uncle Billy" Keen, father of the late R. D. Keene is shown here with a pioneer sulfur duster in Dr. P. Phillips grove in 1912.

Sanford area had experienced considerable expansion in truck farming whereas Orange County had geared itself more to the citrus business. These trends along with the fact that urban developments in both Sanford and Orlando offered choice locations for county government, prompted leaders of that day to cater to these sectional interests by creating Seminole County. In 1910 Orange County had a population of 19,107, but the 1913 change in county lines temporarily reduced Orange County's population. However, the big influx of newcomers during the period brought the population up to 19,890 by the 1920 census.

According to reports of the Commissioner of Agriculture of that period, citrus acreage in Orange County increased in spite of the loss in land area. The acreage of orange trees was reported as 7,334 acres in 1910 and had expanded to 14,576 acres by 1919. Grapefruit acreage increase was even more pronounced, from 392 acres in 1910 to 3,355 acres by the 1920 season. The cost of land suitable for grove sites varied considerably. The late Arthur Clarke who came to Ocoee in 1884 reported purchasing 40 acres of grove land near Ocoee in 1912 for $17.50, for the entire 40 acres!

A severe freeze occurred on February 3, 1917 and much of the citrus crop was destroyed. However, little tree damage was reported

136

although temperatures dropped to the low 20's. Apparently the trees were relatively dormant at the time so that they "weathered" the cold without serious difficulty.

This "freeze" caused T. A. Hakes of Winter Park considerable anxiety because of the new citrus variety (Temple) he had discovered on his home property. Mr. Hakes named the variety in honor of his neighbor, W. C. Temple, who was active on the Florida Citrus Exchange. To protect this special tree Hakes had constructed a twelve foot wire fence around it with a padlocked gate to keep potential budwood thieves away. For protection against the February freeze, he constructed a tent over it with a kerosene heater inside and maintained an all night "weather watch". Thanks to these precautions the tree suffered no damage. In May 1919, the Buckeye Nurseries of Tampa began to offer commercially grown Temple trees to the industry. This was one of many "citrus firsts" that Orange Countians contributed to the citrus industry.

The County Agent program for assisting agriculture came into being in 1914 and that same year John Henry Baker came to Orange County as its first agent. E. F. DeBusk replaced Baker in 1917 with high hopes of being able to work with the citrus industry. However, World War I and Federal Government directives to push a "Food-Fiber and Forage Program" frustrated him. DeBusk resigned in 1919 and his replacement, Charlie Kime was able to do considerable work with citrus growers during his 6-year tenure as County Agent (1919-1925).

Probably the first change that occurred in the local industry indicating a new direction was being taken was the creation of a citrus grove caretaking or maintenance business. Grove caretaking services made their appearances after the big freeze of 1894-'95. Several Orlandoans were in the forefront with this new method of operation. Charles G. Lee, the father of M. Donald Lee and dairyman, T. G. Lee "cared for" several groves owned by other people in the Orlando area. These groves were in the Fern Creek, Amelia Avenues and Lake Underhill area. He also cared for the old Hamlin grove on Mills Street (where the Mediterranean Fruit Fly was first found). When many of these "city groves" were subdivided in the "boom" days of the twenties, Lee got out of the caretaking business.

Walter W. Rose was another pioneer citrus caretaker at this time. He started a Real Estate business in 1913 and sold many citrus groves. Frequently, the buyer would ask, "Who's going to take care of it for me?" To answer that question Rose created the Rose Caretaking Association, Inc. in 1915. With Rose in the endeavor was Emil E. Karst who had come to Melbourne from Kansas in 1912 but decided the mosquitos were too much for him and had moved to

PIONEER CITRUS CARETAKER — Emil E. Karst with some young citrus trees he was planting in his home grove in Orlando in 1919.

Orlando. He was doing grove work there when Rose met him. Rose organized the business and Karst supervised the grove operations and Frank Cullen became the bookkeeper. This arrangement prospered for some 30 years even after Cullen died in the late '30's. Around 1946 Karst brought out the association and changed the name to Karst, Inc. At that time it became a family concern. Today, Karst, Inc. does the grove maintenance, cultivation, fertilization and spraying of some 10,000 acres in 5 counties — Polk, Orange, Lake, Seminole and Osceola, and runs a specialized operation in Martin County. It is one of the largest independent citrus caretaking operations in the state.

Another citrus family that came to Orange County during this period was the E. S. Lawrence family of Gotha. Mr. E. S. Lawrence, his wife, daughter and son Fred P. (later to become Extension Citriculturist) moved to Gotha from Lebanon, Tennessee in November 1918. A second son, Douglas, was born in Gotha in 1922. E. S. Lawrence bought several small groves from the Kegals, Weberkings, and Lau's, and also went into the citrus caretaking business. Teenager, Fred Lawrence, helped his father in this capacity. Fred described these caretaking operations as follows:

> "In the early days (before the Pounds rubber tired Fordson tractors), we operated with mules and horses. We took care of groves as

138

far away as Montverde and Plymouth which meant we would camp out during much of the spray season. It took a six mule (two + two hitch) team to pull the old iron wheeled sprayer up those hills in Lake County and my job (as a boy) was to ride the "off mule" and drive the entire six mules with one line. It was quite impressive to some people to see this long rig swing at the end of the rows, turn the machine and go back down the next row. I was also responsible for the maintenance and operation of the old "Narvo" one cyclinder gasoline motor that powered the four piston pump which generated 350 to 400 pounds of pressure on the two 50' rubber hoses the two sprayers drug around the trees. Most days we would apply seven tanks (250 gallon) of spray but some days only one or two because the motor wouldn't run or 101 other things would happen. On our best days (sun to sun) we would put out 14 to 15 tanks. In those days, spraying was done primarily in the spring and summer. Our pests were even more numerous then than now; rust mite, purple and red scale, cottony cushion scale, mealy bugs, and citrus purple mite or red spiders. In the beginning, we used whale oil soap and/or home boiled lime-sulfur. Later oil emulsion, liquid lime sulfur and more modern chemicals came to be plentiful. We also dusted with "flours of sulfur" prolifically and almost constantly to keep rust mite under control.

In the early days, there were no vacuum pumps to suck up the water from the lakes so you drove the spray machine directly into the lake and dipped up the water with buckets. If the water wasn't close, the then version of the modern day nurse tank was a two-horse wagon with four to six, 50-gallon steel drums with one end cut-out were used. The water was kept from splashing out by draping two heavy burlap bags over the open end of the water barrels."

Probably one of the first major mechanization developments was undertaken by Bill Edwards, President of Plymouth Citrus Grow-

KARST HOME SITE — Emil E. Karst in his 12-acre grove around 1921 at S.E. corner of Delaney and Grant Street in Orlando.

ers Association and Superintendent of the Pirie and Laughlin Estates and involved hauling fruit from the grove to the packinghouse.

In many grove operations the harvested fruit was brought from the grove to a loading point outside by hand cart, called a Georgia buggy. This two-wheeled cart carried two field boxes of fruit, of 90 lbs each. Outside the grove the boxes were transferred to a horse drawn wagon where horses or mules pulled it to the nearest packinghouse. According to Henry Symonds of the Conway area, such a rig transported 25 boxes of fruit and made one or two trips a day depending on the distance to the packinghouse.

Although the Pirie Estate was less than two miles from the Plymouth Citrus Growers Association packinghouse considerable time, manpower and equipment was required to move the fruit. So, in the fall of 1917 Edwards put Reasley Vincent, Sr. on a stripped-down Packard truck to determine whether one man with a truck could move more fruit in a day than four men with teams. Vincent said his maximum speed was only 16 miles an hour. Nevertheless, the demonstration was successful and Edwards immediately acquired another truck. Before long others in the industry followed suit.

Another of Vincent's citrus activities at that period should be noted. He and his brother Lester, may have been the first fruit picker "strickers" in Orange County. The two Vincents were picking fruit (citrus fruit was clipped in those days) in 1912 and were paid 3-½¢ a box by the Plymouth Citrus Growers Association. They "asked" for 4¢ a box but were refused. As a consequence they quit and obtained work building boxes in a Lake County packinghouse.

The farm tractor had begun to appear in local groves by the late teens and in 1918, Hoyle Pounds of Winter Garden became Florida's first Ford Motor Company Tractor dealer. By 1919 he had sold eight tractors. Citrus growers were quite reluctant to allow these iron monsters in their groves to "chew up" the tree roots with their cleated metal wheels, and to compact the soil and break-off limbs as they traveled through the grove. Besides, tractors left no fertilizer behind to benefit the trees!

BOOM AND BUST PERIOD

Years 1920 – 1929

In this period the citrus industry experienced two extreme economic conditions. The Florida land "boom" of the early 20's created much real estate speculation and brought many new residents to the area. Some of these new residents became growers who continued in the industry for many years while others subscribed to the "fast buck" philosophy and soon departed for other pastures. Groves were bought and sold as if there would be no tomorrow. Many new developments "sprang" up in various locations to provide northerners an "opportunity" to "invest" in this exciting industry. The Avalon section, southwest of Winter Garden, is one of the areas that was hotly promoted during the land boom of the 20's.

However, the good times ended when the Florida boom collapsed in late 1925. That was followed by the stock market "crash" of 1929 and the Mediterranean Fruit Fly "find" in Orlando. These severe economic shocks fostered upheavals in the industry that lingered until the beginning of World War II. Consequently the industry experienced a large helping of both the "sweet" and the "bitter" in less than 10 years.

Weather-wise the industry got off lightly because no severe freezes occurred during this period. The hurricanes of July 1926 and September of 1928 raised havoc with certain areas of the state but caused no major problem to the local industry. Perhaps the major weather influence centered around the lack of rainfall in 1927. Only 33.84 inches of rainfall was recorded that year, 17.5" below normal. That record still stands today (1975) as the "driest" year since continuous weather bureau records were begun.

Many newcomers joined the industry during this period although time and space permits mention of only a few. Before mentioning these newcomers it should be noted that in 1924 Dr. P. Phillips started in the Sand Lake area of southwest Orange County what was to become the World's largest tangerine planting. In the same area he constructed his second packinghouse which was hailed in 1928 as the World's largest. According to his son, Walter, the September 1928 hurricane interferred with the construction of this packinghouse somewhat but it was completed in time for fall operations.

One of the newcomers in the Winter Garden area was Mr. Phillip Caruso. He left a produce partnership in New York to begin a Florida citrus operation in west Orange County during the 1925-'26 citrus season. From this beginning lead to the formation of Southern Fruit Distributors, Inc., which today is one of the state's largest and oldest independent citrus growers and processors. Many small growers established "family" groves during this period that later played a role in the Orange County history of this industry. Again, space and time allows mention of only a few unusual stories. The Livingstons, in 1924, started a family grove in the Conway area around five seedling orange tree "survivors" of the 1894-'95 freeze that were planted by grandfather George Livingston around 1890.

Ben A. Carpenter another citrus newcomer established groves in the Turkey Lake area west of Orlando. Carpenter's father, Samuel Preston Carpenter had come to Orlando about 1900 and had told his son of the area's possibilities. In 1925, Ben Carpenter came down from Salem, New Jersey, with the Beacon Hill Holding Company to develop groves for northern investors in the Turkey Lake area. Soon he left that organization and started his own grove which is today run by his son, John A. Carpenter.

A rather unusual turn-of-events brought the A. F. Henderson, A. K. Henderson and J. S. Beerman families to the Clarcona area in 1920! At that time, A. F. Henderson was living in Big Spring, Texas, and had mistakenly received a real estate promotion card intended for his neighbor. This card from the Florida Good Homes Company, a branch of a Kansas City Real Estate Agency, extolled the desirable aspects of Florida living. Because of this card Henderson was influenced to investigate Florida and in the Atlas he read a glowing account of the state. As a consequence he wrote the Kansas City Agency and told them he was interested in the possibilities of their Florida Land promotion. That company notified its Florida representative, a Mr. Baxter, in the Orlando area. After considerable negotiation, the Company arranged to trade Henderson 84 acres of Orange County land in the Clarcona area for 320 acres of his land in the Big Spring area of Texas. (On the basis of the Orange County land at $64.00 an acre and the Texas land at $15.00 an acre). This real estate "swap" was accomplished without any currency exchange!

Actually, this transaction brought three families, A. F. Henderson, his son A. K. Henderson and J. S. Beerman to the Clarcona area. Beerman's wife was Henderson's daughter and young Henderson had married Beerman's sister. These three closely related families were typical of many who got their start in the 1920. They had a family milk cow, they raised chickens, home vegetable gardens together and were pretty well self-sufficient while planting their groves. For a while Beerman worked for Arlie Gilliam and his son, Garrett, in the grove caretaking business. Later he established his own caretaking business and was among the first to mechanize his operation with a Fordson tractor. He helped plant the 70-acre Pentuckett grove on Clarcona Road (now owned by S. G. Battaglia) and the nearby Karl Gebhard grove.

A revealing insight as to costs, and the problems of the small grower of the 1920's, was provided by a bundle of old letters loaned us by Mrs. Julia Oddo who presently resides on her grove on Green-acre Road in the Piedmont area of Orange County. During the 1920's, a neighbor, Gust Jackson, cared for this grove which was then owned by Mrs. Oddo's father-in-law, Charles Fox. At that time

Fox lived in New London, Connecticut, and his grove was one of Orange County's earliest absentee-owner arrangements with the grove caretaking done by a neighbor.

Mr. Gust Jackson, a pioneer grower, came to Piedmont around 1889 after having "dug" for gold in California many years. Jackson was a hard-working individual who gave his best and was completely honest. These traits are revealed in his correspondence with absentee grower, Fox of New London, Connecticut. Some of the more revealing "gems", edited slightly, are presented here:

"January 7, 1924

Mr. Charles Fox to Gust Jackson

Due for picking 3 boxes of tangerines	$ .60
Putting up 3 boxes oranges for Christmas	$ 2.25
January 5 for picking 252 boxes of oranges	$25.20
Hauling the same out of the grove	$ 7.56
	$35.61

"Feburary 23, 1924
Charles Fox from Gust Jackson

For picking 11 boxes of grapefruit	$ .55
Hauling out of the grove	$ .33
For picking 559 boxes oranges at 9¢	$50.31
Hauling same out of grove	$16.77
	$67.96

"Feb. 23, 1924
Dear Mr. Fox

-------Well Mr. Fox what do you think of your orange crop if I am not mistaking it was 1226 boxes that I have shipped and it was good and fine fruit. So you got as much as any of us.

Best regards

Yours truly,
Gust Jackson"

"April 10, 1924
Dear Mr. Fox

-------You will see in the Grower that we have had two days convention in Orlando trying to accomplish a better method to market Florida Fruit. It is no use for me to tell you what was done at the convention as you will see it all in the Grower---"

"Nov. 15, 1924
Dear Mr. Fox

-------Your grove is now plowed and fertilized. In regards to how much fruit you will have I can not say but will say that you will not have half as much as you had last year but your trees are much better than mine this year. We are expecting better prices but expenses will not be any less as help is scarce if you get a Negro and his mule to do one day's work it will cost you $4.50. So picking will not be any cheaper. . ."

"Aug. 10, 1925

--------I realize that you have not had anything but expenses but if you were living here and doing your own work it would be quite different.

Well Mr. Fox I know that you are posted on what is going on here is more people coming in Florida than ever. All hotels and boarding houses are full and some very big deals made. So it looks like to me that if you should like to sell your property, I think that you can get more for it this fall or winter than any time before. But as you can not be here and tend to it yourself, I can not see anything in it for you because everything is so high. We can not think of getting a Negro for anything less than $2.50 per day and he will pick his jobs at that. . .

July and August Expenses (Aug. 26, 1925)

7½ days cutting out dead wood	$18.75
5 days cutting out weeds	$12.50
Hauling out dead wood	$ 4.00
	$35.25
Received by check	$25.00
Balance	$10.25

Gust Jackson"

"Aug. 29, 1925
Dear Mr. Fox

I received your letter of the 23rd and glad to hear from you and I must say that I must congratulate you and your family in your pluck in holding on to your property. After all, this year's nothing but expense. So I surely hope that the day will come that you can get something out of it.

As you know I have more land than what I am using but my boys (John and Carl both born in Piedmont 1892 and 1894) don't want me to sell any of it. So you and I can leave it to the youngsters to take care of.

Kind regards to all.

Sincerely,
Gust Jackson"

"Dec. 19, 1925
Mr. Charles Fox

from Gust Jackson

Banking young trees	$ .50
Putting up 2 boxes of oranges for Christmas	$ .75
Paid for picking 180 boxes of oranges	$36.00
Hauling said 180 boxes out of the grove	$ 5.40
	$42.65

144

Mr. Fox no doubt you think that it is an awful price to pay for picking oranges but it was that or leave them on the trees."

"Dec. 1925

------Well Mr. Fox the fruit crop is going to be very short this season. It was estimated short to start with and now since it is about ready to ship the oranges are splitting and dropping. So it looks like half the fruit is on the ground before they start picking. It is very hard to get any one to pick oranges and with so few that are available, they are very independent so we have to pay more this year. I have two picking in your grove now and the very best that I could do is 20¢ per box for picking. Have heard some that paid 30¢ a box . . . .

"Jan. 15, 1926
Mr. Charles Fox

from Gust Jackson

Spraying insecticide	$ 8.50
Labor	$10.50
Hauling water	$ 2.00
Paid for picking 155 boxes oranges	$31.00
Hauling same out of grove	$ 4.65
11 boxes grapefruit	$ .88
2 boxes tangerines	$ .60
	$58.13

"Feb. 12, 1926
Mr. Charles Fox

from Gust Jackson

25 sacks 3-8-5	$75.90
1 sack 5-8-3	$ 3.77
Freight	$ 7.67
	$87.34

"June 10, 1926
Mr. Charles Fox

from Gust Jackson

For work and fertilizer

March 18 cultivating	$ 4.50
April cultivating	$ 3.50
April 25 ½ day cultivating	$ 1.75
May 6 cultivating	$ 3.50
June 1 cultivating	$ 4.50
June 7 — 25 sacks fertilizer 3-8-8	$91.52
3 sacks castor pomace	$10.01
Hauling and spreading fertilizer	$ 7.00
Cleaning out dead trees	$ 1.50
June 11 cultivating in fertilizer	$ 4.00
	$131.78

"Oct. 19, 1926

Expenses on grove

2 tons citrus fertilizer #10 2-8-10

39.75 per ton	$79.50
Agent's commission	$10.00
	$69.50
Discount with cash with order	$ 6.36
	$63.14
P.P. R.R. Freight	$ 6.60
	$69.74

These reports and bills provide many clues regarding picking costs, fertilizer analysis and costs, general grove costs for pruning and fertilizing in that period.

It was also the unpleasant duty of the caretaker to inform the absentee owner of all the bad news concerning his grove. Here are several items that Jackson wrote Fox on that subject.

On April 28, 1925, Jackson wrote Fox — "The report is that the crop is short all over the state and a new insect is part to blame. It is no use for me to try to explain it but citrus aphid is very destructive. I have seen it and I don't expect to get one box of tangerines next season on account of it. It attacks the new growth and destroyes the bloom and the little oranges so it looks like that we are in trouble again."

In May of 1927 Jackson wrote Fox that the new highway (Highway #441) was being built from Apopka to Orlando and that any day it would cut through their groves. Jackson and Fox both lost several acres to the new highway at that time and again in 1955 when it was widened.

Because the fertilizer industry is such an integral part of the citrus industry, a few observations in this field of endeavor are especially timely during this particular period. One time growers fertilized their small groves through a practice of "cow penning". As animal manures became insufficient to fertilize the larger grove plantings, commercial fertilizers came more and more into general use.

Bill Pease of Winter Garden shared with me by letter, an insight of some of the early history of that industry. Pease wrote — "I worked for the Gulf Fertilizer Co. of Tampa for six years and the Peninsular Chemical Co. of Orlando for three years. I had a wide acquaintance among all the resident growers of that era. Among my competitors selling fertilizer were the following salesmen. All of them have passed on by now.

Bill Appling — Non-acid Fertilizer Co., Lakeland
A. Z. Brown — Wilson-Toomer Fertilizer, Jacksonville

Herbert Lyman — Armour Fertilizer, Jacksonville
Green Rader — Armour Fertilizer, Winter Garden
H. B. Harrell — A.A.C. Fertilizer, Jacksonville
Walter Moorman — Gulf, Orlando

Fertilizer in the 1920's and a few years in the thirties was all delivered by rail. A car load was normally 20 tons in 200 lb. bags. Bill Leffler of Chase and Co. in Sanford started the very popular idea of putting up fertilizer in 100 lb. white bags during the '30's.

Chaco was a well known fertilizer and contained heavy amounts of castor pumice. This castor bean meal was a good organic and sold car load bulk for 14.00 per ton at the plant. Many a housewife during the depression years made shirts out of these white sacks.

Labor in those days was plentiful at $9.00 per week for common grove help. I owned the Packing House that is still standing in Ocoee, which I built in 1934 and sold in 1946. Those days we used to sell a lot of fruit to truckers in bulk. Some of them came from as far away as Canada.

Used to enjoy working with the County Agents of those days as well as the USDA lab and the extension service. W. W. Yothers and Dr. A. F. Camp were very good friends."

Not only were the wages low in those days, but workers expended a lot of energy in physical work. Walter Phillips gave me an affidavit concerning a "work record" established in 1926 which bears quoting. It reads as follows:

"On November 11th, 1926, Walter Phillips of the above address and I, H. J. McInvale of Spring Lake Drive, Orlando, Florida, unloaded six carloads of fertilizer in 200 pound bags, without any mechanical help or other assistance. The bags were unloaded from freight cars to a flat body truck. Then we hauled the fertilizer for approximately three miles and unloaded and stacked it in a barn, at the grove. It took us from 7 A.M. to 5:30 P.M. All the fertilizer was in 200 pound burlap bags. Of course, in those days, people knew how to work and were willing to work.

Signed: H. J. McInvale
Walter Phillips"

A clue to the size of the industry in 1928 is given by Moore when he wrote in his annual report of that year — "there were shipped out of Orange County during the citrus season 1927-28 — 3,345 cars of oranges, 1,421 cars of grapefruit and 817 cars of mixed oranges and grapefruit, this makeing a total of 5,583 carloads of citrus fruit. This approximates 2,000,000 crates which at the price that fruit brought last season enriched the county very materially."

147

Mechanization became more widespread in the late 1920's on several fronts.

Hoyle Pounds in Winter Garden was getting more and more complaints from public officials concerning the "highway eaters" he was selling to growers. Also, his tractor sales were suffering because of the damage they caused when crossing the highways in going from grove to grove. In 1928 Pounds received a patent for designing rims that mounted rubber tires instead of cleated metal wheels. This invention greatly accelerated of tractor sales because it increased their efficiency and speed.

Another invention was simmering in Hartford, Connecticut, in 1929. On top of the Oyster Bar Restaurant, George W. Daughtery, a ventilation specialist, thought of a new method of spraying pesticides. Soon he would be in Orlando (1937) building speed sprayers which would make obsolete grove spraying by hand.

The Florida land boom ended in late 1925 and was followed by the stock market crash in 1929. These items together with the Mediterranean Fruit Fly "find" in the Hamlin grove off Mills Street in Orlando in April of 1929, ushered in an era of severe depression for the citrus industry.

Because the shipment of fresh citrus fruit was in serious trouble in 1929 due to quarantine restriction brought on by the Mediterranean Fruit Fly eradication campaign, Dr. P. Phillips and Philip Caruso both started canning operations that year.

Dr. P. Phillips plant was located at the corner of Orange Ave. and Princeton in Orlando and Southern Fruit Distributors, Inc. (Caruso) opened his canning plant in Winter Garden.

DEPRESSION PERIOD
Years 1930 – 1939

The Mediterranean Fruit Fly eradication campaign had such serious effects on the local citrus industry that it is logical that considerable space be devoted to it. One of the best summaries of this campaign and its many ramifications, was that written by Agent Moore in November 1930 as he summarized his activities for that year. Moore wrote — "On the day of writing this report, the papers are carrying the news of the complete removal of all quarantine regulations on Florida citrus Fruits and Vegetables and of our industry's being restored to the same basis, so far as shipments are concerned, as we were previous to the finding of the Mediterranean Fruit Fly in this county in April, 1929. At this time last year, we did not expect to hear such supremely good news for many years.

148

A major part of this year's work with citrus was connected with the fly eradication program. At the end of our last shipping season when we were expected to clean up the groves and the city, a mass meeting was called by the County Agent to consider ways and means of interesting everyone in the county in this proposition. A little over two hundred representative citizens attended this meeting. Mr. H. A. Ward, large grove owner of Winter Park, was elected Chairman and I was elected Secretary. Men attending from different sections of Orange County selected seven others to serve as executive committeemen and to these this campaign was turned over.

They met immediately in my office, and started on the plans. They met again and again with practically 100% attendance. Our County Commissioners appropriated $400.00 for employing an assistant to me, Mr. C. D. Kime, former Orange County Agent, in this task; and the American Fruit Growers loaned the services of Mr. Clay Binion, one of their most influential local men. The names of the whole committee appear on the attached circular letter, which was the first issued.

It must be borne in mind that the Orange County people had lost more heavily in the eradication campaign than any other part of the state. Their trees had been neglected and had been injured most by the arsenical bait spray. They had been incensed by many acts of wanton or ignorant destruction, and in some instances insulted by subordinate employees who were too ardent in the prosecution of their work or unfit for the responsibility placed on them. The majority of our growers had grievances, and many were thoroughly mad and defiant of any further compliance with regulations of the Plant Quarantine and Control Administration.

The personnel of this committee, however, inspired the confidence of almost all the growers in the county. The news articles and appeals were carefully worded and gave no offense. The men on the central committee each selected a sub-committee as carefully as their good judgment dictated. These various sub-committees divided their territories and made a man to man canvass for the clean up. There were less than a dozen serious objections reported to the central committee from the whole county. We began to give ourselves a pat on the back, and a very strong morale was built up.

This made it easier for the committee to back the next step, which was the application of the two bait sprays called for during the summer by the Plant Quarantine and Control Administration. When the Florida Citrus Growers Clearing House Association came forward with financial help to supply the bait spray materials, and the loans of knapsack sprayers, our people fell into line.

149

In this bait spray campaign the direction of the work and much of its details devolved upon me. But the most arduous duties were efficiently assumed by Mr. C. E. Hawkins, representative of the Clearing House. Every property sprayed had to be reported, and all reports came thru our office, were recorded and one copy sent to the P.Q.C.A. and the other to the Florida Clearing House Association. Our Secretary handled these reports with accuracy and expedition.

The records of the Plant Quarantine and Control Administration show that of the 33,000 acres of groves in Orange County over 97% were properly sprayed with the bait spray by the growers or their agents. The Citrus Exchange Association did most of this work for their members.

When all that had transpired in Orange County during the previous year is considered, I believe this to be one of the most noteworthy accomplishments that any people have ever done, and I firmly believe that the clean up work, and the spray applications finished the job of eradication so ably carried on to almost completion under the direction of Dr. Wilmon Newell."

The end of the Mediterranean Fruit Fly campaign in 1930 brought increased activity to the Dr. P. Phillips canning plant at the corner of Princeton and Orange Avenue in Orlando. Four key employees at this plant, R. D. Robinson, General Manager, Carol Floyd, Plant Engineer, D. M. Smalle, retired canning consultant, and T. J. Kew, chemist, combined their talents to produce a major breakthrough in the canning of citrus. The "flash pasteurization" technique they pioneered and use of chemically inert metal in kettles and other equipment greatly improved juice quality and brought quick consumer acceptance of the canned product. Elimination of the unfavorable "cooked" taste and the metallic off-flavor, resulted in a much better product. An intensive marketing and merchandising program of the improved product made processed citrus an important phase of the citrus industry.

The depression made growers extremely "cost conscious" and responsive to new ideas. This situation enabled County Agent Moore to undertake many grove demonstrations in search of good management answers.

Fertilization was a leading question. Moore wrote in 1931 — "Fertilization of citrus groves is the greatest single item upon which I am consulted. My records show 150 such consultations and I am sure there were others of which I have no record. Results on these are very difficult to get because of so many factors that cannot be controlled in a grove, and the unwillingness of almost all grove owners to leave check plots or to measure and grade fruit. However, one owner at Zellwood is comparing a mineral mixture program with that urged by the fertilizer salesman. No differences are to be noted after ten months. The mineral mixture is just slightly over half the cost of the regular formula."

Depression prices and the cost of various fertilizer materials prompted the Florida Experiment Station to release that year a publication entitled "Fertilizer Recommendations". According to Moore, most of the advice which he had given to growers was confirmed in this publication. He went on to say — "A great deal of money has been saved to the growers whose groves were in condition to justify the use of cheap ammoniates only for a few applications, or ammoniates in combination with potash. One man saved $820 as against his regular schedule of about $1100. His grove seems to be in better condition than a year ago; has a good crop of good quality. A. A. Stuart, Winter Park; A. J. Vaughn, Orlando; P. M. Shannbarger, Pinecastle; Miller-Meitin-Shader, Zellwood; E. S. Lawrence, Gotha; George E. Nace, Orlando; R. E. Kline, Windermere, are some prominent growers who have effected large savings in this way. Their groves rank a little above the average at the present so far as I can judge."

An important long-range cost-comparison project conceived by Agent Moore was launched in December of 1930, under the guidance of Extension Economist Frank Brumley. In this system grove cost records were summarized so that the grower would have an idea of individual costs and how his operation compared to the average.

There were 37 growers in this project initially and 32 of them completed their records for the first year. Through the years, other growers cooperated in this project in other counties about the state to provide a better index of grove costs. This project was continued for 35 years and proved a most valuable yardstick with which to compare costs and returns. These records were also helpful to newcomers who asked, "What does it cost to operate a grove and what can I expect in terms of returns?"

In the late 1920's Moore encouraged growers to plant crotolaria in their groves to improve the soil. This practice grew from year to year so by 1931 he reported — "I bought a club order for growers of 16,700 pounds of *Crotalaria striata* seed and 7,300 pounds of *Crotalaria spectabilis*. They saved in this way about $4,000 in comparison with various retail prices."

Moore's recommendation that growers reduce production costs was not limited to fertilizer. In 1932, he wrote — "Thirteen sprayed for scale control upon my advice. What I consider of more importance is the advice to seventeen grove owners not to spray or dust. One of these told me that on my advice he had cancelled his order

T. A. Townsend of Tangerine (6 feet, 1 inch) is proud of this Crotalaria spectabilis just beginning to bloom. From 1/400 of an acre he cut 8.3 pounds, green weight. In young grove of S. S. Sadler. (1931).

with the Exchange to spray his thirty-acre grove with oil emulsion. Most of the trees are large full-bearing size. The last time it was sprayed it had cost him $187.20. These recommendations cover a total of four hundred eighty-two acres."

Moore also championed biological control methods. In 1933 he reported that: "One of the most spectacular demonstrations I conducted this year was the destruction of a terrific infestation of cottony cushion scale in a tung oil tree nursery and an adjoining citrus grove. These trees looked as if a snow storm had loaded them down, when I released thirty larvae of the Vedalia beetles on December 5th. By March 1st I could not find a live scale or a beetle. Their numbers had increased, they had completed their job and gone seeking food elsewhere. I was disappointed in not being able to get some of the beetles from this place for other infestations of cottony cushion scale. However, in January I had gotten beetles from this demonstration for three other infested properties."

Moore reported that the Dr. P. Phillips Company had established the Chinese lady bird beetles in their large citrus acreage at Sand Lake and that Walter Phillips had offered to supply these beetles to other growers. The beetles were obtained originally from the Florida Experiment Station.

In March of 1933 Agent Moore in cooperation with Dr. O. C. Bryan of the College of Agriculture, and growers Emil E. Karst, Harley Lester and Walter Shaffer, instigated an historic grove demon-

152

stration project that paved the way for a new grove practice of great importance. This demonstration centered around the use of soil amendments such as dolomitic limestone, Ocala ground limestone, superphosphate and colloidal phosphate. Moore summarized his observations and results as follows — "In the Shaffer grove slightly better results are shown in the block receiving finely ground dolomitic limestone. Other blocks received Ocala lime rock, phosphate rock and land plaster (calcium sulfate), with the same and varying other fertilizer materials. In the Karst grove the dolomitic limestone block was much better than the others, last year and this year. The tree condition as to foliage color and abundance, and as to fruit was better. The block next to this, received identical applications except Ocala limestone instead of dolomitic limestone. It had the poorest cover crop and tree condition in the series. No differences have shown up in the Lester grove." This historic grove demonstration "ushered" in the practice of using dolomitic limestone to maintain the soil pH and supply trees with magnesium. In the 1934 freeze citrus trees in good nutritional balance withstood cold better than trees that were deficient in certain nutrients.

Advising growers about their fertilizer problems soon had many imitators. Moore's 1936 report alludes to this situation as follows — "There are five fertilizer factories and one large Exchange mixing plant in Orange County, also agencies of eight large manufacturers. Another of the large Exchange buys on bids, all of the fertilizer used by its members. All these institutions have their "Service" men. Also, Professor E. L. Lord, Mr. W. W. Yothers, Mr. McReynolds, and one or two others sell expert advice to several growers. Some of the grove caretaking organizations have 'fertilizer connections'. What with this array of salesmanship, a county agent, whose 'style is cramped' by lack of much definite information 'founded upon experimental data', and who is supposed not to advise anything that he is not sure will give profitable results, is somewhat handicapped."

An opinion by Moore in 1936 was a preview of the future! He recognized that the time when the county agent could set the pace by a field demonstration had passed and that future county agents could expect competition when recommending new techniques or products.

May 10, 1934 is an important date in citrus history because on that date Dr. P. Phillips had his Sand Lake grove of citrus trees dusted by airplane. Sulfur was used to demonstrate that aerial applications could be used in rust mite control. Aerial dusting of cotton was rather a common practice but this was the first aerial dusting of fruit trees in Florida and perhaps anywhere! The Dr. P. Phillips Company practiced aerial dusting regularly in 1937 and up until 1940. At that time the speed sprayer was sufficiently perfected that the company decided ground spraying was more practical. In 1937 Walter Phillips instigated another aerial first when he arranged for an autogiro to spray a block of their Jaffa oranges at Sand Lake with oil emulsion. The tank held 100 gallons and he used one drum of oil and 50 gallons of water, making this experiment one of the first concentrate-type sprays. However, the nozzles didn't function well and Walter wrote the experiment off as a failure.

A severe freeze hit the industry on December 12 and 13th 1934. As a result of this freeze the Federal-State Frost Warning Service came into being in 1935 to provide growers with advance information on "freezes".

In 1935 the legislature created the Florida Citrus Commission and W. L. "Bill" Story of Winter Garden was a member. Thus, an Orange Countian was a member of the first Florida Citrus Commission.

In 1936, Orange County's citrus acreage was estimated at approximately 35,000 acres. Advice on fertilizing and liming was still information most frequently sought by growers. At that time Moore reported an interesting observation that was confirmed by USDA "researchers" in the 1950's. Moore wrote — "Mr. S. S. Sadler, whom I started on a materials program in 1928, has not used any phosphate on his grove since, except on a block of 16 trees in his seedling grove. These 16 trees do not look nor bear differently from the remainder of the grove." However, Moore could not bring himself to advise other growers to follow this demonstration.

During the 1936-37 season, the State Marketing Bureau recognized Orange County as having shipped the following citrus fruit.

4,877 cars of oranges
1,628 cars of grapefruit
  985 cars of tangerines
1,455 mixed cars

8,945 cars of all citrus

Three items relating to citrus reported by Moore in 1937 are worth noting. He wrote as follows: "I collected and mailed about 3,000 'Chinese' lady beetles, at cost, to eight growers in other counties, for the purpose of establishing them over the state to aid in control of Citrus Aphids. The more widely they are established, the more permanent will they become.

I have instructed several growers how to prepare and apply scale fungus to trees infested with red scale. One reported adequate control in a recent letter. I helped one grower secure a colony of Crypt beetles for control of mealy bugs. I instructed several as to where Vedalia beetles could be obtained for control of cottony cushion scale on citrus and ornamental plants.

The use of magnesium limestone (dolomite) in groves has become so general, partially due to results obtained in this county in one of my soil amendment demonstrations of several years standing, that it is no longer necessary to say much about it."

Before the "depression thirties" folded its tent and departed two Orange Countians laid the ground work for two industry wide "firsts".

In 1937, George W. Daugherty established a machine shop at the corner of Robinson Avenue and Kentucky Avenue (now Orange Blossom Trail) to custom-build his newly patented speed sprayer. This new spray machine would soon become a standard piece of grove equipment all over the world because of its efficiency in applying spray materials.

The other Orlandoan was Dr. Ausker E. "Ed" Hughes, who started a bed of "selected" Parson Brown and Valencia orange seedlings in his backyard at 823 North Magnolia Avenue in December of 1937. The following December Dr. Hughes and his wife transplanted the Parson Brown seedlings to his grove site in Plymouth. In 1941 the selected Valencia seedlings were also transplanted to the Plymouth site.

These "selected" seedlings, especially the Valencias, would become world famous in the late 1950's as virus-free sources of budwood under the State's Citrus Budwood Certification program.

CINDERELLA ARRIVES
Years 1940 – 1949

Several noteworthy events occurred in the period 1940-'49. Perhaps the most significant accomplishment of this period was the processing of the first commercial pack of frozen concentrated orange juice (FCOJ) in April, 1946, by Florida Foods, Inc. at Plymouth, Florida. This company underwent several name changes. It was Florida Foods, Inc., then Vacuum Foods, next Minute Maid Corporation then a part of Foods Division of the Coca Cola Company. This "agricultural first" created an entirely new way of life for the Florida citrus industry. The change from a fresh fruit industry to a processing industry took place in less than 10 years. Even the buying and selling of fruit changed. Fruit prices were based on the pounds-solids (essentially sugars) basis rather than on the box of fruit basis.

An event of almost equally monumental proportions occurred when the first army convoy "rolled" into Orlando August 1940, to set up "housekeeping" at the Orlando Airport. In December, it became the Orlando Army Air Field. This base and its support facility, the Pine Castle Army Air Field was home to thousands of servicemen during the war years. Exposure to the Orlando — Orange County area aroused a love-at-first-sight affection for the area in thousands of servicemen. After the war they descended upon the Orlando area in droves and were a major factor in the chain reaction of urbanization. "Spreading surburbanitis" was to gobble up thousands of acres of citrus groves in Orange County in the 50's and 60's.

In addition to the building storm set off by the military "invasion" several "undesirable weather" storms for the industry visited the county during the 40's.

1940 Freeze Damage

Two severe freezes occurred in 1940, one in January and one in November. A former long-time Orange County citrus grower, C. F. "Fran" Fawsett, Jr., (now a St. Lucie County grower) described this freeze as follows:

"I saw 15 and 16 degrees myself, on properly tested and exposed Taylor minimum recording thermometers.
At such places eight-year old lemon-root Hamlin trees had no wood loss. They dropped the outer shell of leaves but retained most inside leaves.

156

Trees were very dormant and withstood cold better than most people expected. Above 18 degrees there was little or no leaf drop on large trees. January had had a very low mean temperature.

In lower and presumable colder places I saw no thermometers but tree damage was much worse. Leaves died in place on dying wood. Where this happened to full-sized trees I knew temperature must be substantially lower than 15 degrees. I guessed 10-12 degrees.

W. W. Yothers of U.S.D.A. had a grove East of Plymouth in which he reported 10, 11 and 12 degrees on three thermometers. I don't remember how the trees fared — I'm not sure I saw them.

The freezes of Dec. 1934 and Jan. 1935 killed more and bigger trees, all in low areas or pockets, as the second freeze found the trees in vigorous growth. I do not believe temperatures were as low as those of 1940, but tree condition was very vulnerable the 'second time around'."

In addition, growers experienced one of the most destructive hurricanes on record October 1944. Orange County growers suffered large crop losses and considerable tree damage.

World War II brought other problems, mainly scarcities to the citrus industry. Scarcities of equipment and supplies were not unique but a scarcity of labor to harvest the crop was an item for the citrus industry books.

Two public labor camps, one at Gotha and one at Zellwood, housed several hundred off-shore laborers. They were mostly Bahamians and very good laborers they were. Dr. P. Phillips and maybe one for two others erected their own labor camps to house foreign workers and a few citrus organizations used German P.O.W.'s from the Leesburg camp.

The use of off-shore labor was continued after the war until around 1965. However, so many restrictions were put on off-shore labor recruitment that the program gradually dried up.

An interesting view of the local industry during the 40's was found in Moore's 1945 Annual Report. Moore wrote — "For several years there has been a trend toward the purchase of small groves by large operators. There is normally a large turnover in grove ownerships but during this past year an astonishing number of groves have changed hands. During the past few years prices of fruit have been very good, and the groves have been better and more adequately fertilized. The trees are generally in fine condition, notwithstanding damage done by the October 1944 hurricane, and the last winter and spring drought."

With most of the news media emphasizing the war the small band of engineers and scientists that gathered at the small pilot-plant in Plymouth Florida during the winter of 1945 was scarcely noticed.

However, the discoveries made by this group sent shock waves throughout the citrus industry of the world. In 1945, the National Research Corporation working with high-vacuum technology experts in M.I.T. produced an acceptable dried orange juice powder for Army food specifications. John Fox, President of this newly formed company had a tentative contract to produce this product in a pilot-plant operation and wanted to locate near a source of orange juice. After contacting the late Linton Allen of the First National Bank of Orlando, Fox hired Holman R. Cloud as Vice-president and moved to locate this proposed plant next to the Plymouth Citrus Products Cooperative plant in Plymouth.

In the winter of 1945 this small band of scientists and engineers began their mission under Vice-president Holman R. Cloud. There was Henry Cragg, Plant Superintendent; Frank Penn, Chief Engineer; Dr. "Wally" R. Roy, Senior Chemist; Hugh Schwarz, Administration; Dan Draper, Financial Affairs; and Jack Keller, Ken Arnett, and Billy Meadowbrooks, Shift Foremen. This organization known then as Florida Foods, Inc. found that the need for orange juice powder had vanished at the war's end. Furthermore, this young company found itself with a 2½ million dollar plant capable of dehydrating 20,000 gallons of fresh orange juice per day.

Fox directed the staff to investigate the new process developed by Dr. L. G. McDowell (Research Director of the Florida Citrus Commission) which consisted of diluting a fourfold concentrate by adding six to 25 percent of fresh, single strength juice to give a fresh fruit flavor. The first commercial pack of this cut-back concentrate, FCOJ, was turned out in April, 1946.

At about this time the company changed its name to Minute Maid Corporation and undertook tremendous merchandising and advertising programs which began to make FCOJ a household product. Wide spread consumer acceptance of the new product sent the industry "scrambling" to build concentrate plants. This new development along with other changes in processing caused Dr. Phillips to close his single-strength juice canning plant in 1949, after 20 years of operations.

In the immediate post-war years several father-son citrus businesses took on new management procedures. This was accelerated by many of these young men returning from the service. Emil E. Karst bought out the Rose Caretaking organization and with his sons — Art, Chester, George, Loyd, and Roy, renamed it Karst, Inc. Philip Caruso, of Southern Fruit Distributors, Inc. moved his canning plant operations to Pineloch Avenue in Orlando. During this post-war period he was joined by his sons — Austin A., Joseph M., Philip P., and son-in-law John J. Walsh.

In Apopka, R. G. Pitman and his son R. G. Pitman, Jr. (in 1948) started the Florida Ponkan Corporation to propagate and sell his patented mandarin-type orange. However, the poor shipping qualities of this fruit became apparent and the Pitmans changed their citrus operation to meet the demand for standard varieties brought on by the citrus concentrate boom. The Pitman Nursery became one of the largest in the state and R. G. Pitman, Jr., was elected first President of the Florida Citrus Nurserymen's Association which he helped to organize in the early 1950's.

Over in Winter Garden, Roper Brothers joined the cooperative trend by becoming Roper Growers Cooperative in February of 1947.

The Winter Garden Citrus Products Cooperative which had been organized in 1944 as a single-strength juice plant was laying the ground work under Bert E. Roper in December of 1949 to become a concentrate plant. It began operating as a concentrate plant in March of 1950.

Because of the concentrate stimulus, a rash of new grove plantings were made in north Orange County and several other isolated spots. Old timers cautioned that these were cold spots and quite undesirable sites for new groves.·

During the 1940's Orange Countians, T. C. Hawthorne, C. Walton Rex, Wilbur L. Tilden, M. H. McNutt, Dan L. McKinnon, W. L. Story, and R. A. Fendler were appointed to sit on various citrus commissions.

In 1940 Orange County's citrus acreage was 44,600 acres but by 1949 it had expanded to 59,000 acres. Many out-of-state investors became interested in the citrus industry, largely because of the activity generated by the concentrate business. By the end of the 1940's the industry was on a decided up-swing.

"TROUBLES"

Years 1950 — 1959

The currents of the 1950's flowed in many directions but for Orange County's citrus industry the decade might be labeled as one of — "troubles". In the forefront of these troubles were two new virus diseases, a new vine pest, several "hard" freezes and an extremely "wet" year. To add emphasis to these problems, Orange County was "de-throned" from its position as the state's second leading county in citrus production.

Although these two new citrus virus diseases were first discovered in Orange County, they were later found to be wide-spread

159

in other citrus producing counties of the state. Dr. J. F. L. Childs, Plant Pathologist with the USDA Horticultural Laboratory in Orlando, announced in 1950 his discovery of a virus disease affecting Orlando tangelo trees on the Bill Story property south of Winter Garden. The disease, Xyloporosis, was not new since it had been described in Palestine in 1931. However, the cause of the disease was not known. That this disease was caused by a virus and that it was present in Florida added two "firsts" in the record book.

The excitement about this new virus "find" had hardly died down when Dr. T. J. Grant, also of the USDA Horticultural Laboratory, announced in 1952 the discovery of the dreaded tristeza or Quick Decline virus disease in the Winter Garden — Ocoee area of the county and a "positive" find in the Avon Park area.

Apparently these two new virus disease "finds" were not trouble enough because the late Donald Nicholson reported that a strange new weed pest, a vine, had become a major problem in his grove on Grand Avenue in Orlando. He observed this new vine pest first in 1957. However, by 1959 he became alarmed at the rate it was spreading through his grove. After considerable correspondence, the late Erdman West, Botanist and Mycologist at the Florida Agricultural Experiment Station in Gainesville identified this milk weed vine as *Morrenia odorato* Lindl. In a few years thousands of acres of citrus groves all over Central Florida would be infested with this new pest.

These new diseases and the new vine pest were apparently not problems enough because the weather man "slapped" the grower with a series of bad freezes in December of 1957 and January and February of 1958. The development of frozen concentrated orange juice in the '40's had stimulated grove plantings in some very cold locations in the county. After 10 years of mild winters, the owners thought the old timers had been too harsh in their appraisal of these locations. Then came the awakening, a series of freezes in the '57-'58 season that demonstrated once again that land suitable for citrus in Orange County had long since been planted and that all other land was marginal or submarginal.

This was followed by an extremely "wet" year in 1959 with rainfall 12 inches above normal. Groves on low ground, especially in the old vegetable areas of Ocoee and Winter Garden, "experienced" flooding and drainage problems.

The "wet" year of 1959 was followed by a still "wetter" year in 1960! In fact, it exceeded the '59 record by some five inches — 17.32" above normal.

Perhaps the most humiliating news of all came in 1955 when the Florida Crop and Livestock Reporting Service revealed that

160

Orange County citrus production rank had fallen from second to third place and that Neighboring Lake County was now in second place. The "Countdown" had begun.

To further assist in the countdown of Orange County agriculture, the Martin Company of Baltimore bought a 7,300-acre site in southwest Orange County for a defense plant on September 14, 1956. This announcement immediately brought about a frenzy of land speculation. Citrus growers soon discovered that they were first of all in the land business and only secondarily in the citrus business. This new attitude towards land and land-use would cause many new problems. Grove values would increase but so would assessments and taxes.

Those seeking a quick way out of the grove business sold for what they considered exhorbitant prices. However, they watched with amazement as land prices continued to rise. This land speculation sealed the lid on the agricultural "Countdown".

All the news was not discouraging, however. A practice that emerged in the early 1950's was the use of chelated iron to correct iron chlorosis of citrus trees. This discoverey was made by Doctors Steward and Leonard at the Lake Alfred Citrus Experiment Station. In 1952 County Agent Baetzman arranged a demonstration with 17 Orange County growers who had iron chlorosis in their groves. A commercial company supplied the iron chelate to be applied at the rate of a 1/3 pound per large tree. Among the first cooperators to use this material for demonstration purposes in Orange County were — A. H. Bunnell, Lockhart; Neil Dale, Crown Point; Walter E. Dale, Chickasaw Trail; Irene Gundersen, Lockhart; Charles E. Hawthrone, Woodsmere; E. S. Lawrence, Gotha; Ches Magruder, Hickory Nut Lake; Dan McKinnon, Oakland; P. C. Peters, Winter Garden; H. L. Plane, Winter Garden; R. G. Pitman, Jr., Apopka; Dorsey Prescott, Orlando; R. G. Sims, Ingram Road; J. M. Sullivan, Windermere; H. Tanner, East Orange; Mayia Tomyn, Minorville; and C. C. Wilder, Jr., Orlando.

In October 1954, Assistant County Agent H. F. Swanson was appointed Program Leader for Extension citrus activities in Orange County. Upon acquiring a local Citrus Extension Advisory Committee, they recommended he develop programs that would keep growers posted on the latest information concerning all facets of the industry. One of his first projects was to establish a Citrus Production Roundup meeting that would bring the growers the latest research information. These monthly sessions began in April 1956 and continued through May 1972, when they were discontinued because of dwindling attendance.

In June of 1955 Agent Swanson began distribution of the first

161

monthly citrus newsletter in the state. This practice has now been adopted by some 10 other counties.

During the 1950's, the Governor tapped three Orange Countians to serve on key policy making state bodies. Frank Roper of Winter Garden and Frank Chase were appointed to the Florida Citrus Commission. Dr. Ralph L. Miller, Orlando citrus consultant and grower, was appointed to the Board of Control which supervised the state universities, Experiment Station and the State Plant Board.

In 1961 the State Plant Board which had been autonomous since 1915, became the Division of Plant Industry, a department under the Commissioner of Agriculture.

During the mid-1950's Highways #441 and #50 were widened to meet the increasing traffic demands placed upon them. This widening process saw the destruction of several thousand mature citrus trees due to the fact many groves bordered these two major highways. In 1927, this new Highway (#441) passed through the Charles Fox and Gust Jackson groves at Piedmont and both growers lost a good number of citrus trees. Now 30 years later (1957) their descendants saw additional trees removed from these two groves as the highway right-of-way was expanded.

The expansion of these two major highways through the county helped set the stage for the "sizzling sixties" and the grove eaters!

"GROVE EATERS"

Years 1960 — 1969

Growers literally found themselves "floating" into the 1960's. They considered 1959 a wet year because rainfall of 12.4" above normal had occurred. However, when the rainfall for 1960 was tallied, growers found the 17.37" above normal made that year the all time record breaker since continuous weather records were begun locally. That year Hurricane Donna passed through Florida in September and the "eye" passed over Orange County. Many folks believed that it was responsible for the record rainfall but such was not the case. The rainfall in September of 1960 was only 3.98" above normal. September 1945 with 15.87" was the "wettest" recorded above normal rainfall. Actually the cummulative trend started in March of that year when a record 7.13" above normal was recorded and March 1960 with a grand total of 10.54" rainfall is still the wettest March on record.

In addition to the record rainfall, the 1960's also set a low temperature record for the century. On December 12, 1962 a large mass of artic air moving into the state and created a disastrous freeze with temperatures ranging from 15°F to 20°F in many locations on the morning of December 13th. The strong winds associated with this hard freeze largely nullified the natural protection devices such as high ground locations as well as artificial ones. Groves located on hill tops were literally "blasted" by the freezing winds whereas some groves in lower locations were shielded somewhat. Under normal conditions cold air settles in the pockets and low ground areas and citrus trees in such locations experience more cold damage than on high ground locations. Because of the wind velocity from the '62 freeze reversed this situation and hurt many high ground groves worse than those on low ground. Those who viewed the damage from the air, reported that Lake Apopka had moderated the cold front considerably and that groves south of the lake were a normal green whereas groves east, west and north of the lake exhibited all degrees of cold damage.

Of all the groves damaged by the '62 freeze, the Glenn Brown grove on the Round Lake Road north of Zellwood at the Lake County line won the "conversation" honors. The owner had "elected" to try his newly installed overhead irrigation system as a cold protection device. However, the low volume of water, emitted an inadequate amount of heat. Furthermore the continuous spray combined with the extremely low temperatures and high winds, proved disastrous. The wind driven spray turned to sleet and built up on these large trees until many split and fell apart under the weight of the ice formed. The scene in this grove next morning was like a fantastic winter wonderland. A solid sheet of ice covered the ground. Trees were split apart as if a tornado had passed through and yard-long icicles hung from all the trees. This "cold protection technique" eventually caused the complete removal of all trees and the replanting of the entire grove.

As Orange Countians recovered from one of the worst freezes of the century, they received more bad news from another direction. For years they had enjoyed being the #2 county for citrus production but then when Lake County dumped them into 3rd place they believed that their 3rd place position was assured for years to come. However, when the 1963-'64 production figures were tabulated Orange County found itself "bumped" down to 4th place. St. Lucie County had not been seriously hurt by the freeze and with many new groves coming into production it could expect increased future production each succeeding crop year. Orange County could see the handwriting on the wall. Its days as one of the "Big Three" in citrus production were numbered!

Nevertheless in February 1964 Orange County recorded a

"family" first for local citrus record books. Lee Mathews, the first Production Manager of Plymouth Citrus Growers Association retired after 30 years service (1934-'64). His son, William H. "Bill" Mathews was appointed to replace his father in this position.

The year 1964 signaled another "first" but of an unwelcome kind for the local citrus industry. That year a single adult weevil of the sugarcane rootstalk borer weevel, *Diaprepes abbreviata,* was found in a citrus nursery in Apopka. This "find" was the first ever in the state but it alerted plant inspectors to double their inspections. In 1968, many "finds" were made in the Apopka area. Thus Orange County became the first county in the state to acquire this insect pest from Puerto Rico. These discoveries were followed by others and today (1975) the infested area is quite large in north Orange County. To date no control measures are in sight.

The big freeze and the sugarcane rootstalk borer weevil both helped set the stage for the urbanization of many groves. However, it was the announcement on November 15, 1965 which showed that the "grove eater" era had arrived. On that historic date Walt and Roy Disney announced their selection of a site in southwest Orange County for the new Disney World entertainment complex. What the Martin Company announcement of September 1956 did for Orange County land speculation was just a sample of the urbanization boom that the Disney announcement triggered. This super entertainment complex fostered all kinds of urban development that literally "gobbled up" groves.

Added to that, the construction of Interstate Highway #4, the Sunshine Parkway (later re-named Florida Turnpike) and the Beeline Expressway through Orange County during this period "gobbled up" hundreds of acres of citrus groves and opened up large tracts to urbanization.

On the more peaceful side several Orange Countians were appointed to the Florida Citrus Commission in the 1960's. Those who served were — Henry Cragg, Frank Chase, George T. Carson, Robert S. Kazaros and Earl M. "Duke" Crittenden.

A change also took place in local Extension activities in the field of citrus as the '60's drew to a close. County Extension Director Swanson assumed full administrative responsibilities for the local Extension staff and John L. Jackson, Jr., Extension Agent II — Citrus Multi-County, became Extension Program Leader for citrus activities in Lake and Orange Counties.

In retrospect the '60's can be listed in the history books as the beginning of the countdown for the Orange County citrus industry. Even the famous "Orange Avenue" in downtown Orlando began to lose its former economic prestige to outlying shopping centers. The citrus industry as well as names of streets and businesses associated with it no longer had the same glamour as when the orange was king. As one wag put it, "its time to change the state flower from the orange blossom to the concrete clover leaf, our state flower should be symbolic of the times!"

BICENTENNIAL THOUGHTS

Years 1970 – 1975

Judging from the experiences of Orange County's earliest citrus pioneers such as Sidney O. Chase, J. R. A. Tucker, James E. Hill, William C. Roper and Hugh Hungry McClure, the local citrus industry appears to have reached its centennial anniversary in the 1970's. Some would set the first date prior to Florida's becoming a state but it must be remembered that citrus plantings earlier than 1870 did not exist in the area now known as Orange County. Consequently, trends had already been established which indicated that the citrus industry was on its way out before its hundreth birthday! Evidence of this is contained in the citrus inventory reports released by the Florida Crop and Livestock Reporting Service, as follows:

YEAR	TOTAL CITRUS ACREAGE, ORANGE COUNTY
December 1969	65,961
December 1971	60,567
December 1973	56,320

As an unpleasant comparison it is pertinent to note that in Orange County, California, the home of another Disney entertainment complex the citrus industry has declined at a much faster pace. According to the Farm Advisor, H. Leonard Francis, their citrus industry is going out of business at the following rate:

YEAR	TOTAL ACREAGE, ORANGE COUNTY, CALIFORNIA
1947	76,000
1950	65,000
1955	47,000 (Disneyland opens)
1960	34,000
1965	24,000
1968	21,000 (Estimate)

PEOPLE AND CITRUS LIKE MILD CLIMATES — West Covina, California citrus area in 1948 and the same area a few years later.

Many American cities sprang up around the best farm land in an area, although the locations of some cities were determined by access to rivers, harbors and railroads. However, as more and more people are attracted to an area, the adjacent land becomes converted to housing and a new population center results. To be a part of such a transition is one thing, whereas moving to an area after the transi-

166

tion, is a vastly different experience. Thus the citrus groves that were once a part of Orlando have given way to urban development triggered by the vast flood of people that descended upon Orlando since 1940.

THE LAST ONE — The Mary S. Compton grove on South Orange Avenue and Michigan is the last commercial citrus grove on Orange Avenue (1975).

Orange Avenue is the principal thoroughfare through Orlando and the last commercial citrus grove located on it, as of today (1975), is the Mary S. Compton grove located at Michigan and South Orange Avenue. Miss Compton, now in her nineties, told me that when she, her brother, mother and father acquired the property in 1925, they were "way out in the woods". Although the Comptons had moved from Chicago they didn't feel at the time that they were too distant from downtown Orlando. However, many of their friends believed the Comptons had located "too far out in the country". Today, the Compton grove is completely surrounded by business enterprises and the area is zoned commercial. Soon it will be another place where — "a good grove once stood". To speed the exodus of the grove the property was denied assessment on an agricultural basis several years ago and must now pay property taxes on the basis of its **potential** urban-use rather than its **actual** grove use.

Promoters, speculators and similar public-spirited interests have long known it was to their economic advantage to have land reclassified to a so-called "higher and better" land-use category. Converting citrus groves to urban use involves real estate commission fees, engineering and architectural services, and other renumerative operations. However, this "flurry" of economic activity is short-lived and consideration should be given to the long-range effects.

Citrus groves are highly compatable with out hydrological cycle whereas urban land-use is not. For 70 years Orlando has been cov-

167

ering up land with impervious layers of asphalt and concerete. It is now finding most of its land-locked lakes thoroughly polluted with storm runoff water from these urban areas.

However, a far more serious problem is beginning to raise its ugly head and the get rich-quick boys need to do some reconsidering. Otherwise a major disaster will occur when the land-use — rain cycle circuit becomes overloaded.

The citrus area west of Orlando and south of Highway #50 (north of Disney World) is recognized by hydrologists as the county's prime underground water recharge area. Since this citrus area "captures" the rainfall that recharges the entire Orlando area's ground water supply, land-use devoted to citrus has served the urbanite well. However, this citrus area is becoming "whittled away" by urbanization and the ground water recharge potential is being reduced. Furthermore, more and more water supplies are being withdrawn daily to meet increased urban demands. The well could run dry! It has happened in other areas.

Many students of rainfall cycles contend that urban development creates conditions that can alter rainfall. Whether this be true only a long range study of 75 years or more can substantuate and by then it would be too late.

Nevertheless it is worth noting that since the last "wet" year (1960) the past 14 years have totaled up to a 41" rainfall deficit! The last five years reflect an ever increasing trend toward deficit rainfall and whether this is in proportion to urbanization, is anyone's guess. These last five years are shown below:

YEAR	ORLANDO OFFICIAL RAINFALL RECORDS
1970	- 7.41" Deficit
1971	-11.28" Deficit
1972	- .28" Deficit
1973	+ 4.00" Surplus
1974	- 6.99" Deficit

In recognition of the importance of citrus to Orange County, a special citrus tree planting ceremony was held at the County Court House on November 22, 1963. Upon that occasion, Commissioner of Agriculture, Doyle Conner, County Commissioners and local legislators planted a Valencia orange tree on the Court House grounds. This tree symbolizes the citrus industry that has meant so much to the county and from which the county derives its name. However, one wonders if it will still be there 50 years from now or whether future Court House expansion will see it removed?

The Countdown moves on.

168

CHAPTER V
History of the
Ornamental Plant Industry

A person seeing for the first time the numerous ornamental plant nurseries in the Apopka, Plymouth, Zellwood area of Orange County and learning of its great economic importance, invariably wonders what caused the industry to locate in Orange County.

Perhaps a brief account of the early history of the industry will put the situation in perspective. In a special article on the "foliage industry" in the Orlando Sentinel, November 19, 1972, Linda Tomlinson wrote that the background of "Florida's role in the foliage industry began in Springfield, Ohio, in 1912, when a Mr. Powell sales manager of a Springfield Floral Company thought of growing the expensive Boston fern outdoors in Florida. Powell shared his idea with Harry Ustler (there were three Ustlers, Harry, Frank and John) an order clerk of the company. Together they discovered that in Florida Boston Ferns could be produced for a fifth to a tenth the usual cost.

Harry Ustler came to Florida to look over the area and set up shop and expected Powell to follow. However, Powell was unable to come to Florida due to financial problems and Ustler realized he lacked the necessary funds to begin planting the Boston fern. To bide his time Ustler took a job as a waiter at the Altamonte Springs Hotel. There he became acquainted with W. P. Newell, one of the hotel's guests. The two men became friends and Ustler shared the fern growing idea with Newell.

Newell advanced the necessary capital and the two men established the first Boston fern operation in a slat shed near Lake Eola in Orlando, that was previously used for growing pineapples.

The Lake Eola site was used only a short time before these men moved their fern growing operation to some land that Newell owned in Apopka.

According to Paul Ustler his father Frank started Ustler Brothers Fernery in 1917 and was joined by Harry and later by John. However, it was Harry Ustler who was the first to come to Florida. The birth of the idea of growing Boston ferns unquestionably originated in Springfield, Ohio but it was Harry Ustler who brought the idea to Florida. It was his enthusiasm for the fern business which encouraged brother Frank and his son Paul to come in 1917 to be followed by John in 1920.

This historical vignette provides some clues regarding the individuals who "pioneered" the growing of Boston ferns, but the question of "why Orange County?", remains unanswered. In the absence of other data, I believe that Newell and Ustler were attracted to the area and did not meet in Central Florida entirely by chance.

Around the turn of the century, Florida was not generally regarded as the "Land of Flowers". Stories concerning mosquitoes, rattlesnakes, alligators, and swamp fever convinced many visitors that "where" they visit in Florida should be carefully selected. Even in those days the Orlando-Winter Park-Maitland-Altamonte Springs-Apopka-Zellwood area of Central Florida was regarded as something of a tourist mecca. As a matter of fact, the Orlando slogan of "The City Beautiful" originated in 1908 according to Orange County historical records. Mrs. W. S. Branch, Sr., the wife of a prominent civic leader and a worker in beautification efforts, suggested the slogan.

Neighboring Winter Park, called itself "City of Homes" and home of Rollins College, shared with Orlando top billing as an attraction for northern visitors. Even the rural areas of Orange County were endowed with natural scenic beauty. This was recognized at an early date because the beautiful Laughlin and Pirie Estates were both early "horticultural show places" in the Zellwood and Plymouth areas of northwest Orange County. Several people connected with these two estates would become actively involved in "pioneering" the Boston fern industry.

In retrospect, historians will probabaly concede these natural beauty assets were responsible for attracting Newell and Ustler to this section of Florida. Had they been attracted elsewhere in the state, Orange County may well never have gained such prominence in the production of ornamental plants.

In addition to the scenic beauty assests of the area, there were two eminent horticulturists living in the area who were beginning to make some major contributions in their horticultural activities just after the turn of the century.

Dr. Theodore Mead had come to Florida in 1881. He lived in the Eustis area five years before moving to the Oviedo area (then northeast Orange County) in 1886. For the next 50 years Dr. Mead did extensive plant breeding work with orchids, amaryllis, crinums, caladiums, gladiolus as well as with many other tropical plants and trees.

In western Orange County (Gotha), Dr. Henry Nehrling was also making many outstanding contributions to the horticultural world with his enormous introductions of tropical bamboos, palms and other plants along with his hybridization work. Dr. Nehrling had established his Palm Cottage Gardens in Gotha at the turn of the century. Thus, it was only natural to expect the area to attract other pioneer growers of exotic plants.

FIRST COMMERCIAL PLANTING OF CALADIUMS — Dr. Henry Nehrling is shown inspecting his caladiums at Gotha, Florida March 21, 1917. Dr. Nehrling first introduced caladiums to Florida and as a result of his introductions an industry was born in Highlands County in the 1920's. Photo courtsey step-son Robert D. Mitchell.

FORMATIVE YEARS

1900 — 1919

It is obviously impossible to recognize every pioneer horticulturist, native born or early settler. There are just too many. However, we shall attempt as many as we can manage.

At the turn of the century Orange County was distinguished by having two eminent horticulturists in residence — Dr. Theodore L. Mead and Dr. Henry Nehrling. Throught the years these two made many direct and indirect contributions to the local industry. We hasten to point out that the men were not alone in this field and one of the first women active in this area was Mrs. John Mays Caruthers of Orlando. In 1908, Mrs. Caruthers had a hobby of growing pansies, violets, and sweetpeas in her backyard. Friends and visitors kept asking her for bouquets 'til this "hobby" blossomed into the first

171

florist business in Orange County — Caruthers Violet Dell Florist! Her small Lord and Burnham greenhouses at Gunby and Lake Streets, built around 1916, were probably the first commercial greenhouses in Orange County.

Another who later started his own nursery was Robert D. "Bob" Mitchell who arrived in Gotha in 1910 at the age of 11. His father had come to Florida for his health but died soon after coming. Later, his mother married Dr. Henry Nehrling of that community, a pioneer ornithologist, botanist and horticulturist. Dr. Nehrling was also a collaborator of the office of Foreign Plant Introductions and his gardens at Gotha contained exotic plant introductions from all over the world.

Young "Bob" Mitchell was awarded a scholarship to Washington University in St. Louis and also studied at the Missouri Botanical Gardens under George Pring, Professor Alex Laurie and many other distinguished horticulturists. Later he returned to Orange County, started his own nursery and made several major contributions to the local industry.

Mr. and Mrs. Jones Vincent and their seven children came from Texas to Zellwood in 1911. They intended to start a vegetable farm on the newly opened Apopka marshland. His intentions never materialized but all four of their sons — Reasley, George, Jim, and Lester Vincent went into the business of growing Boston ferns in the 1920's. Reasley and Lester Vincent would later establish nurseries and florist concerns of their own in Zellwood that their sons would continue and follow in their footsteps. Also, Lester's grandson would later become affiliated with the business. This pattern of families starting with Boston ferns in the 1920's and continuing in the ornamental plant business for the next 50 years became the pattern for the local industry. This "in the family" tradition of growing ornamental plants from one generation to the next provided a continuity and strength to the industry.

Martin J. Daetwyler arrived in Orange County about the same year as the Vincents. He started a citrus nursery in the Pine Castle area about the time Ustler and Newell were beginning their Boston fernery. In the early 1920's, Daetwyler began to specialize in the landscape business and soon had one of the largest nurseries of this kind in Central Florida. He also had a large business of selling peat for garden use.

Daetwyler's nursery operations were also the starting point for several future nurserymen. Mr. Mulford B. Foster joined Daetwyler in 1924 and several years later established his own Tropical Arts Nursery and later gained international recognition as an authority on bromeliads.

Ken Soper worked for Daetwyler after school during the late 1920's and later as a full time employee. Later he worked for McColley's Bamboo Nurseries, Inc. while running his own nursery on the side.

John Rice Springer was another pioneer horticulturist in the early teens who wore two hats. Springer, one of the University of Florida's earliest agricultural graduates, came to Orange County in 1915 to work for the John Schnaar Insecticide Company. Later he was a pioneer grower of leatherleaf ferns and Orange County's first nursery inspector.

Another pioneer horticulturist during the teens was Texas emigrant Victor Pilat. He came to Apopka in 1918 from the famous King Ranch in Texas to try his hand in growing Boston ferns.

Native-born Orange Countians who also played key roles in the 1920's or "Foundation Years" were Harry M. Smith, Winter Garden; Mallory Welch, Wallace Champneys, and Gillen McClure, all of Apopka.

OLD TIMERS — Orange County's first nursery inspector John Springer (left) examines foliage plant with pioneer foliage grower Harry Smith — Smith built first commercial foliage greenhouse in Orange County. *Photo Winter Garden Times.*

Harry Smith was born in Winter Garden in 1904. He and his father, George Thomas Smith, started a landscape nursery, ultimately became one of the largest foliage plant nurseries in west Orange County.

Wallace T. Champneys was born in Apopka in 1908. His father, William T. Champneys, was one of those "converted" to the fernery business by pioneer W. P. Newell in 1918.

Mallory Welch, born in Apopka in 1897, began growing Boston ferns around 1922. Welch's record of growing only Boston ferns

173

from 1922 to 1958, earned him the title "Dean" of Boston fern growers. Although the Ustlers grew Boston ferns all those years, they did so in later years only as a side line crop.

Gillen McClure, native Apopkan (1889) started growing Boston ferns in the early 1920's and was in and out of the business with his son George who re-entered the ornamental plant business in a big way in 1972 by buying the Ustler's nursery.

The ornamental plant industry experienced its first major freeze on February 2, 1917. It was the contributing factor for moving the beginning of the caladium industry from Orange County to Highlands County, in a round about way.

According to John Springer, February 1st was "shirt sleeve weather" but during that night a severe cold front moved in. The next morning it was 19° at Springer's home in the Conway section southeast of Orlando. Springer said "ice formed" in a pitcher inside his home!

Dr. Nehrling was so disheartened by the extensive damage experienced at his home in Gotha as a result of this severe freeze that he moved his operations further south.

A friend invited Dr. Nehrling to use his property near Naples. However, this Naples site was reclaimed by the heirs in 1924 and Dr. Nehrling was asked to move. He was offered a site near Sebring and moved several truck loads of his prized caladiums there. Later the deal fell through and certain parties acquired his prized caladium bulbs.

Dr. Nehrling returned to Gotha and died shortly thereafter (1926).

So, the freeze of 1917 caused the first collection of caladiums in Florida to move from Orange County to Collier County and finally to Highlands.

It should be pointed out the many small ferneries established during the formative years by Ustler, Powell, Pilat, Champneys and others, were backyard ferneries of ¼ to one acre in size.

FOUNDATION YEARS
1920 – 1929

When the year 1920 rolled around, several ferneries were operating in the Apopka area. These stimulated others to go into the Boston fern business during the early 1920's. Several who started ferneries in the Apopka area during this period were – W. W. "Wade" Walters and his young wife Mary, MacFadden, McFarland, Mallory

Welch, Tom R. Smith, John William Smith, Leslie P. "Ted" Waite and Gillen McClure.

Mr. William Edwards, Superintendent of the Laughlin and Pirie Estates, was instrumental in starting a four acre Boston fernery in Zellwood. Mr. Reasley Vincent was foreman of the Laughlin Fernery and Reasley's brothers, Jim, George, and Lester were also in the fernery business during the early 1920's. Claude Bell and E. W. Fly both had ferneries in the Zellwood area and William Edward's son, Steward, had a fernery at Plymouth and another near Lake Gem.

The fern business became so active in the Apopka area in the early 1920's that in 1924 the City of Apopka adopted the slogan, "The Fern City."

The year 1924 was a monumentous one because of a new fern variety. That year, John R. Springer, Orange County's first nursery inspector discovered a "leatherleaf" fern at Frederick W. Fletcher's florist establishment located at Lemon and Jackson Streets in Orlando. Springer was so impressed with this new fern variety that he immediately obtained some stock plants and started a leatherleaf fernery in the Conway area. He hired a William Hayward to help him operate his nursery while he continued as a nursery inspector for the State Plant Board for a seven county area.

Shortly after becoming associated with Springer in this operation, Hayward's wife visited friends in South Portland, Maine. A next door neighbor, E. S. Marsell, heard of her "glowing report" of the fern business in Orange County and promptly came to Orange County to investigate the situation. He was favorably impressed and as a result bought out Fletcher's entire stock of leatherleaf plants for $6,000. He bought some property in Zellwood off Round Lake Road and established a leatherleaf fernery. E. W. Fly joined him for several years in this business.

There are two versions of the origin of this new species of fern in the Orlando area, Springer's and Marsell's. According to Springer, Fletcher was an orchid grower and probably obtained this fern as packing material in a shipment of orchid plants from Brazil in the early 1920's. Marsell believed that Fletcher bought the leatherleaf stock material from a floral company in Auburndale, Massachusetts in the early 1920's. In either case, John Springer was the first to grow leatherleaf ferns commercially in Florida. He has a check for $14.40 from S. S. Pennock Company, wholesale florist of Philadelphia dated July 14, 1924 that establishes his first shipment of this fern. He received three cents a leaf.

The Zellwood Fern Growers marketing activities preceded those of the Orange County Fern Growers Association. An Orange County

Chamber of commerce publication of the mid 1920's provides us with an insight into the business of fern growing of that period.

"The fern growing industry, represented by the Zellwood Fern Growers' Association, a co-operative organization of fern growers, is one of the prosperous and successful organizations of this section. The association was organized in 1922 and shipped their first orders in 1923. The total spring business was 285,000 ferns. The business grew and prospered until the season of 1925-26 showed a total shipment of 850,000 ferns with an approximate value of $62,775. With the business rapidly expanding the year 1926-27 will witness a shipment of considerably over one million ferns. The market for the Zellwood ferns is the entire United States and parts of Canada and the varieties of asparagus plumosa and asparagus spengeri, shipped under the trade-mark 'Dewkist' are well known throughout the entire country, particularly in the larger centers.

Interesting, it is, to know that the association of fern growers has twenty-one members and that the acreage under shed is nearly forty. To clear the land, shed, stock and prepare for irrigation, costs in the neighborhood of $3,500 for each acre. A good average yield an acre is something like 14,000 ferns in the fall and 40,000 in the spring. The cost of production annually is around $1,500 an acre."

Mr. William Edwards, a leader with the Zellwood Fern Growers and in community affairs, "spear-headed" the creation of the Apopka Fern Growers Association. The purpose was, improve the bargaining position of fern growers with buyers by uniting all fern growers under one marketing organization. This, he accomplished in 1928 and secured John Masek from the accounting firm of Potter, Potter and Bower in Orlando as Sales Manager of this co-operative.

As with any industry-wide organization, not every one chose to become a member. Some major growers who did not affiliate were — W. W. Walters, Tom R. Smith, Mallory Welch, and Gillen McClure.

Shortly after this industry-wide organization was established in 1928, the stock market crashed and economic conditions of the country went into a tail spin. Also, the Mediterranean fruit fly appeared and the ensuing eradication campaign of 1929 and early thirties, did nothing to help the ornamental plant industry or its new marketing co-operative. These factors led to the Apopka Fern Growers' collapse in 1934.

A landmark in the history books of the ornamental plant industry occurred in 1928 when there was the "first" recorded attempt to grow a foliage plant for the trade.

While on a visit to his parents in St. Louis in 1928, fern grower W. W. Walters met D. S. Geddes, a florist in the area who did business with Walters. While visiting Geddes' greenhouse, Walters saw some *Philodendron cordatum* and asked for some of the plant material to try in his Apopka fernery. He planted the Philodendron so it could grow on a trellis his fernery. However, this method of growing was not attractive for this plant because it sends out roots at every node. The rank growth that occurred with this vine type culture impressed no one favorably and after two years Walters destroyed his test planting of Philodendron.

How this tropical plant came to be widely grown in various St. Louis greenhouses during the 1920's is a story in itself.

R. D. "Bob" Mitchell, who was first to grow *P. cordatum* commercially in Orange County in 1930, provided us an insight to its historical background. Since he attended horticultural classes at the Missouri Botanical Gardens in the late teens and early 20's while a student at nearby Washington University, Mitchell became well acquainted on the horticultural activities of the Gardens.

According to Mitchell, *P. cordatum* was first introduced into the St. Louis area by the Missouri Botanical Gardens from its substation in Bogota, Columbia. This introduction was made in the early 1920's and Dr. Jesse Greenman, a taxonomist with

PHILODENDRON PIONEER — Robert D. "Bob" Mitchell of Shore Acres Nursery off of Holden Avenue in Orlando was first commercial grower of *Philodendron cordatum.*

the Missouri Botanical Gardens was the individual who properly identified and named this new plant introduction.

Growers in the St. Louis area were growing it extensively as a greenhouse plant by the mid 1920's.

After working in the St. Louis area for several years Mitchell returned to Orange County in 1929 and established his Shore Acres Nursery just off Holden Avenue in south Orlando.

The activities of other pioneer horticulturists during the "Foundation Years", should also be recognized because they were to play important roles in the industry for the next several decades.

Billy Glenn, Editor of the Orlando Sentinel newspaper in the 1920's, visited Mulford Foster in West Palm Beach and told him his landscape talents were needed in the Orlando area. Foster came to Orlando in 1924 and worked for M. J. Daetwyler as a landscape architect for several years before he started his Tropical Arts Nursery.

About this same time (1926) Harry M. Smith and his father, George T. Smith started a landscape nursery in Winter Garden.

At this same period, the Caruthers' Violet Dell Florida establishment was located on Delaney Street across from the Al Coith Park in Orlando. By the end of the 1920's the Caruthers had moved their retail florist shop on Court Street to the San Juan Hotel building in downtown Orlando where it would occupy this prominent place for the next 20 years.

A World War I Veteran who was attracted to the Apopka area to go into the fern business was Hugo Pilat. The fact his father was already in the fern business was another reason for his settling in Apopka in 1921. During the 1920's he worked for W. P. Newell and W. W. Walters before starting his own florist business in Plymouth during the 1930's.

The 1920's also saw an influx of a great many young men into the business who became partners with their fathers or someone else and who would go on to become some of the foundation nurserymen of the industry for the next 50 years.

In 1926 William T. Champneys' son Wallace, reached the age to go into the fernery business as his partner. Champneys' nursery would be one of the first to have a greenhouse in Apopka by early 1930 and it would continue as a family nursery so typical of a good many nurseries that began in the 1920's.

The middle 1920's saw Raymond Clay Hogshead bringing his family from Virginia to try his hand in growing ferns. After clearing his tract in the Plymouth area in 1927, he was ready for his first crop of ferns in 1928.

Also during the 1920's several school boys were getting "exposed" to the ornamental plant business and who would later use this horticultural experience to devote their lives to the ornamental plant business, for the next 40 or more years!

For instance, there was the Mahaffey brothers, Jim and Tom, whose father, C. O. Mahaffey figured if they had a 3/4 acre fernery, it would keep his boys busy and "off the streets" during non-school days. Since his business was concrete construction, Mahaffey instilled in his sons the desire to make their fernery pay its own way. So in 1926 these recently transplanted Georgia boys got "exposed" at an early age to the nursery business. Jim remembers in 1928 he was earning $60.00 a week working in the fernery while the principal of the Apopka High School was earning only $50.00 a week at his prestigeous postion. The Mahaffey boys also worked in several nurseries during their school days. Mallory Welch remembers contracting with the boys for weeding his fernery.

178

Verne Buck, Joe Wofford and Ken Soper were other "school boys" who worked for various ornamental plant nurseries during and after school hours during the 1920's.

Soper worked for M. J. Daetwyler Nurseries in Pine Castle from 1926 to 1929 during "off school" hours. Then in 1929 he became a foreman after graduation and worked for Daetwyler for the next 10 years. He started a nursery of his own and also worked for Bamboo Nurseries for 17 years (1951-1968).

Joe Wofford worked at the C. R. Lott 5-acre leatherleft fernery on the Clarcona Road in the late 1920's. Later in 1932 Wofford became foreman of the fernery. In the 1940's he went into the service and upon his return in 1946 he purchased the fernery and has operated it until the present time 1974.

Verne Buck another school boy who worked in various nurseries, came to the area from Tennessee in 1921. Buck's father was in the construction business. So Buck's exposure was similar to the Mahaffey boys. He worked For Ustler Brothers, Champneys, and Tom R. Smith fernery. In 1933 he graduated with Tom Mahaffey and a few years later he joined the John's organization in 1935.

By citing these various individuals and their activities during the 1920's it becomes increasingly obvious why this period might be referred to the Foundation Years. Many of these individuals and their families would be associated with the ornamental plant business down through the years. Some would have a third generation of the family involved in the same business some 40 years later!

FERN DEPRESSION YEARS

1930 – 1939

Long-time ornamental plant grower Tom Mahaffey described this period in the history of the Ornamental Plant Industry as the "Fern Depression" period.

For many years growers had relied on the Boston fern as their money crop. There was no incentive to diversify the industry so every new fernery just added to the overall marketing problem. When the fern market started to fall apart because of the stock market crash, the fern growers found themselves in serious trouble.

Furthermore a major problem associated with the Boston fern was its seasonal nature in that growers harvested two crops of ferns a year. After Memorial Day in May, the selling and harvesting of ferns was closed down for the summer months. Then after a growing season of several months the industry was ready for another period of harvesting and selling.

This cyclic economic activity and poor economic conditions generally, prompted growers to look for other indoor foliage plants to breathe some new life into the industry.

Since *Philodendron cordatum* became a commercial foliage plant during this period and later became the "money-maker" for the industry, a historical account of this particular foliage plant is in order.

Robert D. "Bob" Mitchell of the Shore Acres Nursery adjacent to Lake Jessamine off Holden Avenue, was the first to grow and sell commercially *Philodendron cordatum* in 1930. Although Wade Walters was first to grow it, he was not successful in finding a market for it. Mitchell's contact as a former student and landscape architect relations with the Missouri Botanical Gardens paid dividends in this regard. After graduation from Washington University in St. Louis, Mitchell had worked several years in that area before moving back to Florida in 1929.

One of ·"Bob" Mitchell's "Missouri contacts" from his Washington University days was Glenn Turner then head of the National School of Floral Design. In the early 1930's Turner visited Mitchell in Florida and encouraged him to grow *Philodendron cordatum*. Turner promised to talk it up all over the country and to send him customers. Florida was a more logical place to grow *P. cordatum* than St. Louis and Turner thought Florida could produce this plant more profitably. So with this encouragement Mitchell ordered 500 plants from Frank Serloff and Company of St. Louis and started growing this foliage plant commercially in 1930. So historians can record that W. W. "Wade" Walters "first" grew cordatum in Orange County and Florida but Mitchell was the first to grow it commercially. The credit for stimulating a market for this plant must go to Glenn Turner and his travels about the country in his National School of Floral Design activities.

Mitchell was also the first to introduce Chinese Evergreen, *Aglamena simplex*, into Florida (1930). Again, Mitchell's contacts with key personnel at the Missouri Botanical Gardens unlocked the door.

George Pring, Superintendent of the Gardens had suggested that Mitchell, through the U.S. Consul in Shanghi, China, make contact with a shipper for this plant. Through this Chinese exporter Mitchell received some bare canes of the Chinese Evergreen in late 1932 or early '33. Other local growers also secured propagation material of this plant but according to the timing of these shipments Mitchell was "first" with this new Orange County introduction.

Mitchell was also the first grower in the county to grow Silver Marble pothos. He secured the stock plants from the Bourdet Floral Company in 1940.

In 1930, another new ornamental plant was entering the commercial trade in the county. B. M. Sangster of South Orlando purchased half an acre of amaryllis bulbs from Dr. T. L. Mead. By 1953, Sangster had expanded his amaryllis planting to over 70 acres and the size of his operations earned him the title "Amaryllis King of the World".

In 1935, Mulford Foster made the first of his many plant collecting safaris that later earned him the title of world's authority on bromeliads. On this first trip, he went to Mexico, West Indies, Central and South America and brought back over 200 plant specimens of the bromeliad family. All were new to horticulture.

Another important milestone was the construction of greenhouses for growing foliage plants. According to John Springer, nursery inspector of that period, Harry Smith of Winter Garden completed the first large commercial greenhouse around 1929 or early 1930 and Wallace Champneys of Apopka was the next to follow.

These houses saved these owners from severe plant losses when the hard freeze of December 12 and 13th, hit the state in 1934.

The slat sheds and smudge pot heaters were powerless against a freeze of this magnitude. As a matter of fact, growers had no forewarning that such freezes were expected.

According to Tom Mahaffey, citrus and ornamental plant growers were generally "warned" of approaching cold weather by a passing train. In those days, if a train traveling south encountered severe weather in Georgia it would tell Florida folks of the approaching cold front by tooting its whistle for five long blasts. In the early 1920's, Apopka growers were forewarned of potential freezes by W. T. Berry, agent for the Seaboard Railroad in Apopka. Berry obtained reports of freezing weather by telegraph and passed these on to interested growers. After the severe 1934 freeze, the Federal-State Frost Warning Service was instituted to forecast by radio the approach of freezing weather throughout the state.

Two of today's growers, Reasley Vincent, Jr. and Ed Fly, recalled their boyhood experiences in firing nurseries in the 1930's. Fly remembered "firing" one of his father's slat houses to protect the chinese Evergreens. A rat ran through the shed and in the excitement of shooting it, the slat shed caught fire and destroyed all of his father's stock plants! Vincent's experience was more serious and left him with physical scars. As a 10-year old boy he was assisting his father in the firing operations one cold night when his "slop apron" became saturated with fuel oil and caught fire. He became terrified and started to run. However, his father caught him and rolled him the dirt to extinguish the flames. The scars from these burns on his leg are a constant reminder of that painful experience. Others were less fortunate and several fatalities were recorded. Wood was the principal fuel for heating ferneries at the early period and Mallory Welch remembered being told that smoke would prevent freeze damage. To test that idea he soaked piles of sawdust with oil and ignited them during a freeze. Plenty of smoke was created but the ferns still froze!

During the "Fern Depression" several recent high school graduates joined the ranks of full time employed nurserymen. Jim Mahaffey graduated from Apopka High School in 1932 and started his own nursery. The following year his brother Tom followed suit. Verne Buck a high school graduate of '33 joined John Masek in 1935 and was put in charge of buying, selling and shipping. When the Apopka Fern Growers Association folded in 1934, Masek bought plants from individual growers and contracted for ferns and other foliage plants. By 1939 John Masek had the nucleus of a marketing outlet around which to build his own nursery, later known as "John's".

POTTING FOLIAGE PLANTS at John's Nursery in Apopka.

Two high school graduates moved up to foremen in nurseries and later developed their own nurseries. Ken Soper became a foreman for Daetwyler in 1931 and continued there for 10 years. Joe

182

Wofford became foreman of C. R. Lott's leatherleaf fernery on Clarcona Road. After a period in armed services he returned in '46 to buy the fernery. In 1934 Raymond C. Hogshead moved to the Miami area to start a nursery there. However, his wife and son, Raymond B. "Bunny" Hogshead continued to operate the nursery in Plymouth.

E. W. Fly and E. S. Marsell dissolved their partnership in the leatherleaf growing in 1931 and both went their separate ways. Fly decided to grow Boston ferns and other indoor foliage plants and Marsell specialized in the leatherleaf to the point of becoming the county's largest grower.

The 1930's marked the appearance of another floral concern in Orange County. Hugo Pilat decided after having worked for several fern growers for the past 10 years it was time to start his own business. So he started Pilat's Florist in Plymouth in 1931, a time of great uncertainty. Today, some 44 years later, Pilat is still a going concern!

Julian Nally arrived in Orange County in 1934 when his parents acquired the old Nehrling Estate near Gotha. Under his stewardship it once again became a horticultural garden with an unusual floriculture endeavor!

In 1934, Harry Smith and his father sold 200 five-ton truck loads of landscape plants to the Ravine Gardens in Palatka. This sale caused them to enter the foliage plant business and to grow sansevierias, bromeliads, and Ficus species.

In the late 1930's the Wallace T. Champneys Nursery added azaleas to their list of ornamental plants which already included Boston ferns, leatherleaf ferns, *Sansevieria laurentii, Sansevieria Zeylanica* and others. These trends to diversify with new plants indicated the era of "one cropping" was a thing of the past for the nurserymen.

The 1930's witnessed a temporary departure from the nursery business by pioneer grower Mary Walters. Because of the death of her husband she had to take up outside employment to raise her family. Since she loved the nursery business she vowed she would return when conditions provided her the opportunity. (In 1944 she returned and today her son and grandson are in business with her).

In reviewing the agricultural industry of the 1930's, County Agent Moore mentioned more and more often in his annual reports the ornamental plant industry.

During the 1920's, citrus, dairy, vegetables, and poultry were the big money makers in the agricultural family and the ornamental industry was a "stepchild" in that no mention was made of it in agents annual reports.

In 1931, when the Orlando Chamber of Commerce instituted a program to bring 1,000 new farmers to the county over the next 5 years, K. C. Moore prepared a summary sheet on the possibilities in the ornamental plant business. He wrote as follows:

For Bulbs, Ferns & Ornamentals: "Acreage required from one to five acres, capital investment high per acre. Special skill and temperament necessary. These things are in the luxury class and in normal times the returns on investment are satisfactory!" No doubt Agent Moore considered citrus, vegetables, dairying, and poultry to be in the major industry category with beef a minor category item. The ornamental plant business was considered a luxury item with little future in the depressed economy of the 1930's. Between the depressed national economy of the 1930's and the war clouds of World War II on the horizon, the ornamental plant business looked anything but bright. Nevertheless the industry managed to forge ahead during the 1940's.

EMPHASIS ON FOLIAGE PLANTS
1940 – 1949

The ornamental plant industry of Orange County began with the Boston fern in 1912, but after the "fern depression" set in around 1934, the industry looked for new plants for indoor use. Some of the plants investigated and tried during the 1930's were: *Sansevieria zeylanica, S. Laurentii, Ficus elastica, Euphorbia lactea, Euphorbia meritolia,* peperomia, pothos, *Philodendron cordatum* and *Aglamena simplex.*

Knowledgeable growers of that period, credit the late Dr. John Masek with quantity sales of these new indoor plants in the late 1930's and early 1940's as the moving force for converting the industry to the foliage plant business.

The "fern depression" ended the Orange County Fern Growers Association in 1934. At that time John Masek started developing a system of mass-merchandising the new indoor plant varieties. Masek leased several ferneries and also bought plants from other growers such as Clay Miller, John Springer, R. D. Mitchell, to mention a few. This was a new merchandising concept for the industry and it started a trend that was helpful for growers who were unable to mass-merchandise their plants. Masek started building his own nursery in 1939 and Verne Buck became his chief co-ordinator of activities. No doubt Masek's many activities during the early 1940's breathed new life into the industry during the period of transition and economic uncertainty.

However, during this period of the early 1940's other nurserymen were still active in various other aspects of the industry. Mallory

184

Welch and the Ustler Brothers continued growing Boston ferns while E. S. Marsell, C. R. Lott and John Springer were major producers of the leatherleaf fern. Wallace Champneys, the Mahaffey brothers, Harry Smith and others were gearing their operations more and more to these new indoor foliage plants. At the same time B. M. Sangster was growing amaryllis in the Conway area, Mulford Foster was doing well with bromeliads and M. J. Daetwyler was doing likewise with landscape plants in the Pine Castle area.

County Agent Moore recognized these activities in a section of his 1940 annual report by writing — "This county is the center of amaryllis bulb production and there is a large industry involved in the growing of ferns, asparagus plumosa and ornamental plants".

The 1940 Census of Agriculture revealed the ornamental plant industry of Orange County became 4th in income and was within $3,000 of being in 3rd place as these figures show. The value and rank of importance of agricultural commodities in the 1940 Census of Agriculture were as follows:

RANK OF IMPORTANCE	COMMODITY	# OF UNITS	VALUE
1st	Citrus	1,422	$2,943,056
2nd	Dairy	47	$ 321,164
3rd	Vegetable	34	$ 199,793
4th	Horticultural Specialty	74	$ 197,062
5th	Poultry	108	$ 117,734
6th	Livestock	20	$ 29,073
	TOTAL		$3,966,816

Several major freezes in 1940 destroyed a great many plants. Wallace Champneys lost all of his Sansevierias and others claimed similar losses. The temperature records show that the county experienced temperatures in the low 20's and down into the teens on January 27, 28, and 29th and again on November 16th and 17th of that year (1940).

These "freezes" coupled with memories of the 1934 freeze no doubt convinced many growers that greenhouses were a necessity and not an expensive luxury. Some growers believed that Harry Smith's and Wallace Champenys' expensive greenhouses were impractical liabilities. However, the freeze caused many to re-evaluate the practicality of greenhouses for plant protection.

At this time Peter Pearson appeared on the scene. Tom Mahaffey described him as the "father of the glass houses" for the industry. Mrs. Mary Odom described her first encounter with Pearson which occurred one cold morning about daybreak. She had been firing all night with the crude smudge pots of that era when in "popped" Peter Pearson dressed in a heavy coat, muffler, and gloves.

TYPICAL GREENHOUSE —
This one at John's Inc. occupies an acre under glass.

His opening remark was — "It seems to me you folks could devise some other means of heating your plants". Peter Pearson brought many second-hand greenhouses from Chicago in the early 1940's and sold them to many nurseries in the Apopka — Plymouth — Zellwood area.

With the advent of World War II many local nursery men left to go into the service. To mention a few there were Jim Mahaffey, Joe Wofford, Raymond B. "Bunny" Hogshead, B. P. Nelson, Reasley Vincent, Jr., and Verne Buck.

There were even a few new nursery "starts" during the early 1940's which might be considered unusual with the appearance of World War II and all of its drain on men and resources.

The O. F. Nelson and sons B. P. and Earl began growing African Violets and Orchids in Orlando. This backyard activity later led the Nelsons to become major producers of ornamental plants in the Apopka area.

In 1944, Mary Walters, now Mary Odom, decided the time was right for her to get back into the nursery business. With her new husband in the service and her children old enough to help her, she borrowed some money and established her Wayside Gardens Nursery.

Several other happenings in the 1940's should be noted because of their historical place in the development of the local ornamental plant industry.

Out in Gotha, Julian Nally began growing gloriosa lilies that had been introduced there by the late Dr. Henry Nehrling. Nally found florists all over the country quite enthusiastic for these attractive flowers as corsage items. Service men ordered these attractive corsage blooms in lieu of orchids for their wives or girl friends so this unusual florist item built up to a sizeable business during the war years.

186

In 1942, the Laughlin Estate at Zellwood became Hampden Dubose Academy. This transition altered the activities of Reasley Vincent, Sr. who had been affiliated with the Estate for over 20 years. Vincent left to start his own nursery. With his knowledge of azaleas acquired at the Laughlin Estate, he started his nursery at Zellwood with 150,000 seedling azaleas. Later, he and his son, Reasley, Jr., expanded the azalea operation into a large foliage nursery. Another case of a nursery that got its start during the war years.

In the late 1940's, right after the end of World War II, there were several other events which took place that need to be recorded because of their historical impact on the industry in the years to follow.

Raymond Clay Hogshead who had left Orange County to establish a nursery in Miami in the 1930's, went on a plant safari to Costa Rica during this post war period. According to Tom Mahaffey, Hogshead brought back many tropical plants and introduced them to the trade.

Mulford Foster another world traveler for plants, also was active during this period and acquired more recognition for his tropical plant explorations. In 1945, his book, "Brazil, Orchid of the Tropics", was published.

Al Dudley, of the Aldot Farms adjacent to Long Lake, came to Apopka because of an unusual series of events.

Dudley and his neighbor, Hans Stimpfle were both in the ornamental plant business at Hicksville, New York prior to World War II and both saw the market potential for *Philodendron cordatum*. It was Dudley who wrote in 1940 to Harry Ustler urging him to devote an entire greenhouse to the production of this particular foliage plant. Ustler replied that this item was already overplanted and he refused to devote that much space to an item doomed to failure!

During World War II Dudley went overseas on a civilian military project. While in the service he and Hans Stimpfle, his neighbor, vowed to move to Apopka when the war was over and grow Philodendrons. So, in 1945 Dudley and Stimpfle came to Apopka to look for a place to establish a foliage nursery. However, Stimpfle wasn't impressed with the area and returned to Long Island. After examining several locations Dudley settled on his present site near Long Lake.

Robert H. (Bob) McColley was another out-of-stater who also came to the area in the late 1940's and later would make a name for himself in the industry.

In 1949, McColley rented the site of the present Winter Park Drive Inn Theater and Hollieanna Shopping Center in Winter Park for his first venture into the ornamental plant business.

This was the situation at the end of the 1940's. The stage was set for great expansion of the ornamental plant industry in Orange County.

AN INDUSTRY IS BORN

1950 – 1959

Continued growth of the ornamental plant industry in the 1950's soon placed it among the leaders in economic value. The three Census of Agriculture reports during this period illustrates the importance of the industry.

CENSUS YEAR	RANK IN COUNTY	NUMBER OF UNITS	VALUE OF PRODUCT
1950	5th	183	$1,851,975
1954	2nd	221	$2,542,999
1959	2nd	263	$8,585,508

During this period, 1950 – '59, the ornamental plant industry became Orange County's second most important agricultural industry.

In keeping with the changing times the City of Apopka changed its slogan from "Fern City" to "Foliage Capital".

The importance of this industry was further recognized in 1957 when Agent Swanson requested the State Extension office in Gainesville to put up matching funds for an ornamental plant specialist for the Orange County Extension staff. Once the state office agreed, a similar request was made to the Board of County Commissioners. This budget request was co-operatively funded by the state and county and on November 1, 1959 William E. Colburn was hired for this new position.

The Job Description called for 30% of his time to be devoted to the ornamental plant problems of homeowners and 70% of his time to be devoted to commercial industry problems. A few years later Colburn resigned to go into private business. Today, he is owner and manager of Cypress Creek Nursery, Inc., a wholesale landscape plant nursery in southwest Orange County. Bruce Barmby assumed this position upon Colburn's resignation in 1961.

There were two major problems which occurred during the 1950's that dealt "body blows" to the industry. One was the Korean War that started in August of 1950 and continued for several years. The other was a series of severe freezes with temperatures in the low twenties on December 12 through 14th of 1957 and January 9 through 11th and February 4th and 5th, 14th, 17th, 18th through 22nd of 1958.

The effects of the Korean War on the foliage industry is not reflected in census reports. Unlike World War II, the Korean War did not completely disrupt the economy. It affected primarily the lives of individuals. Men called into service had their lives interrupted and this worked personal hardships. Some of those who were affected were C. M. "Mac" Walters, Jack Christmas, Larry Cobia and Earl Nelson, to cite a few.

The problems created by the severe freezes of the 1957 — '58 season were probably more serious for the ornamental plant industry than the Korean War. For example, it terminated Mallory Welch's long record of growing Boston ferns. Welch started growing Boston ferns in 1923 and grew this one variety continuously for the next 25 years despite the influx of a long list of new indoor plants through the years. Other growers dropped this item after the "Boston fern depression" or took other indoor foliage plants to supplement their operations, but Welch did not. However, after the disatrous freezes of the 1957 — '58 season, Welch decided that the Boston fern was too difficult to grow.

Julian Nally of Gotha, experienced hardships not associated with the weather. Nally had built up a nation-wide market for flowers of the gloriosa lilly, *Gloriosa rothschildiana*. He "inherited" these bulbs with the old Nehrling Estate and developed this flower into a highly sought-after corsage item during the war years. However, by 1955 his gloriosa plant had become so generally infected with a virus disease that Nally had to destroy all of them. He continued to grow several varieties of bromeliads, however.

During the 1950's several nurseries made major changes in their operations. Robert H. "Bob" McColley moved his Bamboo Nursery from Winter Park to a site on the Clarcona Road just off Highway #441. Ken Soper, a Daetwyler Nurseries employee for 10 years, joined McColley. By having an experienced employee as Soper to do the routine nursery business, McColley was able to devote his extra time to experimenting with the hybridization of Philodendrons.

The Fernwood Nursery of Plymouth also made some major changes. Ed Fly bought out his father's interest in 1950 and began a program to expand the nursery his father had started in the 1920's.

The O. F. Nelson and Sons Nursery on Lawrence Road (now Sheeler Avenue) was in the development stage in 1950 when O. F. Nelson quit his job with Central Paper Company to devote full time to the business. Shortly thereafter his son B. P. Nelson quit his job with Hughes Electrical Supply to assist full time and in 1959, the other son Earl quit his job as Assistant County Agent in Manatee County to make a three-way family partnership.

While these various foliage plant nurseries in the Apopka area

189

were expanding, B. M. Sangster's 70-acre amaryllis bulb-growing operations in the Conway section began to decline. The expansion of housing units in that area was the problem. As more of this land became more valuable for housing developments, Sangster was unable to lease land for growing amaryllis bulbs. Because of his age and failing health, Sangster decided not to move to a new location.

The 1950's recorded several "firsts" in the ornamental plant industry of Orange County. For example, Mulford Foster, of the Tropical Arts Nursery in Orlando helped establish the International Bromeliad Society in 1950 and became its first President. He also became the first editor of its Journal.

Jim Mahaffey of Apopka established a "first" of sorts, he constructed his 50,000 square feet fiberglass greenhouse in 1952. This new greenhouse was a major topic of conversation of that day. Jim also built the first greenhouses in the Hobe Sound area of Martin County in 1950 — '51. Today, these nurseries are known as Gulfstream Nurseries.

Another ornamental plant industry "first" of the 1950's was the hybridization of a new variety of Philodendron by Robert H. "Bob" McColley of the Bamboo Nurseries. Bob's first successful Philodendron hybrid "Florida" was released to the trade in the mid 1950's. Because of the color and leaf characteristics of *P. lacinithium*, one of its parents and the cold tolerance inherited from its other parent *P. squamiferm*, the new hybrid was readily accepted.

Emerald Queen and Burgundy were two more successful Philodendron hybrids created by McColley and released to the trade in the late 1950's. Later McColley's hybrids were patented and released differently.

The totem-pole practice for *Philodendron cordatum* was a successful idea that emerged in the early 1950's. Exactly who originated this concept is now unknown but the early experiences of one pioneer are worth noting. Al Dudley of the Aldot Farms, near Long Lake in the Lockhart area, remembers producing some totem poles with *P. cordatum* in 1948. He tried selling some to Caruthers of Violet Dell Florists but was refused. They could see no market for this item on a totem pole. Dudley left a half dozen of the *P. cordatum* totem poles with DeVane the florist. However, they were slow movers. Obviously, Florida customers were not ready for this item. However, at the florists conventions in St. Petersburg, Florida and Savannah, Georgia, in 1950, Dudley interested several out-of-state buyers and soon the totem pole item caught on.

In the 1950's the industry sought other channels of transportation than railway express for shipping plants. For historical reasons some old transportation charges for shipping leatherleaf ferns should be noted. According to John Springer a pioneer grower of Orlando, railway express gave growers a flat rate for shipping leatherleaf ferns in wooden boxes containing between 600-800 leaves. Some of the charges, according to old shipping invoices, were as follows:

1952 Boston, Mass.	15 lbs. of Ferns	$2.01
1953 Boston, Mass.	15 lbs. of Ferns	$2.01
1953 Philadelphia	15 lbs. of Ferns	$1.81
1953 Washington, D.C.	15 lbs. of Ferns	$1.78
1954 Memphis, Tenn.	15 lbs. of Ferns	$2.01
1956 Boston, Mass.	15 lbs. of Ferns	$2.39
1958 Boston, Mass.	15 lbs. of Ferns	$2.94
1957 Boston, Mass. (June)	15 lbs. of Ferns	$2.39

INDUSTRY BIG DEALS

1960 - 1969

During the 1960's the ornamental plant industry undertook several "big deals" which revealed that it had developed some muscle. Up to this time, the interests of the industry were so diversified that any unified action was next to impossible. By the 1960's however, the idea was generally accepted that the industry needed a state research unit to work on horticultural problems. The industry also needed a co-operative buying organization that would save the grower some money. For these two needs industry leaders banded together to demonstrate that muscle is a necessary ingredient for action.

The 1960's also saw many new plants introduced to the trade. McColley of Bamboo Nurseries and Larry Cobia of B. L. Cobia Nursery, both introduced several patented new varieties that they created or found. Raymond B. "Bunny" Hogshead introduced *Maranta crythroneura* to the trade during the '60's. Jim Foster of Perrine, Florida had obtained the stock plants of *Maranta crythroneura* from Brazil but encountered problems in trying to produce quality plants for the market. R. B. Hogshead discovered that soluble salts were hampering growth of these plants and causing their unthrifty appearance. By correcting the condition he was able to produce healthy plants the trade would accept.

In the early 1960's Nelson's Nursery introduced container-grown roses to the wholesale trade, creating another "horticultural first" for the industry.

However, there were some unfortunate events that occurred during this period that should be recorded of this historical significance. Dr. John Masek, pioneer nurseryman and founder of John's Inc., died in 1964. That same year the Caruthers sold their Violet Dell Florist business after 50 years of continuous operation!

191

One of the first "big deals" the industry attempted was to secure a university research unit to work on problems connected with growing ferns and foliage plants. The need had been made known previously but was rejected by University of Florida administrators. Several industry leaders believed the time was opportune for another attempt.

Jack Christmas, of the Oakdell Nurseries, was President of the Central Florida Chapter of the Florida Nurserymen and Growers Association (FNGA) in 1962. Christmas and County Agent Swanson discussed ways in which the request for a research facility might be revived. Both agreed that Dr. J. R. Beckenbach, then Director of the Florida Agricultural Experiment Stations would have to be convinced first. In recognition of this need, Professor Alex Laurie, of the Whistling Pines Nursery at Dona Vista and formerly on the staff of Ohio State University, was invited to carry the ball because Dr. Beckenbach had been a student of Professor Laurie's.

In October of 1962 Professor Laurie arranged to have lunch with Dr. Beckenbach and Dr. E. W. McElwee, Ornamental Horticulture Program Leader at Gainesville to discuss the ornamental plant industry's need for a research unit.

Professor Laurie was told that Dr. Beckenbach would neither "block" or "push" for such a research unit, and as long as the industry pursued the matter independently and did not interfere with present research budgets and requests he would remain neutral. Dr. Beckenbach said that $150,000 would be required as a separate and independent appropriation for the building and to secure a research staff. He stipulated that the land for such a facility would have to be donated. All of this would have to be done by the industry without upsetting any of the current Experiment Station budget requests!

Professor Laurie reported this information to Jack Christmas, President of the Central Florida Chapter of FNGA. John H. Talton, a local nurserymen and then Orange County Commissioner, became a prime mover of this project. One of the first steps decided upon was a strategy move to get Director Beckenbach, together with the Ag Council and industry leaders to agree on the merit of the project.

If the project was approved at the highest level, it could be expected to pick up support as it went along. To this end Representative Henry Land of Tangerine suggested that if the project could get the approval of the State Legislature all of the other bits and pieces would automatically fall into place. Representative Land said he would sponsor the industry resolution concerning the need for a research unit into the House of Representatives and he would get his colleague, the late Senator Beth Johnson to introduce the companion bill in the Senate. A resolution of this kind requiring no financial support would be acceptable to members of the Legislature and could provide a springboard for future action. This was the strategy behind the two joint resolutions which were passed in the 1963 session of the Legislature.

With this psychological victory secured, industry leaders went to work to secure the necessary funds. The next promotional phase fell to county Commissioner John H. Talton of Apopka. Commissioner Talton secured a county appropriation of $20,000 to purchase a site in the county for such a research facility. Several sites in the Apopka area were selected for consideration and after consultation with Dr. John Sites, the new Director of Experiment Stations, it was agreed the site on State Road #437 next to the county's Magnolia Park was the most desirable. This tract was formally purchased by Orange County on September 20, 1965 and deeded to the state to provide the necessary acreage for the construction of the foliage plant research center. The research center was funded by the Legislature, constructed and officially dedicated in November of 1969.

Another "big deal" by the foliage plant industry was the creation of the Apopka Growers Supply, Inc. in 1965. Allen Poole, General Manager, described this new industry venture as — "a cradle to the grave horticultural supply company." According to Poole, the prime movers who brought this supply company into being were Ralph Faircloth, Roy Stutzman, Verne Buck, Paul Faircloth and Norman Hickerson, Ground work for this organization was begun in 1964 and it was officially launched in July of 1965 when the horticultural supply company bought out the old Hill Greenhouse Company.

At the time of its purchase (1965) the Hill Greenhouse Company was doing an annual business of $150,000. In August of that year, Allen Poole was hired as General Manager and Assistant Secretary of the Horticultural Supply Company. There were five other employees and during the first year five more employees were added. The sales expanded to $725,000 with profits of $33,000 that first year of business. By the end of the fiscal year ending June 30, 1974 sales had expanded to 7½ million dollars and profits to over a half million! Employment had reached 100 and a branch facility had been opened at Stuart and another branch would open soon in Ft. Myers. All of this activity in strictly "hard goods" made the AGS the largest horticultural supplier in the United States, according to General Manager Poole. As of October 1974, the AGS, Inc. was in the process of merging with the Vaughn-Jacklin Corporation. If consumated this would result in an over 40 million dollar over-the-counter public trading company.

Like any other period in the history of the industry, the 1960's also witnessed some changes in ownership and management of various nurseries. Some were within "the family" and one resulted in a new trend for the industry.

In 1967 Robert D. Mitchell, Jr. resigned his position as southeastern sales representative of the George J. Ball Company to join his father in his Shore Acres Nursery adjacent to Lake Jessamine near Holden Avenue in south Orlando.

Jack Christmas of Oakdell Nurseries, bought out his father and began to expand the business in 1960. He was one of the first nurserymen to employ the new carbon dioxide generator in his operations. That same year (1960) B. L. Cobia started his nursery in Winter Garden.

In 1962, a series of events occurred which later lead to the development of a corporate conglomerate on the local agricultural scene. Tom Mahaffey, pioneer grower, sold his three nursery sites to the Stutzman Brothers — Roy, Bob, and Don — of Chicago.

Looking back on this sale, Mahaffey said he tried to "hide" this money in the citrus business and the disastrous freeze of '62 almost convinced him he had succeeded! Temperatures dropped into the teens and the losses experienced by the industry were the worst since the famous 1894-'95 freeze.

For the next five years Mahaffey tried his hand at growing citrus before returning to the nursery business, in 1968. His son, T. O. Mahaffey, Jr. joined him in this second nursery operation.

In 1969, a Houston firm called Stratford of Texas, Inc. was engaged in corporate agriculture. They decided to acquire leading businesses in the floriculture industry under the name, United Horticulture, Inc. Stutzman's Florida Foliage was United Horticulture's first acquistion. Paul Faircloth's Park Avenue Nursery, Harry Smith's Winter Garden Ornamental Nurseries, Ralph Faircloth's Nursery and Imperial Builders, a greenhouse supply outlet in Apopka was acquired later. These several corporate entities became known collectively as the Green Thumb Corporation.

Another accomplishment of the 1960's was the introduction of several new ornamental plants to the nursery trade. Also, the Nelson's assembly-line technique of mass-producing container grown roses on the *Rosa fortuniana* (double Cherokee) rootstock created a new line of ornamental plants for Florida home gardeners. For years, Florida home gardeners had tried to grow roses but after a year or two the plants languished and died. As a result roses were treated more like annuals. However, this new rootstock adapted to Florida soils proved to be the ingredient necessary for success. The success of Nelson's assembly-line technique of mass-producing almost a hundred different varieties of roses on this new rootstock made the name

Nelson's Florida Roses almost a variety name rather than a trade name.

The 1964 Census of Agriculture report cited the ornamental plant industry as having 293 production units and producing horticultural products valued at $7,063,865. By 1969 these figures had almost doubled.

This new change in the economic importance of the local foliage plant industry prompted the "City Fathers" of Apopka to again change their city slogan again. The slogan now became — "Indoor Foliage Capital of the World."

The Florida Foliage Festival, 1965, focused attention on the foliage industry as an important segment of Orange County's economy. Various nurseries erected special displays in downtown Apopka and competed for various awards. The Governor, Commissioner of Agriculture and other dignitaries participated in the Festival. Thousands of visitors visited the displays and toured the nurseries that held "Open House" tours. In 1972 the name of this annual event was changed to World Foliage Festival.

INTERNATIONAL DEVELOPMENTS

1970 - 1974

With all of the urbanization pressure — high land values, high taxes, competition for labor, increased vandalism and a host of related pressures in the early 1970's most other agricultural endeavors experienced downward trends. This was reflected in the economic units and the acreage involved. However, such was not true for the ornamental plant industry. It continued to grow and expand in size and importance.

As a matter of fact, it was the only agricultural endeavor in Orange County that could view the future with confidence.

The foliage plant industry began to acquire international recognition during the early 1970's. For example, the Mahaffey's, Tom and Jim, Bob McColley, John Marsell, Norman Weir, Earl Vaughn and Green Thumb, Inc. were among those who had established operations in Central America during the '70's for the production of unrooted stock material.

Another development with international overtones was the short course program begun in 1971. That year a National Tropical Foliage Short Course was initiated to bring together industry people from all over the world and to provide information for everyone interested in the use, marketing or production of foliage plants. There were over 250 registrations from 17 states and three foreign countries. The National Tropical Short Course was repeated in 1974.

Over 710 people registered from 37 states and five foreign countries.

In concluding this history of the Orange County ornamental plant industry, emphasis was focused mainly on people because people more than plants made the industry what it is today and what made it so different from other agricultural endeavors was the "family" nature of the endeavor. It was a business to make money but the nature of the work seemed to be a strong magnet for drawing the children of owners into the business.

VETERANS ALL — Pioneer ornamental plant growers and the year they came to Apopka. Left to Right — Elwood Ustler (1917), Mallory Welch (born - 1897), Hugo Pilat (1921), Paul Ustler (1917), Mrs. Mary Odom (1921), Tom Mahaffey (1919), Jim Mahaffey (1919), Verne Buck (1921).

There are any number of second generations of family members involved in nursery operations. There are several such as Wayside Gardens and Lester B. Vincent and sons in which a third generation member of the family is in the business.

The late W. W. "Wade" Walters was the first to try growing a foliage plant in 1928 and then died before seeing the industry move from ferns to foliage plants. Today, his widow Mary Odom and their son C. M. Walters, and now his son, Cline, are engaged in the production of many foliage plants and carrying on the family tradition.

CHAPTER VI

History of the Vegetable Industry

The vegetable growing or truck crop industry, more than other branches of agriculture "wandered" about the county before returning to the promised land where it began. These wanderings covered some 26 years and several generations of growers before the pilgrims found their "promised land".

In the early 1900's the organic soils in northwest Orange County, between Lake Apopka and the Zellwood Community, were hailed as the vegetable "promise land". News of this area sounded far and wide, brought many pioneer families to the county. However, after several disastrous years of trying to reclaim these organic soils from Lake Apopka the vegetable industry abandoned that site and scattered to various flatwoods locations in the county. Thus, most of the vegetable farmers operated on small areas of flatwoods soils near Ocoee, Winter Garden, and Oakland, in western Orange County during their ensuing 26 years of exile. At the end of that period interest was rekindled in the Apopka marshland area. This resulted primarily from the "know how" learned with similar soils near Lake Okeechobee.

However, the new generation of "black gold prospectors", with better "know how", still experienced some of the same hardships that the "suitcase farmers" experienced a generation before.

This "suitcase" appellation resulted from the rapid movement of black gold prospectors to and from this new farm frontier. As one group arrived, the previous group would often be leaving with few possessions packed in a suitcase. A few disastrous crops were sufficient to wipe out the newcomers and make room for another group to try its "luck". The rapid turnover of growers gave a gambling reputation to the area that was more notorious than some of the country's leading gambling establishments.

Because weather and market hazards can change success into disaster overnight, vegetable growers are generally considered the big gamblers in the agricultural family. However, growers farming these organic soils found themselves fighting additional odds because of the weather and water hazards peculiar to the area. Fortunately, a number of growers survived these odds and became highly successful. It is this group that gave this farm area the good name it eventually acquired.

In 1969 the crops produced in the Zellwood District were valued at $11,676,267 and caused Orange County's vegetable production to place fifth in Florida and twenty-first in the entire United

States! So it seems worthwhile to devote some attention to the history of this industry before the pioneers of that period are all gone. Through interviews with several pioneer settlers of that period and with one of the original sod-busters of the first "black gold rush" considerable firsthand information was acquired.

Arthur King, the lone survivor of the original "sod-busters" was 86 when interviewed (July 22, 1971). His recollection of his personal farm experience was clear and he had extensive knowledge of the farm period between 1910 and 1914. Mr. King died December 15, 1974 at the age of 89.

Several children of the first pioneers were also interviewed, Hamilton Jones; George, Lester, and Bannella Vincent; and Ralph C. Osborn a native born (1907) Zellwood resident. As a boy, Mr. Osborn remembered playing with horse shoe relics of that era. A breed of horse, referred to as Montana mustangs was used to work these wet, spongy soils because heavy horses were not adapted to these conditions. Furthermore, these small horses were fitted with a special shoe similar to a snow shoe in order to provide extra traction on soggy soils. When a horse lost a shoe it would hold up that foot until the farmer retrieved the shoe. The animals evidently "sensed" if they put their weight on a "shoeless foot" on those soggy soils they would bog down. According to Mr. Osborn the special horse shoes were obtained through catalogue orders and that horses' front legs were commonly wrapped with burlap to prevent leg damage from the cumbersome "muckshoes".

Three "eyewitness" accounts of the Apopka marshland history was interviewed: Arthur King pioneered in the period 1909 through 1914, Ken Jorgensen, a successful grower was one who pioneered during the re-opening of the Zellwood Drainage and Water Control District in the period 1944 to date, and Arch Hodges the Engineer and Superintendent of the District from 1946-1972.

Turning the clock back to those pioneer days, we find two ex-Tennesseans — James W. "Sawgrass" Jones and Arthur King — trying to convince their former neighbors to come to Zellwood. Mr. Hamilton Jones, son of "Sawgrass", provided information on his father's promotional activities. Mr. Jones died in February, 1973. Arthur King, another whom "Sawgrass" Jones influenced to come to Zellwood also talked with us before his death. The Vincent Children — Lester, George, Clifford, and Bannella, told of their parents being recruited for the Zellwood project by Jones and King. This migration of friends and relatives from Tennessee started with James W. "Sawgrass" Jones, formerly of Columbia, Tennessee. The others came from the Mt. Pleasant area of Tennessee.

In 1904, the James W. Jones, Jones Vincent, Tom Morton and John Morton families had moved to Texas to try their hand at farming there. James W. Jones and his family settled near Grand Prairie, Texas, and the others settled near Ovilla, Texas. According to Reasley Vincent he said "they first went to Texas to get 'conditioned' before moving on to Florida!"

Around 1908, James W. Jones heard glowing reports of a fabulous new farmland area being developed from the Apopka marshland near Zellwood, Florida. These reports put out by the Guarantee State Bank of Dallas, Texas described the Apopka marshland soils as being like black gold just waiting for farming prospectors to develop them into the richest farmland in America! In 1909 Jones traveled to Zellwood to see this area firsthand. He was impressed with its great potential and became its most ardent supporter. As a result Jones was nick-named "Sawgrass" Jones.

Jones wrote Arthus King his young friend in Tennessee and advised him to come down right away. In the meantime, he returned to Texas to get his family and to tell his Tennessee friends in Texas about this fabulous new frontier.

Arthur King arrived in December of 1909 and King, being single and only 24 at the time, was eager to farm despite the many handicaps. King said that compared to the farmland he had just left in Tennessee the area looked like one big manure pile just waiting to be farmed.

"Sawgrass" Jones and his family arrived from Texas in early 1910. Jones' enthusiasm got him a "non-paying" position soliciting his friends to buy tracts in this new farm frontier. Arthur King bought 10 acres of the recently opened marshland for $100.00 an acre, and started his first farming operation in 1910.

Jones and King both advised their Tennessee friends in Texas to join them in this promised land which "offered" so much more than Texas. Before bringing their families, Tom Morton and Jones Vincent came to see it for themselves. They returned to Texas convinced of the correctness of their friends' appraisal of the area. Upon their return to Texas, Tom Morton and Jones Vincent convinced John Morton and Harry and Lee Gregory to come to Zellwood. In late 1911, several Texas families — Tom Morton, his wife and two children; his brother John Morton with wife and five children; Jones Vincent with wife and seven children; and Henry and Lee Gregory, chartered a pullman car for the trip to Florida. They rented a freight car to transport their farm equipment and assorted livestock. George Vincent, son of Jones Vincent, was "selected" to ride in the freight car with the equipment and livestock.

The pullman car carrying the Texas families arrived in Zellwood on December 1, 1911 and George Vincent with the livestock and equipment arrived on the following day.

ARRIVAL DAY — The several families that arrived in Zellwood December 1, 1911 from Texas to begin a new farm life.

Before long this group convinced other Tennessee friends and relatives to join them. The Fieldings, Flys, Holts, and the Letsingers were among the later settlers to follow. George Vincent remembered that the promoters had constructed a tower so new arrivals could climb up and get a good view of the tremendous expanse of the marshland.

However, of all these families, only Arthur King bought some of the Apopka marshland and attempted to farm it. The others became involved in citrus and other activities in the area but none participated in the vegetable growing venture.

The black gold prospectors soon found that farming this marshland was next to impossible. The low nature of the area located on the north side of the lake made it subject to frosts early in the fall and late in the spring. The cold hazard was difficult to plan around because a cropping schedule for the area had not been worked out at that time. However, the major problem was lack of water control. As a result, the area was so soggy that work with horses was next to impossible even when equipped with special muckshoes. Rain and breaking dikes were an ever present problem. However, as one disgusted group left another group of enthusiastic new comers would arrive fully expecting to succeed in this area. The rapid coming and going of farm prospectors gave rise to the "suitcase" story.

Mr. King remembered particularly the problems of trying to store potatoes grown on these mucky peat soils. For some unknown reason, potatoes grown on these soils rotted quickly. King remembered that this condition was thought to result from low potash and phosphorus content of the soils. He remembered ordering sulphate of potash and superphosphate from the Wilson-Toomer Fertilizer Company in Jacksonville to correct this condition and believed that the storage life of potatoes was improved. Since this experiment was conducted about 1912, it may have been the first organic soil field demonstration in Florida.

King supplied produce to several stores in the Mt. Dora area and picked up the old produce and replaced it with fresh on a weekly basis.

LOOK AND BUY — Observation tower adjacent to the Apopka Marshland around 1912. Potential buyers could get a better view of this farm area that was being promoted as "Black Gold".

Around 1914 King decided that the cold and water problems were too much for him and that his "promised land" had disappeared. As a result, he ended his peat soil farming and started a citrus nursery on some high sandy land in the Zellwood area. From this nursery he established a grove nearby. He also practiced carpentry as a trade and during the Florida "boom" of the 1920's he worked as a carpenter in Pompano Beach and Ft. Lauderdale. Because of his frequent absence from the county he became one of the earliest members of nearby Plymouth Citrus Growers' Association.

By 1917, King's estimate of the farming potential of the Apopka marshland was accepted by the few remaining individuals. According to Ralph Osborn the spoilage of a carload of potatoes sent to Philadelphia in 1917 was the straw whcih finally broke the camel's back. The Zellwood farm area was abandoned and Lake Apopka was allowed to "recapture" the mucky peat area once again. Equipment abandoned on the farm site at that time was found when the area was redrained some 26 years later.

In the twenties, the Florida Humus Company operated on the edge of the area and dug peat from the marsh. A Chamber of Com-

PIONEER VEGETABLE GROWERS — Ken Jorgensen (left) of the Zellwood Farms a pioneer of the second opening of the Apopka marshland in 1944 discusses with Arthur King his recollections of the period he farmed there in 1910-1914. Picture taken September 24, 1973.

merce publication of the late 1920's described this operation as follows: "The muck is poured into open concrete drying bins, each containing sixty tons. Spread to a thickness of twelve to eighteen inches. The water soon drains away and the Florida sun dries off the greater part of the moisture in just a few days. The partly dried muck having a consistency and color of brown felt is then transferred to the drying plant where the moisture is reduced to about 10 per cent. The finished product contains from three to four per cent ammonia and is sold in sacks and in bulk. The capacity of the plant is twenty tons each day when running full time".

For the next 20 years the Apopka marshland dropped completely out of the farming picture and reverted to being trucked off and sold by the ton!

When inadequate water control caused abandonment of the Zellwood area the vegetable industry moved to the flatwoods soils in Orange County. On these more sandy soils growers controlled water levels rather effectively with tile drainage systems.

In 1925, County Agent Kime reported that — "1200 acres of commercial truck and gardening have fallen off because of the immense real estate development causing frequent changes in property ownership!!"

Today, some 50 years later, another real estate boom is occurring in Orange County but the vegetable industry is not experiencing any particular problems. The land ownership is now stabilized and builders have learned the hard way not to build structures on these unstable mucky peat soils! The flatwoods soils used for vegetable production are so isolated that they appear safe from development for the time being. However, some old vegetable growing areas of the 1930's and 1940's were later converted to citrus production and certain of these areas are now being converted to urban use!

In 1926 Kime resigned as County Agent, and K.C. Moore replaced him. A first concern of the vegetable industry as reported by

Moore was to secure seeds of vegetable crops adapted to Florida conditions. In 1927 he reported spending considerable time on the Orange County Chamber of Commerce Committee in pursuit of this problem. Agent Moore recommended to this committee a seed breeding and investigational department for the Experiment Station. What happened to this resolution and the Chamber's efforts in its behalf are not recorded. At least the Chamber had an agricultural committee in those days and was interested in the welfare of agriculture. This concern has long since departed from the present day Chamber.

As might be expected, marketing vegetable crops periodically becomes a problem and 1928 was such a year. In his annual report of that year Agent Moore wrote: "Large operators have pretty well figured out their problems except those of marketing. These marketing problems are concerned mostly with competition from foreign countries. Within the last half dozen years the imports of winter vegetables have grown from a few carloads to 3,791 carloads shipped into the United States and Canada, our national market, from Mexico. During the same season Cuba exported into American markets 32,798,000 pounds of fresh vegetables, the Bermuda and the Bahamas 588,203 bushels, making a total of about 170,000,000 pounds for the winter season. The large truckers (vegetable growers) have the opportunity, if they want to use it, of about as good a sale proposition as I have found in the state. One of the growers in the Winter Garden section has established so good a reputation for the quality of vegetables shipped out of his packing house and has acquired such valuable experience and has pursued a policy of such just dealings with the growers as to give them about as good service as they could get. He is working this on what is the equivalent of a cooperative basis."

The competition of foreign vegetables mentioned in 1928 is a problem that concerns Florida growers today.

Agent Moore summarized Orange County's vegetable production in his 1928 report as follows:

Mixed	635 Cars	Celery	28 Cars
Cucumbers	566 Cars	Corn	4 Cars
Lettuce	417 Cars	Potatoes	2 Cars
Peppers	196 Cars	Tomatoes	2 Cars
Romaine	63 Cars	Beans	1 Car
Cabbage	53 Cars	Eggplant	1 Car
Melons	48 Cars		

The total of 2,016 carloads of vegetables shows Orange County had a sizeable industry for those days.

In 1929 the Mediterranean fruit fly was discovered in Orange County and as a result all horticultural interests faced a major disaster. Hundreds of acres of local vegetable crops were destroyed because of quarantine restrictions.

Notwithstanding the Mediterranean fruit fly, marketing was a problem in 1929. In his 1929 Annual Report Moore wrote — "Marketing continues to be our greatest problem. The shippers of vegetables in the western part of the country have the privilege of the service of perhaps the best salesman among the farmers of the state, Mr. M.C. Britt of Winter Garden. Mr. Britt operates a large vegetable packing house as well as two truck farms. His high standard grade and pack and his thorough acquaintance with marketing practices and his fairness, all make for the growers as good facilities as most cooperatives and better than many in the state. Consequently, I have not considered it wise to suggest a cooperative sales organization for truck. But since the Farm Board began to function, Mr. Britt has discussed with me some of the phases of the Federal Marketing Law that might make a cooperative desirable for his community. It is possible that we will work some plan out that might help."

However, all vegetable marketing in 1929 was not on the scale of carload lots sold to out-of-state buyers. Many small gardeners produced vegetables in excess of their needs to be sold on the local market.

A Farmers Market was established in Orlando in 1926 to meet this need and Agent Moore reports the volume of business done by this market in his 1929 Annual Report — "Having succeeded despite many terrific obstacles for poor people to face, they sell at their market about $75,000 worth of products each year. Their manager, Mr. W.H. Brown, is the main story. They sell vegetables, flowers, poultry, rabbits, ornamental plants, etc. When they are unable to produce these things, they buy them to hold their line of customers."

Agent Moore reported several humorous incidents which are too good to let pass. "A big fellow blew in one day to get information on handling muck lands, drainage and irrigation. He stated that he was farming near Taft. His farm turned out to be 20 feet by 30 feet garden with a few strawberry and a few cabbage rows!" In another situation, a fellow came into Mr. Moore's office raising a terrible fuss about the Plant Board's destroying all his vegetables. Since he was wanting immediate reimbursement for the crops destroyed in the Plant Board's Mediterranean fruit fly campaign, Agent Moore figured a farm visit was in order to appraise the value of crops destroyed. He found another backyard tract of about 20 or 30 feet in size!

Frequently the man whose entire income depends upon a crop makes less fuss over a disaster than the backyard gardener. Perhaps the commercial grower is "conditioned" to adversity. The backyard gardener often can't or won't accept adversity and looks for a "whipping boy". All too often the County Agent fulfills that role too.

The year 1930 brought unfavorable rainfall to several vegetable areas in the county and three growers' crops were destroyed by high water that year. Moore sought research information to answer the many technical questions that commercial vegetable growers were beginning to ask, especially on fertilization practices and vegetable varieties adapted to Orange County conditions.

Searching for answers, Agent Moore went from farm to farm observing the successful growers. The most successful practices were passed on to other growers. This "observation" practice is widely used by agents because thoroughly researched answers to all questions are simply not available. However, there are always certain farmers who do not care to share trade secrets with their competitors through the County Agent! We found this out from an interview with the late L.W. (Billy) Tilden, who with his father L.W. Tilden were at one time one of the leading vegetable growers in western Orange County. According to Mr. Tilden his father once said — "Educating agents on farming techniques which would be shared with competitors results in the County Agent being more of a hinderance than a help!" The L.W. Tildens, father and son, M.C. Britt, Clarence G. Tilden, L.M. Austin, Morgan and Henry Britt, Brown and Burney Cannon, J.H. Briley, Harold Henschen, and Fred and Raymer Maguire were successful vegetable growers in the west Orange County area in the 1920's and 1930's. In those days vegetable tracts varied from 5 to 40 acres. Mr. Tilden's 40-acre single vegetable crop planting was one of the largest plantings in the south during the early 1930's.

A commercial vegetable farm operating in *eastern* Orange County is mentioned only once in the various agents Annual Reports. In 1930, P.H. Shepherd of Christmas was reported to have raised some good vegetables but had too much for the local trade and was too far from a shipping point. Railroad facilities is one reason why the vegetable areas were located mainly in western Orange County rather than in the eastern part. Cold protection afforded by Lake Apopka, one of the largest lakes in the state, was another important factor.

Production of vegetables on sandy flatwoods soils required good water control and Moore emphasized this fact in his 1930 Annual Report as follows: "By long experience the commercial truck growers of this section have arrived at the conclusion that it is too hazardous to attempt to grow vegetables in large acreages without water control. Their lands are smoothed and tiled, and the tiles so laid and connected as that they may be used for sub-irrigation. This practice requires large investments, and experienced drainage engineers are employed."

In 1931 Moore reported that browning and leaf burning occurred to the 15 acres of cabbage owned by the Sadler Brothers of

Oakland. This problem was found to be a fertilizer burn and flushing water through the tile drain system in the farm corrected it. This demonstrated another reason for good water control.

The depression, coupled with the adversities resulting from the Mediterranean fruit fly campaign, caused disastrous economic conditions in Orange County. The Orlando Chamber of Commerce undertook a campaign to strengthen the local agricultural economy by encouraging people to engage in various agricultural pursuits. County Agent Moore wrote a series of "fact" sheets that were handed or mailed to people who inquired about coming to Orange County to take up some agricultural activity.

One of these fact sheets makes interesting reading in the light of today's food problems. Mr. Moore wrote — "Vegetable production is more hazardous than other lines. Commercial truck growing is not undertaken by experienced growers, except on land that is tiled and irrigated. The cost of tiling and irrigating ten acres will require approximately $200 per acre. The acreage required will vary with kinds of crops grown. For example, a strawberry farm requires less land than one planted to such crops as beans and cabbage. Farmers should grow a crop of corn following the winter vegetable season. If you contemplate raising winter vegetables, you should locate in a section of the county where winter vegetables are now grown. The reason for this is obvious — marketing, production, etc." One wonders how many new vegetable growers were recruited by these efforts of the Chamber of Commerce?

Weather conditions were most unfavorable in 1932. Moore reported that year as the driest, warmest twelve months he had experienced in Florida. (He evidently forgot 1927, the driest year on record). Those truck farmers who were unable to irrigate lost practically all their labor and investments. The adverse weather conditions also increased the nematode problem. In answer to that problem Moore pushed the use of *Crotalaria spectabilis* in the truck fields rotation as a means of controlling the nematodes. The seriousness of the nematode problem in 1932 should dispell any illusions that growers may have about the "good ole days". Every generation has its problems but growers in 1932 seemed to have had more than their share!

In 1932 something new appeared on the horizon, the "Subsistence Garden". Today, we have another emphasis on home gardens because of economic conditions! During World War II days they were referred to as "Victory Gardens". Apparently home gardens wax and wane according to times. According to Agent Moore the "Subsistence Gardens" were a cooperative venture between the City of Orlando and the Orange County welfare workers. Seeds and fertil-

206

izer were donated by public spirited citizens and given to people who were unable to buy them. Some 48 city lots were plowed up to provide areas for planting "Subsistence Gardens".

The agricultural agent must communicate with the novice and back yard gardener as well as the commercial grower but sometimes he wonders if anyone gets the message. For example, N.W. Seegar, a successful commercial vegetable grower of that period wrote a letter in appreciation of Moore's services as follows: "We have carried out your advice and suggestions each trip to our farms and want to say that they have been very helpful to us indeed. I feel that your service is very valuable, and as always glad to have you make us visits as well as to come when we call you."

In 1933 a new nematode control was recommended by Agent Moore and he mentions that several large growers satisfactorily controlled nematodes by using calcium cyanamid. This material was also a high carrier of nitrogen and calcium and had a sweetening effect on the soil during the period that the cyanide gas was begin evolved. Also it destroyed germinating weed seed and soil inhabiting insects.

The effects of the depression were still severe in 1933 and there were many requests for vegetable garden information. Over 700 lots of seed and fertilizer were dispersed in cooperation with the Orange County Unemployment Relief Committee according to Moore.

However, the extremely dry spring of 1933 nullified most of the home gardening efforts and created additional problems for commercial vegetable growers. Thrips on cabbage, cucumbers, and celery became a major problem. Over 200 acres of cucumbers were lost as a result of thrip damage.

The first annual Central Florida Farm and Home Institute program held at the Magnolia School Building on Thursday, August 10, 1933 emphasized vegetable production. The speakers and their topics reflect the interests and problems of those times.

DR. J.R. WATSON — Florida Experiment Station
      "Report on Experiment Work Controlling Root Knot"
J.R. GUNN — County Agent, Kissimmee
      "Discussion & Open Forum on Truck Crop Insects"
A.P. SPENCER — Director, Gainesville
      "Aims & Accomplishments of Extension Service"
DR. W.B. TISDALE — Pathologist, Florida Agricultural Experiment Station
  "Fundamental Principles Underlying the Control of Truck Crop Diseases"
PROFESSOR ALEX JOHNSON — Sanford
      "Discussion & Open Forum on Truck Crop Diseases"
DR. O.C. BRYAN — Florida College of Agriculture
      "Soil Factors Involved in Growing Truck Crops"

Many now famous names are on the above list but the day of the general practioner has long since passed. Nowadays researchers are more specialized.

The year 1934 was the beginning of the end of vegetable growing on the sandy flatwoods soils in Orange County. Vegetable production on the organic soils in the Lake Okeechobee area were beginning to make their impact on the local industry. That year Moore wrote that: "Large scale truck farming is on the wane in Orange County. Five of our largest operators have 'gone broke' within the past three years. Two have lost their farms. Several causes contributed to this: the depression, over-confidence in their ability coupled with lack of available information from any source on many production problems, and competition from other and more forward areas of the state."

The punch line in Mr. Moore's statement shows that he is provoked, because the Experiment Station staff of that period (1930's) helped vegetable growers in the Everglades at the expense of the Orange County growers! Here's what Moore wrote on this subject: "The Everglades Experiment Station has worked out information that enables farmers on that type of muck and peat to produce abundant crops at less cost than truckers on other soils and other types of muck can produce them for.

The Experiment Station workers deserve the highest commendation for the efficient speedy way in which they did *that* job. But it is a devastating irony of fate that tax money partly paid by truckers in the many other sections of the state on millions of dollars invested in land, irrigation, etc. should be used to open up a vastly rich deposit which may be more sorely needed many years hence. This is especially hard since much of the farming in the Everglades is done by transient operators. But such has been the profligate march of progress in get-rich-quick America."

However, within a decade Agent Moore would find this research information most helpful to Orange Countians as they returned to the Apopka marshland.

A severe freeze in 1934 lead to the creation of the Federal-State Frost Warning Service for Florida and Ray Shearouse, the local representative of this new service, was stationed in Orange County. One of the observation stations in the county was established on the vegetable farm of P.H. Britt in Winter Garden.

In 1935, 30 truck farmers applied for emergency crop loans under the F.C.A. and Moore found himself busy devising plant schedules, itemizing the quantities of seed needed and costs of fertilizers and spray materials for each crop. Responsibilities for these government economic programs of the "depression" period severely taxed the already overworked County Agricultural Agent.

The depression continued to foster interest in market gardens and the low capital investment required for this agricultural endeavor was another factor. Mr. Moore reported in 1935 that "growth in the number of small truckers for local selling to housekeepers, to stores and to truck drivers for hauling north. In looking over my list I find nine in this class that have come within the year. I cannot encourage this kind of venture except where water control facilities exist or can be installed. However, I cannot take an aggressive stand against it, for most of these operators make enough to keep off relief rolls. So it is my policy to render any practical assistance I can toward solving production, out-look and marketing problems for them."

The year 1936 found Agent Moore struggling to carry out an administrative directive to organize a county-wide Agricultural Planning Council to examine all agricultural problems and develop recommendations for programs of action. Agent Moore prevailed upon some 25 agricultural people to serve on this Agricultural Planning Council. Five people, Rich Briley, Oakland; J. A. Boone, Orlando; W.N. Seegar, Ocoee; P H. Britt and C. G. Tilden, Winter Garden, represented the vegetable industry.

After several meetings these busy men found the objectives of this program too nebulous to justify their time and efforts. An example of the all too common administrative directive to do something (practical or not), at least go through the motions because we need it for the record! No doubt, such administrative shadowboxing will always be with us.

By 1937, vegetables produced on the muck soils in Palm Beach County were forcing the Orange County flatwoods vegetable growers out of business. Mr. Moore reported that — "a large part of the acreage of truck farmers in this county has been planted to citrus trees, and the present large commercial vegetable production is in the hands of less than a dozen men." The State Marketing Bureau reported 894 cars of vegetables shipped from Orange County in 1937. Some growers sold their produce through the farmer's curb market at Garland and West Colonial in Orlando. In 1937, the 9th year of its operation, this market did about $80,000.00 worth of business.

Orange County shipped 1,000 cars of produce in 1938. In that year Moore asked a certain prominent and successful grower to serve on the Extension Advisory Committee which he had been directed to create. The grower declined in no uncertain terms saying — "I do not have the time nor will I take the responsibility. Too many things can go wrong with Florida farming." It is a wonder that similar statements don't happen more often with today's generation of farmers. However, one farmer said as much recently when he remarked — "Everytime I go to a meeting it costs me money back at the farm." Many things can go astray when the grower is not there to give personal supervision. Busy and successful farmers don't attend meetings for entertainment. Only an urgent need will justify the grower leaving his massive investment where supervision is as critical as in a large manufacturing plant. Asking such a person to spend his time attending committee meetings, talking in generalities about various problems is to say the least presumptuous. We never seem to learn from past experiences!

Approximately 3,000 acres were devoted to vegetable production in 1939. But the relative importance of various crops was not reported.

Mole crickets were a problem again in 1940, the worst epidemic of mole crickets that Moore had ever seen. Truck farmers were advised to mix one pound of calcium arsenate with about 30 pounds of pulverized poultry manure as bait. This treatment proved quite successful. Agent Moore went to Lakeland and Plant City to investigate the plans for free distribution of bran and calcium arsenate by Federal and State Government Agencies. However, he found out that Orange County growers did not qualify for assistance under this program because they were late in applying.

Another insect problem that involved unusual control measures was a build-up of aphids in some of the vegetable fields. Since ladybird beetles were an effective control measure, Moore ordered six shipments of convergent ladybird beetles and during the week of November 17, 1940 released 79 gallons of these beetles in pepper fields. One hundred and four gallons of these beetles at a cost of $320.00 was involved in this special biological control program (there are approximately 30,000 beetles per gallon).

The clouds of World War II began to appear on the horizon in late 1940 and interest in national food production began to accelerate. This "rekindled" interest in the rich marshland area near Zellwood that was abandoned some 23 years before.

As to who did what and where and when, in this second attempt to re-develop this area, several versions exist. However, nearly everyone agrees that the late Judge Charles O. Andrews, Jr. was really the "father" of the Zellwood farm area in that he created the legal vehicle which brought the Zellwood Drainage and Water Control District into existence. When Judge Andrews was a member of the Florida Legislature (House of Representatives), he drafted the necessary legislation to create the Zellwood Drainage and Water Con-

210

trol District Act. It was this Act that secured the necessary financing and engineering to bring this development into being.

In 1941 the Zellwood Drainage and Water Control District was organized as a municipal corporation under a special Act of the State Legislature (Chapter 20715). Those familiar with the legal aspects of this Act credit Judge Andrews with creating a landmark piece of legislation. If this Act had not been properly drawn up so as to withstand all kinds of legal attacks and maneuvers, the District would probably have failed during the trying years of the area's early development. It should be pointed out also that Judge Andrews served as President and legal advisor to the Board of Supervisors of the District from its inception until his death in September of 1969. Thus, Judge Andrews guided the District through its financing problems and in its struggles with various groups as well as controversies relating to Lake Apopka.

Mr. George B. Hills prepared the original engineering design for the District. Following that, a local citizens committee was required to establish the value of the land proposed for development. According to E.S. Marsell of Zellwood, he, Harlow Barnett and Leroy Smith, both of Tangerine, set the value at $150.00 an acre. With the value of the land to be developed established and a plan for development drawn up, an application was made to the Reconstruction Finance Corporation for creation of the Zellwood Drainage and Water Control District. A Reconstruction Finance Corporation loan was granted in the amount of $142,500 for Unit #1 (approximately 2,589 taxable acres) and $257,500 for Unit #2 (approximately 6,000 taxable acres). In the course of the construction, additional funds became necessary and the R.F.C. granted a supplemental loan in the amount of $87,500.

During these early years, Mr. Richard Whitney, of New York, was a principal owner because his properties were pledged for loans from a New York bank. When Mr. Whitney encountered financial difficulties in the repayment of these loans, the bank sent their trouble shooter, John F. White, to assist in liquidating these properties. In 1945, Mr. White bought the New York bank's interest and obtained a loan of $200,000 from Connecticut Mutual Company to create the Florida Humus Company, of which he became President.

At about the same time (1945 & '46) W.T. Cox of the Connecticut Mutual Company, made an intensive study of the area and recommended that his company buy out the R.F.C. This they did in 1946 with $487,500 of 4% Zellwood bonds. The purchase was made at par and represented all of the securities of the Zellwood Drainage and Water Control District.

Proper management of the water was the primary requirement of the Drainage District and a network of major canals was built so that the water level on each farming tract could be maintained individually and without regard to the other tracts. Gus Wenzeloof, the first Superintendent of the Zellwood Drainage and Water Control District, was replaced by Arch Hodges on March 1, 1946. According to Hodges a section of land (640 acres) was normally ditched as follows: One ditch 660 feet from the line, followed by a second ditch 1,320 feet from this one and two more ditches 1,320 feet apart followed. A final ditch 660 feet from the proceeding squared off the section giving it a uniform grid system of water control.

VEGETABLE FARM AREA — In the foreground is a portion of Lake Apopka which is two feet higher than the farm area. In background is the pump house located in the #2 Unit of the District. A system of canals, ditches and mole drains enables each farm to maintain its own water control levels.

Units 1 and 2 each had its own pump house, with three diesel pumps handling 42,000 gallons per minute. Lake Apopka was two feet higher than the nearby farm land so water from the lake could flow into the District canals by gravity flow. Pumps moved the water throughout the network of canals. From the main canals, each individual farm tract can regulate its own water levels.

Moving water from the District back into Lake Apopka required extensive pumping because of the two foot difference in elevation.

This elaborate water system was supervised full time by the superintendent who was answerable to the Board of 5 Supervisors. This Board was set up to provide the overall management of the

District. It also sets the annual tax per acre that provides funds to maintain the 11 miles of levees separating the lake from the farm land, together with all the bridges, roads, canals of this 9,000 acre private tax Drainage and Water Control District.

This system of managing its affairs under a municipal corporation responsible to the taxpayers within the District has withstood the test of time. The sound thinking of the late Judge Charlie O. Andrews, Jr., made the landowners responsible for their own destiny. This vital principle was not employed when the area was first opened to farming at the turn of the century and at that time it was impossible for each farmer to control the water level adequately within his farm area.

As an aid to recapturing the historical highlights of the reopening of this promised land, we have both written and "eyewitness" accounts. The first written account of what occurred was recorded by K.C. Moore in his 1943 Annual Report as follows: "In the spring of this year the acres of commercial vegetables planted in Orange County was approximately doubled by the draining and opening up of a large area of peat soil at Zellwood on the north side of Lake Apopka. The company now owning this tract completed drainage ditches and pumping facilities to adequately control the water. About a dozen farmers who had experience in the Everglades section grew crops of cabbage, beans, potatoes, and corn there in the spring. A large acreage is now under cultivation. Turnips, kale, cabbage, spinach and carrots are being grown under contract with the large new dehydrating plant on the property. I arranged a conference between the Zellwood growers and Dr. F.S. Jamison in July. At that time they questioned him on the many details of fall planting. The most important of these related to varieties and kinds of vegetables and to the proper fertilizer amounts and ratios. This was a most satisfactory meeting, and the growers believe it will result in an increased yield, and a better grade of vegetables. In April a frost did some damage to beans and tomatoes and an early frost in October has done slight damage. These were the latest and earliest frosts, respectively, recorded in about 25 years. I have assisted these Zellwood farmers in various ways, and our county Machinery Rationing Committee (this was the period of World War II) has rendered them valuable services in obtaining needed equipment."

The frosts early and late encountered that first year showed that this hazard was still to be reckoned with. Then too, the temperatures of the area could be expected to average from 8 to 10 degrees lower than Orlando temperatures during a severe cold snap.

These cold hazards and the lack of information on what crops

213

were best suited to the area were important factors during this early trial and error period of the District.

The timing of crops relative to the frost hazard was brought into sharp focus again in 1950 when frost in late April (7th & 8th) killed over 700 acres of sweet corn and sent many growers scurrying for their suitcases. Besides learning to "farm the weather" in this new location, farmers desperately needed technical information of all kinds. The kind and amount of fertilizer to use, the varieties of crops best suited to these muck soils, and control of insects and diseases were problems these growers had to overcome during the trial and error period. They literally wrote their own text book as they went.

However, this need for technical information might be called chickens coming home to roost! In 1934 Agent Moore resented the Everglades Experiment Station's assistance of so-called "transient operators" on the muck soils of South Florida that were competing with Orange County growers on flatwoods soils. Now, nine years later, Agent Moore found himself in desperate need for just such information for his growers on muck soils. An interesting example of how views can change with the passage of time. It should be noted that the Extension Vegetable Crop Specialist, F.S. Jamison drew on these results quite freely and shared them with Zellwood farmers at a 1943 conference. Because Dr. Jamison had worked with Palm Beach County growers for several years, he could give firsthand information to Zellwood growers.

In 1944, vegetable growers on flatwoods soils were again plagued with mole crickets. The problem became so serious that USDA Entomologists in cooperation with the State Plant Board provided 71,000 pounds of mole cricket bait at no cost to local growers. This was distributed to 114 growers at the rate of 30 pounds of bait for each acre infested. Assuming 100 percent infestation, there were 2,367 acres of flatwoods soils in vegetable crops in 1944.

World War II created severe labor and farm equipment problems for vegetable growers. In 1944 Agent Moore made a survey of the number of acres of vegetables lost for various reasons. In the Winter Garden area four growers lost an aggregate of 862.5 acres and five growers in Zellwood lost approximately 1,027 acres. The causes were shortage of labor, frost damage, diseases, insects and prices. One grower believed that if the prices had been better, the labor could have been found. Another believed that if labor had been ample, farmers would have lost money anyway because they would have continued shipping to a declining market. During the 1944 crop season severe marketing problems caused the Zellwood growers to ask for assistance and Moore called Extension Economist, D.E. Timmons for help.

Moore's 1944 report noted 2 items from 1943. One was the November 1943 meeting of Zellwood growers concerning fertilizer supplies, especially of high potash formulas such as 0-9-12, and 0-8-24. Mr. Howard Thulberry, Field Survey Representative, War Food Administration, and several representatives of fertilizer manufacturers attended the meeting. The second item was the request of A.P. Spencer, Director of the Extension Service for information on nematode problems in Orange County. The response to Spencer's inquiry "shook" Mr. Moore. He reported — "I did not myself fully realize until I had read these letters how tremendously costly the nematodes were, although I have contended for some years that they are our most serious pest".

1945 was another bad year for mole crickets on flatwoods soils although vegetables on the Zellwood muck soils did not suffer. Some problems arose from the free insecticide supplied to growers for mole crickets. According to Moore's report, "Mr. P.E. Britt of Winter Garden generously permitted us to use his packing shed as a storage and distribution point. Some 15,100 lbs. of bait were alloted to 16 truck farmers in that area on a basis of 30 lbs. of bait per acre of crops, and 120 lbs. per acre of seed bed. Approximately 2,600 lbs. were distributed to 20 vegetable growers from the county barns in Orlando."

Further on Moore reported that 36 farmers received the bait and used it on the following crops and acreage:

CROP	ACRES	CROP	ACRES
Peppers	168 7/8	Strawberries	8
Cabbage	166 6/8	English Peas	7 6/8
Escarole	29 5/8	Turnips	4
Beans	21 4/8	Broccoli	3 2/8
Potatoes	19 6/8	Beets	2 1/8
Eggplant	19 2/8	Carrots	2 1/8
Cucumbers	15 7/8	Commercial Flowers	1 5/8
Lettuce	11	Onions	1 2/8
Tomatoes	10 6/8	Okra	1
Squash	9 3/8	Celery	4/8
Seed Bed	8 4/8	Corn	4/8
Collard Greens	8 2/8	Cauliflower	3/8

Moore reported that the 1945 mole cricket eradication program led to some "criticism" because the free government assistance did not benefit everyone! Farmers in the Zellwood area complained that cut worms and *not* mole crickets were their very serious problem. Because bait could not be secured for control of cut worms, the amount we distributed this year was less than half of last year's distribution. Our Zellwood farmers' criticism was fair; cut worms were just as serious for their crops as mole crickets were for crops on sandlands, so why should some farmers be given free insecticide to control one well-established insect, whereas other farmers be denied to control another?

That same year Moore reported another problem with discrimination overtones. In 1945 the City of Orlando passed an ordinance that required peddlers of agricultural produce to take out a license or to present a certificate from the County Agent stating that they are known to be farming in Orange County or adjacent counties. According to Moore this was for "the protection of our local farmers against outside competition!" A grower's permit is still required for farmers who peddle their farm produce, but it is not interpreted as protection against outside competition. It simply allows a farmer (regardless of what county or state he grows his produce in), to sell this produce direct to the consumer without a commercial peddler's license. However, an individual buying produce from a farmer for re-sale becomes a peddler and requires a commercial license.

An unusual event in 1945 was the use of German war prisoners by Zellwood growers and some citrus packers in the county. Labor was quite scarce near the end of World War II and the use of P.O.W.'s was one method used to meet that need. After World War II ended late in 1945, vegetable growing expanded on these newly opened peat soils. By the late 1950's vegetable growing on sandy flatwood areas in the Winter Garden area of West Orange County was a thing of the past and much of the vegetable area was planted to citrus.

The Zellwood pioneers, Ken Jorgensen, Bob Stewart, Arch Hodges, C.R. Clonts and son Rex Clonts, the late O.C. Calhoun, Grant Lust, "The Hoopers", Clarence Welling and Billy Long came to the area soon after it was opened and "stuck it out" through the hazardous shakedown period. A brief account of their activities is in order. Each one's accomplishments provided hope for others that this area would become a major production area for vegetables. Their watchword might well have been — "There's more in the man than in the land".

The Dean of Zellwood farmers today is Mr. Ken Jorgensen. He was among the first to arrive. In 1944 he came from Rochester, N.Y. as a technical advisor to the Beechnut Packing Company. Beechnut was one of the first major companies to purchase land in this newly developed area. At that time they were pioneering the production of baby foods and their Zellwood operation was for the purpose of growing vegetable crops during the fall, winter and early spring months. In the summer months Jorgensen, went north to help the company buy produce from growers nearer the processing facilities.

It was soon obvious to Beechnut's officials that the Zellwood farm area was too far away and production was too uncertain. The

216

1944 hurricane did not help matters. These difficulties convinced Beechnut officials that they should terminate their Zellwood operations and put their 600 acres up for sale.

In 1947 Ken Jorgensen, Bob Stewart, and Frank Dutton formed a corporation (Zellwin Farms) and bought out the Beechnut Company's farm facilities. In the early 1950's Mr. Dutton sold his interest to Jorgensen and Stewart. These two original pioneers survived the hazardous "trial and error" period and built their partnership into the largest and most successful farm operations in the area. Today, Zellwin Farms operates some 3,000 acres of muck farm land in Units #1 and #2 of the Zellwood Drainage & Water Control District. Zellwin Farms also owns and operates some 1,400 acres of irrigated sandy farm land nearby.

A non-farmer, who came on the scene in 1946 and played a key role in stabilizing the area during the hazardous trail and error period, was Arch Hodges. Mr. Hodges replaced Gus Wenzeloff, first Superintendent of the Zellwood Drainage and Water Control District and the farming interests were fortunate to have his services. Coming from Clewiston and being familiar with the muck soils of that area and their water management problems, Mr. Hodges was a great asset. His knowledge was especially helpful in 1958 when the high water level in Lake Apopka was a serious threat to the entire farm area. Several breaks occurred in the main levee of Unit #2 and only emergency repairs averted a major disaster. Following this emergency, the District authorized a complete overhaul of the levees to strengthen them against future problems.

In September 1960 the "eye" of hurricane Donna passed over the farm area. A major disaster was averted only because of the measures taken by Superintendent Hodges. He spent all night watching the pumps and water levels in the main canals.

Hodges' dedication and his willingness to institute new methods was a major factor insuring the success of this new farm area as far as water control was concerned. Since water control or rather the lack of it was the major cause of the failure of the area in the teens, his was an important contribution. Hodges retired in 1972 after 26 years on the job and was replaced by T.C. Yon. Mr. Yon worked under Gus Wenzeloff in constructing various phases of the project and the water management of the District continues under competent supervision.

Another pioneer who persevered was O.C. Calhoun. Mr. Calhoun's operation was exceptional in that he came out of retirement to undertake this new farming frontier operation. At 60 years of age he started growing vegetables in the District in 1946 and was actively farming at the time of his death in 1972, at the age of 84! Mr.

Calhoun also came to the District in an unusual manner. He had grown cotton and fought the boll weevil in South Carolina for the first 40 years of his life. He farmed in Texas for several years. In 1946 he retired and moved to Mt. Dora. In Mt. Dora, Calhoun became acquainted with Jim McGowan of Oviedo, who suggested forming a partnership to farm in the new Zellwood Drainage and Water Control District. Calhoun and McGowan purchased 80 acres of the peat land to grow late spring celery. In 1947 they planted a fall crop of beans and in the spring of 1948 they acquired another 70 acres of land to grow celery and sweet corn.

Their first venture in sweet corn growing proved timely. Although yields were only about 75 crates to the acre, the market price of $3.00-$3.50 per crate brought a good return and sufficient financial independence that in the summer of 1948 they divided their assets and each went his separate way.

When sweet corn proved to be a "money crop" in the Zellwood area many growers put all their money in it. However, the disastrous late frost of April 7th and 8th, 1950 ruined many and caused another "suitcase exodus" of growers from the area. However, a few hearty souls stuck it out and among these were — Jorgensen, Stewart, Calhoun, Welling, Lust, Clonts, and the Hoopers.

William D. (Billy) Long was perhaps the youngest farmer to survive the early hazards and become a successful grower. He came to Zellwood in 1953 at the age of 23, after three years of training at V.P.I. and with experience on his father's farm in Virginia.

Being single, he moved into a boarding house in Zellwood with assets consisting of a second-hand tractor, a disc and $1,000. The first year he leased 60 acres of land and put in a crop of sweet corn. This proved remunerative because there were no late "frosts" that year, the market was good and his yields were good. His first year's operation was successful but several succeeding years nearly wiped him out. Today, Long Farms comprises 1,500 acres of vegetable land (800 acres of muck soils in the District and some 700 acres of nearby flatwoods). He also has an interest in a vegetable pre-cooling plant and operates a packing shed with the Lust Brothers, also pioneers of the trial and error period.

Grant Lust, originally from Ohio and a former P-51 pilot, arrived in Zellwood in 1949 to operate a crop dusting service. He rented some land from Hooper Farms and soon his farming line was doing better than his crop dusting business. Then he persuaded his brother, Marlon, to join him. They expanded their operations gradually, and in 1955 another brother, Cloyd, came down. In 1956, Calvin, the third brother, joined the business.

Of the farms that began back in the trial and error period when the District first opened, Lust Farms was one of the most successful. People with previous farm experience failed and left but Lust, a World War II pilot, showed that other factors also influenced success on this new farm frontier.

Hooper Farms is another situation where unusual credentials determined success. In 1948 the father, M.M. Hooper a station manager in North Birmingham, Alabama, retired from the Southern Railroad at the age of 62. The family operation consisted originally of Mr. M.M. Hooper and sons Foley and Eric. Later the younger brother Frank joined the operation as did Foley's son Robert and Eric's brother-in-law, Pat Green. They farmed 1,700 acres of muck soils in Orange and Lake Counties. In July of 1948, Mr. Hooper and his son, Eric, (then in the service) toured Florida looking for a suitable site to start raising cattle. On this trip they happened to visit the newly developed Zellwood Drainage and Water Control District. Both were impressed with the possibilities of the area for vegetable production rather than for cattle operations. Their enthusiasm was such they purchased 265 acres in Unit #2 of the Zellwood District from J. W. Piowady. In October, 1948 Foley, the oldest son, left the American Cast Iron Pipe Company in Birmingham and brought his family, father, mother and young brother, Frank, a fifth grader to Zellwood.

The second son, Eric, an Annapolis graduate, class of 1946, still had a year of military service to complete but after completing his military service in 1949, he too joined the family in the Zellwood farm venture. As the family farming operation expanded over the years, the roles of the various members changed. Brother Frank completed college, and joined the family operation. Eric's brother-in-law Pat Green, and Foley's son, Robert did likewise. M.M. Hooper, now in his late 80's assumed an advisory and bookkeeping role, which left the other members free to concentrate on production and marketing of the various crops. What began originally as a cattle safari to Florida grew into one of the area's most successful vegetable farms!

Clarence Welling, a Michigan celery grower also came to the Zellwood area during the trial and error period. Welling frequently came to the Daytona Beach area to visit a relative. On one of these winter trips he visited the Zellwood area and was impressed with the similarity of the area with his Michigan farm land. He bought 30 acres in 1952 and moved his family to Apopka in 1954. The first couple of years he grew celery along with sweet corn. Soon afterwards he started growing "greens" — turnip, mustard, and collards — during the winter months and sweet corn in the spring. In 1965 his son Jack joined him in a partnership and eventually expanded their operations to 300 acres in the Zellwood. area.

Another pioneer family that helped to establish the farming area was C.R. Clonts and his son Rex. C.R. Clonts started growing celery in the Oviedo section of Seminole County in 1927 and his son Rex, joined him in 1940. In 1949 they purchased 630 acres in Unit #2 of the Zellwood Drainage and Water Control District. Their crops have been mainly celery and sweet corn but in the early farming operation they grew some escarole and chicory.

From this brief insight into the background of the pioneer growers, it is interesting to note that many had little or no experience with vegetable growing. However, many who did, found that the soil conditions, weather factors, and uncertainty of cropping seasons were so different that their previous experience in other areas helped very little. Learning by trial and error was the rule. Those that could, succeeded, whereas many others became "suitcase casualties". Most Zellwood growers agree that sweet corn is the crop that saved the area from failure.

Control of the corn ear worm made this crop a success and credit for this goes to the (then) wonderful insecticide D.D.T. After it was demonstrated that D.D.T. could control corn ear worm, the method of application and timing had to be worked out. This development occurred around 1947. The grower that first marketed a crop of sweet corn and demonstrated the possibilities of this crop at Zellwood is believed to be Pearle Stutzman.

Over the next few years, many varieties of sweet corn were tried in order to find the variety best suited to the growing conditions of the Zellwood area.

CORN HARVEST AT ZELLWOOD — Mule train technique of harvesting sweet corn at Zellwood — a bygone harvesting practice.

William D. (Billy) Long is credited with introducing Gold Cup sweet corn, the variety that today constitutes 75% of the sweet corn acreage grown in the Zellwood area. Long obtained the seed for this variety while visiting his father's farm on the eastern shore of Virginia in 1956. After a successful 10-acre trial planting in the spring of 1957, it soon became the favorite of other growers. Good market acceptance increased its popularity.

The importance of the sweet corn crop alone by various crop years is shown by the data compiled by Carl W. Sprang of the Zellwood Sweet Corn Exchange as follows:

YEAR	ACRES	CRATES	DOLLAR VALUE
1961	3,636	1,134,904	$2,894,005.00
1962	4,460	1,141,760	$2,020,915.00
1963	4,224	1,119,640	$2,351,244.00
1964	4,308	1,249,320	$3,623,038.00
1965	4,980	1,324,949	$2,755,893.75
1966	4,426	1,195,000	$2,285,779.75
1967	4,751	1,429,613	$3,345,294.50
1968	4,596	990,880	$2,271,429.25
1969	5,066	1,241,301	$2,507,428.00
1970	4,697	1,347,928	$3,663,384.00
1971	4,684	1,089,337	$2,438,002.00
1972	4,379	1,138,214	$2,580,464.00
1973	4,512	1,487,504	$3,485,836.50
1974	4,914	1,400,576	$4,371,392.45

This history of the Zellwood Drainage and Water Control District would not be complete without the names of those who have farmed in the area. Some names may have been overlooked and for this, we apologize.

INDIVIDUAL OR FIRM	TYPE OF AGRICULTURAL ENDEAVOR
Leon Sewell	Vegetable Crops
Lawrence Hughes	Vegetable Crops
Walter Hull	Vegetable Crops
Chapman Brothers	Vegetable Crops
Thurman Knight	Vegetable Crops
Ken Jorgensen	Vegetable Crops
Bob Stewart	Vegetable Crops
Frank Dutton	Vegetable Crops
O.C. Calhoun	Vegetable Crops
Julius Dingfelder	Vegetable Crops
A. Sapperstone	Vegetable Crops
Pearle Stutzman	Vegetable Crops
C.R. Clonts & Associated Growers	Vegetable Crops
Chase & Company	Vegetable Crops
L.B. McLeod	Beef Cattle
A.J. Rusterholtz	Dairy Cattle

INDIVIDUAL OR FIRM	TYPE OF AGRICULTURAL ENDEAVOR
W.R. Rust	Cattle
Dick Whittington	Cattle & Vegetables
Roach Brothers (Claire & Dallas)	Vegetable Crops
William D. (Billy) Long	Vegetable Crops
H.F. McGowan	Vegetable Crops
Grisham & Crum	Sod
Ohio Farmers — Frank Gaedy, Andy Couch, George Weasel, Ray Shey	Vegetable Crops
Jack Conrad	Vegetable Crops
E.L. & Jack Gerwig	Vegetable Crops
Clarence & Jack Welling	Vegetable Crops
Harry DeRyke	Vegetable Crops
King Carden	Vegetable Crops
Mrs. Mae Borders	Vegetable Crops
Charlie Grinnell	Vegetable Crops
Lester Bill Vincent	Vegetable Crops
Paul Wolfe	Vegetable Crops
Dan Stroup	Vegetable Crops
Clarence Beall	Vegetable Crops
Glenn Allen	Vegetable Crops
Buster Williams	Vegetable Crops
Dick Crates	Vegetable Crops
Mark Ambs	Vegetable Crops
Lust Brothers — Grant, Marlon, Cloyd, and Calvin	Vegetable Crops
Hoopers — Foley, Eric, Frank, & M.M.	Vegetable Crops
George Long	Vegetable Crops
Emory Rice	Vegetable & Cattle
"Red" Tedder	Vegetable Crops
Bob Reedy	Vegetable Crops
Morton Tarte	Dairy
T.L. Smith	Cattle
Earl New	Vegetable Crops
Norman Hickerson	Caladiums
Wallace Champneys	Landscape Plants
Carl Miller	Vegetable Crops
J.W. Piowady	Vegetable Crops
Frank Scott	Vegetable Crops
Don Carroway (O.P. Swope owner)	Vegetable Crops
Ernest Neel	Vegetable Crops
Charlie O. Andrews, Jr.	Cattle
Charles Nieblick	Vegetable Crops
Harry Bairstow	Cattle
R.C. Potter	Vegetable Crops
Bill Kerchoff	Glads
Harry Smith	Caladiums
J.B. Register	Vegetable Crops
Harold Maguire	Vegetable Crops
Richard Whitney	Vegetable Crops
Lake Coleman	Vegetable Crops
Ben Bernie	Vegetable Crops
Henry Thurston	Vegetable Crops
Orlando Farms — Bloomberg & Tarlow	Alfalfa

INDIVIDUAL OR FIRM	TYPE OF AGRICULTURAL ENDEAVOR
Mark Wustman	Vegetable
Tom Stavey	Vegetable Crops
Tony Mobarick	Vegetable Crops
Herb Behrings	Vegetable Crops
Lake Charm Fruit Company — Bob Foote	Vegetable Crops
Rust Bardwell	Vegetable Crops
D.R. Laddy	Cattle
Lamantia Bros.	Vegetable Crops
D.R. Holt	Cattle
Buckeye Farms	Vegetable Crops
(Mewenites) Hostetlers	Vegetable Crops
W. Bass	Vegetable Crops
Wm. Wysong	Vegetable Crops
Leo Uffurd	Vegetable Crops
Bislinghuff	Vegetable Crops
Benbow	Cattle — 1949
Ralph Long	Vegetable Crops
John Gardner	Vegetable Crops
Owen Killingbeck	Vegetable Crops
Lewis Bros.	Vegetable Crops
Champion	Cattle
Roper Bros.	Vegetable Crops
Marc Miller (Del Pan)	Vegetable Crops
John Wane	Vegetable Crops
Wm. Hutchinson	Vegetable Crops
Lee Ramsbottom	Vegetable Crops
Florida Nursery	Woody Landscape Plants
Central Florida Nurseries	Woody Landscape Plants

At the present time (1974) the vegetable farms in Orange County on muck land and on sand land are as follows:

MUCKY PEAT SOILS

Lust Farms	Mark Ambs
Long Farms	Duda Farms
Zellwin Farms	Dan Stroup
Hooper Farms	Clarence Beall
Chase & Company	Charlie Grinnell
Clonts & Associated Growers	R.C. Potter
Ohio Farmers	Dick Crakes

SAND LANDS FARMS

Zellwood Farms
Long & Scott

What the future holds for the local vegetable industry is uncertain as it has always been. However, the loss of these valuable soils along with pollution problems associated with Lake Apopka could

223

bring a "Countdown" for this industry similar to what other agricultural endeavors have, and are presently experiencing.

Recognizing these long-range problems now and implementing solutions, are ways of insuring that this important agricultural industry will remain a part of the county's economy for years to come.

CHAPTER VII

History of the Dairy Industry

According to local historical records thousands of cattle roamed the wooded areas around Orlando in the 1880's. These were beef cattle and local milk supplies came from a can. Mrs. Amanda Ford brought the first milk cow to Orlando in 1884. One might say this was the beginning of the dairy industry in Orange County.

In 1884, the territory comprising Orange County differed considerably from its present day boundaries. In fact, three years after the first milk cow appeared in Orlando, the area was divided to make three counties, Orange, Lake and Osceola. In 1913, Seminole County was carved off leaving the Orange County we know today.

In the period from 1884 to 1900, dairying in Orange County was primarily a family type operation although several local residents sold their surplus milk to their neighbors. One of the earliest family — surplus milk producers in the county, was the C. Fred Ward family of Winter Park, the parents of one of Orange County's progressive pioneer dairymen — Carroll L. Ward, Sr. The C. Fred Ward family started their family dairy in Winter Park in 1906 with four cows — two of their own, one owned by an uncle and one by a grandfather. Milk was delivered in the Winter Park area by a horse and wagon twice a day. The cows were milked by hand and the milk was strained, bottled and delivered to their neighbors all within a few hours. This was done twice a day because they had no equipment for refrigeration or pastuerization of milk at that time.

The Ward's Lakemont Dairy prospered and soon bought out the Ahik and Harris family dairies. By the 1910-'12 period, the Ward Dairy operation became sufficiently large to install milk coolers and deliver milk only once a day. In 1917, the Ward's son Carroll L. Ward assumed operation of their dairy and carried on the family operation for the next 40 years. The Ward herd consisted of grade Jerseys in the early days and in 1937 he began to acquire a few registered Guernseys. By 1942 he had changed the entire herd over to registered Guernseys. At the end of World War II his 200-cow herd was producing 700 gallons of milk a day. When Mr. Ward's son, Carroll L. (Bud) Ward, Jr., returned from the Armed Service, a 3rd generation of the Ward family became active in dairying.

In 1952 the Wards sold their Lakemont dairy routes in Winter Park, Maitland and Orlando to T.G.Lee. With the disappearance of the Lakemont Dairy plant and milk route, the Wards became producers for the T.G. Lee Dairy. The Wards continued to produce milk at their Winter Park location 'til 1957 when the senior Ward divided his herd and sold his portion to terminate his many years of dairying in Orange County. The land, approximately 1,000 acres adjacent to the city limits of the rapidly expanding Winter Park had become quite valuable for urban development. So with the sale of this valuable property for urban development it necessitated Carroll L. Ward, Jr. moving his herd to Lake County, near Astatula to continue the family tradition of dairying. He continued as a producer for T.G. Lee and is still doing so at this time (1975).

The site of the original Lakemont Dairy is today occupied by Winter Park High School and several housing developments known as — Brookshire, Winter Park Pines and Golf Side.

A strange sequence of events has occurred in the area relative to the pasture grass situation. The Ward Dairy had one of the earliest plantings of pangola grass in the county (1930's). When the area was converted to "city pasture" and to hundreds of homes, St. Augustine, centipede and bahia became the preferred "pasture" grass of the new owners.

The Shader Dairy at Fairvilla was another pioneer dairy family of the "teens". Myer Shader provided us with some of the background history of their farm. Shader said his father, brothers and Jake Meitin started this 15 Jersey cow dairy in 1913. He remembered the state was building a brick road from Orlando to Apopka in 1915 and his family picked up chipped pieces of brick to help build a paved floor in their barn.

SILAGE OPERATIONS OF YESTERYEAR — (left to right) — Myer Shader, his father Israel A. Shader, and brother Isadore, stand in front of their forage chopper and wooden silo at their Fairvilla Dairy Farm July 1919.

In 1918 they sold their milk route to the Datsons and became producers only. Myer Shader left the dairy farm in 1933 but other members of the family and relatives continued the dairy up 'til 1949.

Because of their religious doctrine the Shaders conducted their dairy farm in the early days different from neighboring farms. They kept the Jewish Sabbath (Saturday) strictly so they had one of their neighbors (the Eunices) milk their cows on their Sabbath.

226

Also, a week prior to their Passover holiday, 4 cows were put on a diet of beet pulp and alfalfa so that no grain was in their feed. This milk was handled separately and marketed in compliance with this religious doctrine.

Talking to Stanley J. Shader about the Shader Dairy, he said — "you might point out an unusual 'first' about me". He said, "in 1925 when I was born at the old Florida Sanitarium and Hospital my parents paid their hospital bill with products from the farm". The hospital had a grove nearby and a great deal of manure from the Shader Dairy farm was used to fertilize the grove.

In 1949, the mixed herd of some 80 cows was sold to Tommy Knight and after 36 continuous years the Shader Dairy ceased operation.

T.G. Lee, another pioneer Orange County dairyman, started his operations about the same time as Carroll L. Ward, Sr. but did so quite differently. T.G. Lee's father, Charles T. Lee, was a prominent citrus grower and the family dairy involvement consisted of a single milk cow that Mr. Lee purchased. In 1925 T.G. Lee purchased a cow and a calf. Around these three dairy animals began the dairy career of T.G. Lee which would lead to his becoming one of the largest independent dairy farms in the entire state. His first dairy plant consisted of a 10 foot square milk room next to the milking barn. His pasture area was between Colonial Drive (Highway #50) on the north, Robinson Avenue on the south, Primrose Avenue on the east and Bumby Avenue on the west. One of Orlando's largest shopping centers occupies this site today.

At first, Lee sold his milk to a local distributor. Later he added enough customers to establish his own milk route and made his deliveries from a Model T Ford coupe, which also served as the family car during "off" hours. By 1934 Mr. Lee's operations had reached a size that required a milking parlor which was constructed on Bumby Street. Later, when the herd and farm operations were moved to the Conway area south of Orlando this site became the T.G. Lee milk processing and distribution center. Lee's dairy was next door to the Orlando Air Force Base during World War II. Later it became Herndon Airport. It was the result of urban encouragement into the area that prompted Lee to move his herd from the Bumby site. However, a small portion of Lee's herd was maintained on the "city pasture" tract adjacent to Colonial Drive for several years. During the middle 1950's this "city pasture" was "converted" to a multi-million dollar shopping complex known as Colonial Plaza Shopping Center. At that time Lee's farm and herd operations were conducted at the Conway site while the processing and distributing phase of operations were conducted at the old home site at Bumby Street and Robinson Avenue.

For his progressive leadership in dairy farming and in milk plant operations, T.G. Lee was designated "Dean of the Florida Dairy Industry" at the American Dairy Science Association meeting at the University of Florida in 1970.

Of the several hundred people active in dairying in Orange County through the years, Ward's and Lee's dairy operations are "singled out" for special comment because of their progressiveness and the fact that each was active in dairying more than 40 years. As of January 1975 Lee was on the threshold of beginning his 50th year of continuous dairying, a record for Orange County and for Florida as well.

The producer-distributor type of operation of these two dairymen was typical of the pre-World War II dairy period in Orange County. It was an era of rugged individualism with few industry-wide group activities. The daily work routine was endless, as every one knows who has ever worked around a dairy. Consequently, dairymen had little time to attend meetings because they not only milked cows, but processed, bottled and distributed their product. Any meetings to be attended had to be of the highest priority to justify the time away from their 24-hour operations. Also, since they were directly in competition with one another, there were very few mutual areas of concern because of the competitive nature each found themselves in as both a producer and distributor.

DAIRY PIONEERS — (left to right) T. G. Lee and Carroll L. Ward, Sr. look over diary museum items of yesteryear's industry. August 1971.

The number of dairy farms in the county varied considerably at different times in this pre-World War II period and the number of cows per herd varied from 10 to perhaps 50 cows for the largest herd in the county.

These records from County Agents annual reports, (except for the official Census of Agriculture figure in 1940), reflect the ups and downs of dairy farming in Orange County.

YEAR	NUMBER OF COUNTY DAIRY FARMS
1925	85
1927	50
1928	64
1937	62
1938	50
1940	93

For the physical and financial make-up of the Orange County dairy farms in the late 1920's we are indebted to former County Agent, K.C. Moore. In 1926-27 Agent Moore wrote that "A short questionnaire was prepared by me for the purpose of showing to the businessmen of Orlando the value of the dairy business to the city as an enterprise. The following are some of the figures:

Total value of 50 dairy farms	$1,115,000
Value of buildings	$ 187,000
Number of milking cows	1,350
Value of cows	$ 176,400
Value of other equipment	$ 61,875
Number of calves and heifers	244
Value of calves and heifers	$ 11,250
Number of bulls	75
Value of bulls	$ 9,850
All have pastures	
Yearly value of pastures	$ 31,750
Number of helpers employed	120
Wages paid helper per week	$ 2,440
Wages paid helper per year	$ 122,000
Weekly cost of delivery (too low)	$ 800
Daily milk production (gallons)	2,500
Value at .40 per gallon	$ 1,000
Average production per cow per day through the year	$ 1.85 gallons"

For a capsule documentary of the local dairy industry during the 1920's, 30's, and early 40's, we are again indebted to Agent Moore for the thorough reports he made of these periods.

For example, in the 1926-27 period, he reported working with the Orange County Milk Producers Association, a community corporation, called Fairvilla Dairies, Inc. Perhaps the most important thing the association accomplished that year was to get certain changes made in a new milk ordinance proposed by the City Health Officer. According to Moore, this organization was "strong enough to get almost every provision they wanted, at the same time safeguarding the city's milk supply".

This association also helped its members buy feed co-operatively (an early version of today's Farmer's Cooperative Exchange). Through buying a carload lot every three weeks in summer and every two weeks in winter dairymen saved about 50 cents per hundred pounds of feed.

An historically interesting item of the late 1920's, is the account of perhaps the first dairy lobbyist in Orange County and possibly the state. In Moore's 1928-29 report, P.T. Donahue appears as having been a representative lobbyist for the local Dairymen's Association at the previous legislature, as follows: "Mr. Donahue took an important part in getting the new dairy act drafted and accepted by

229

the committee of the legislature handling it." Whatever this act meant to the dairymen of that period we have no knowledge except it rated special mention by Agent Moore.

Controversy, like death and taxes, seems to be one of those inevitable things. An issue that became quite controversial in May of 1931 was a new milk ordinance that the City of Orlando adopted in order to conform to the "Standard Milk Ordinance", of the United States Public Health Service. County Agent Moore found himself attempting to convince dairymen that — "It was their duty to support it as a protection to their customers and as a means of increasing their business."

In July, 1931 the Manager of Southern Dairies, Inc. of Miami conferred with Orange County dairymen and Agent Moore on the feasibility of building a plant in Orlando. Southern Dairies, Inc. decided on the basis of their findings, that the Orlando area was not a good potential market for their services at that time. Apparently the producers were satisfied as to how they were marketing their product and were not ready to turn that phase of their industry over to an outside company.

Economic conditions were poor in the early thirties and Moore believed that a pasture improvement program for the local dairy industry would be the best program he could "push" to help the industry. To that end he enlisted 8 dairymen in a pasture improvement demonstration but the weather and other circumstances thwarted this endeavor. In his 1931-32 report Moore wrote — "A new ordinance and dairy inspector in Orlando required dairymen to spend most of their capital in meeting the new regulations. Also, the unprecedented drought made grass plantings impractical in the spring and oats, rye, barley, vetch Austrian peas impractical this past fall."

In the early 1930's both the weather and economic conditions seemed to be working against the local dairymen. To add to these problems, there was a move afoot to gain a competitive advantage in the market place through price cutting. As to this situation Moore wrote — "The Orange County Milk Producers Association of which Mr. Lee was President, worked hard on a cooperative movement to protect the wholesalers in their contacts with distributors, and to protect the retailers against unwarranted price cutting."

By 1932-33 local dairy problems had become so great that Agent Moore was devoting most of his time to this commodity field. He helped the Orange County Milk Producers Association fight against price cutting and to adopt a fair price code. In this regard he devised a questionnaire to gather data on the cost of production and

230

related information. His efforts in this industry-wide effort were recognized by Commissioner of Agriculture, Nathan Mayo.

From an historical point-of-view it is of interest to review some of the dairy matters Agent Moore found himself concerned with in 1932-33. Among those cited by Moore were — "Fifty-one visits to dairy farms for such reasons as: dairy association matters, pasture making and care, decision as to purchase of herd which I advised against, decision as to purchase of land for a new location which I advised, dehorning calves demonstration, three diseased cows, accompanying veterinarian to determine source of poisoning from plants, feed formula, low cream content of milk, tattoo marking of registered bull calf, etc." He further noted, "I have attempted whenever it was timely to impress on our dairymen that they can produce milk cheaper if they will improve their pastures or plant better grasses — especially centipede. Four of these centipede pastures have been started this year. Other dairymen have planted napier grass, sudan grass and para grass at my suggestion."

The educational activities engaged in by Agent Moore in 1932-33 would be beneficial today with two major exceptions. Since artificial insemination has made the raising of dairy bulls unnecessary, registration of a bull calf would be an out-dated practice. Centipede would no longer be recommended as a pasture grass. A few years after this period Agent Moore secured some pangola grass cuttings to establish some trial plantings in the county. It soon became the most popular pasture grass in the county and centipede became a product of a bygone era.

By 1933-34, the Orange County vegetable industry found it difficult to compete with the Everglades farming area so that dairying had become the second most important agricultural endeavor in the county. That year the dairy industry brought $346,700 into the county. Commenting on the milk supply and demand situation of that period Mr. Moore wrote — "The dairies and privately owned cows, produced all the fresh fluid milk and cream needed by Orange County residents with the exception for a few 'tourist months', when some cream was imported."

In 1934-35 Agent Moore wrote — "I have worked with the Orange County Milk Producer's Association throughout one of the most trying years in the history of local dairying. The one big problem has been getting cooperation on the part of the State Milk Control Director. From our point-of-view, the association has done everything possible to aid the producers and the producer-distributors to comply with the rulings of the Board, and to get a living from their dairies. Space does not permit going into detail. It has been a heartbreaking fight for most of the leaders. The opinion is held among the dairymen that it is almost hopeless to fight the well organized and financed distributing companies whose greed is generally known. During the first half of the year feed prices were low and supplies abundant, and it was difficult to arouse much interest in home production until too late to do much planting. The fight with the Control Board occupied the dairyman's thoughts during the winter and spring when planting should have been done. Through the fall months it has been too dry to plant winter temporary pastures.

However, I have been instrumental in getting one silo built and in locating available corn on truck farms to help fill two others. I have, throughout the year, hammered away at dairymen to grow more of their roughages, or to save all the hays they could find. The unusually constant summer rains interefered. Silos must be built for saving roughages." From this brief look of a critical period of past dairy history, we note that County Agent Moore was counselor, comforter, catalyst and prophet for the dairy industry.

The County Agent frequently collides with controversial issues in his educational endeavors. It was in this regard that Moore wrote of a situation which occurred during the 1934-35 period as follows — "Our dairymen have gone through another hectic year in their marketing problems and controversies. They have made my office headquarters and come to me with their troubles. The State Milk Control Board has not enforced its orders, and the small number of retail dairymen who want the code enforced are helpless. I could not get out into the fight because I had 'clients' on both sides of the question."

Twenty-five years later (1955) a similar situation occurred when several Orange County dairymen requested County Agent Fred Baetzman to schedule an educational meeting to discuss the "pros" and "cons" of a Federal Milk Marketing hearing in Orlando. Other dairymen were "against" such a meeting. County Agent Baetzman had friends on both sides so he decided not to get involved! The Assistant County Agent, H.F. Swanson was given the responsibility of presenting both sides of this controversial issue and letting the dairymen decide what they preferred. Swanson asked Economist William E. Black from the University of Florida to discuss "pros" and "cons" of Federal Milk Marketing Orders. However, when the meeting was held the dairymen showed little interest. It should be noted that 10 years later a marketing order for milk was voted for and adopted by the producers in the Central Florida Milk Shed.

Anyone who works with an agricultural group must be prepared to weather storms within such an organization due to differences of opinion. Those who are inclined to think their generation is the only one to experience such difficulties needs only to read history and be

232

appraised of events. Moore provides us an insight into the dairy difficulties of the 1935-36 season with these comments — "The local organization has almost been broken up by dissentions and lack of leadership. I have not considered it advisable to make any efforts yet toward a reorganization; and Mr. Hamlin L. Brown, Extension Dairy Specialist, concurs with me in this opinion."

With these comments on what transpired within the dairy industry Moore felt it his responsibility to start a different program upon which the association could build. He felt a silage crop demonstration could be a means of unifying the industry around a common interest. In 1936 Moore wrote — "it is hoped that we can get dairymen to studying means of producing more of their feed, and increasing the average production per cow; and stop fighting over prices and price control. The continuous fight for the past 2½ years has greatly hampered progress or cooperative effort. Most of it has been with the Milk Control Board, or have felt that whatever functioning this Board has done, has reacted to the advantage of the distributors and a few chislers."

Another problem the dairymen were experiencing in the mid to late 1930's was the way the Bang's disease tests were being conducted. Moore reported the program might ultimately work to the dairymen's advantage but the larger operators were experiencing heavy losses. The relationships of the dairymen and the Bureau of Animal Industry got so "strained", Moore felt it was his responsibility to try to smooth out the difficulties. He made a special trip to Jacksonville to personally discuss the matter with Dr. Cole, the State Representative of the Bureau of Animal Industry. Moore reported he helped two groups of one- and two-cow owners to get together so that they could benefit by this program of remibursement for Bang's reactors.

As if the Bang's program was not enough to have to contend with at that time, the required dipping program for the cattle tick also created its share of problems for the dairymen. Moore reported that during the winter and spring a controversey developed with officials in charge of dipping. Because of reinfestation a number of dairies and individual cows were required to be put back on a dipping program. As a result many were injured by the dip, careless rough handling, and extreme cold weather all added to the complications of this program. Dr. Knapp, State Veterinarian made some procedural changes in the program but apparently the losses dairymen experienced were not reimbursed under the program.

In reviewing the summary of educational activities by Moore in the field of dairying during 1936 many "out-dated" services are revealed in light of today's industry needs and activities. For instance,

Moore reported having — "helped with the registration of calves, writing other County Agents about (2) registered bull calves for sale, dehorning cows and young calves, furnishing information on state sanitary regulations of dairies (4), formulae to give balanced ration from lists of feeds available, advice on care of pastures, putting truck growers who had corn for sale in touch with dairymen wanting to buy it for silage (4), looking over farms to determine their adaptability for dairying (2), inspecting for screwworms (several), diagnosing and suggesting treatment for skin troubles, milk fever, salt sickness, mineral deficiencies, bag troubles, etc. for farmers of limited means unable to pay a veterinarian, talking and writing to numerous farmers from other sections with references to the dairy situation and possibilities."

This recap of activities provides us an insight of the generalist role the County Agent performed in those days. He was also a practicing "lay" veterinarian which was evidently acceptable in those days under existing conditions but in today's specialized and complex world, the County Agent's role would be entirely different.

For instance, what was the role of a veterinarian during that period of the 1930's as compared to today's demands of a veterinarian? In response to this question it was our good fortune to be able to interview a interview a pioneer Orange County veterinarian, just prior to his death in 1972, to secure the veterinarian's point-of-view in those "depression years".

Dr. W. Monroe Lynn D.V.M., first came to Orange County in 1917 as a civilian employee of the army to carry on a hog vaccination program. He was transferred to an out-of-state army base in 1918. When Dr. Lynn left, however, County Agent DeBusk said it became his responsibility to carry on the hog vaccination program.

In July of 1926, Dr. Lynn returned to Orlando to open the first Veterinary Hospital in Central Florida.

The Florida "boom" had just burst and few people could afford a veterinarian for household pets. Consequently Dr. Lynn's calls were primarily farm animals and these were primarily horses and mules. Dairymen called him only when it looked like they might lose a prized milk cow. Many of Dr. Lynn's clients paid for his services with farm commodities such as milk, meat, eggs, or vegetables. Reflecting on those days of large animal practice he pointed his finger at nephew Dr. David Lynn's animal hospital nearby and said — "we did not work in air conditioned office and treat lap dogs and pussy cats, we had to go out into the field to see our sick patients!" Looking back it is quite apparent pioneer Veterinarian W. Monroe Lynn and the dairymen of that period had a lot in common. They needed each

234

other and most of their transactions in goods and services did not involve currency.

Dairy Herd Improvement through testing and record keeping was becoming more and more a way for progressive dairymen to upgrade their herds. So in 1937 Agent Moore felt it was time to undertake such a proposal for local dairymen. He visited with 58 dairymen to "sell" them the merits of this program. Only two dairymen, Lee and Ward, responded to Moore's efforts. However, between them they had one hundred seventy-five cows eligible for testing, a number insufficient to create a Dairy Herd Improvement Association for Orange County. They affiliated with the nearby Pioneer Dairy Herd Improvement Association of Volusia County of which County Agent Fred Baetzman was Secretary.

This response failed to discourage Agent Moore and up to his retirement in 1946 he tried to convince Orange County dairymen of the need for production testing. The early ground work done by Agent Moore along with Baetzman's acquaintance with most Orange County dairymen through his activities with the Florida Jersey Cattle Club and related activities, enabled him to organize an Orange County DHIA group in 1949, three years after he became Orange County Agricultural Agent.

By 1940 the screwworm had become the major concern for both dairymen as well as cattlemen. Twenty-nine dairymen reported nine screwworm cases in the two months of September and October. Since dairymen inspected their animals more closely than cattlemen did, the problem had by these findings become quite serious.

Beginning in the 1940's some major changes took place in Orange County dairying. More and more dairymen became producers. The processing and distributing of milk was left to those specializing in this phase of the industry. This new era of specialization fostered greater cooperation among local dairymen. Prior to this, anything that might benefit a colleague was largely considered to their competitive disadvantage. One of the first cooperative undertakings in the early 1940's was formation of the Farmers Cooperative Exchange at Pine Castle. This cooperative endeavor resulted from the difficulty that local dairymen experienced in obtaining feed. The importance of this feed cooperative is well illustrated by the volume of business conducted through the years. In 1945, the Co-op sold $194,500 worth of feeds and general farm products to patrons. By 1970 sales had expanded to $1,290,000! During this period there were two fires and several changes of location in the Pine Castle area. The present facilities, established in 1947, have undergone considerable expansion and remodeling and in 1958, they converted to bulk operation to keep abreast of bulk-feed handling techniques installed on the patron's dairy farms.

It is perhaps noteworthy that from its inception in 1940 through 1973, the Farmers Cooperative Exchange has had only four Presidents and five Plant Managers. The Presidents were: R.C. Macy; B.W. Judge, Sr; Carroll L. Ward, Sr; and T.G. Lee. The Plant Managers during this 33-year period have been — Henry Burch, J.C. Crissy, J.C. Tyson, Albert Jones, and Donald D. Platt, who is the current manager.

Carroll Ward, Sr, a former President, said that in 1943 this association saved him when he found his former sources of feed suddenly cut off. By becoming a member of this cooperative he was able to get the feed supplies he needed. Even after dispersing his dairy herd he has continued as a member in order to buy feed and supplies he needs for his beef cattle.

Not only did World War II create feed supply problems for dairymen but between the demands of the Armed Forces and other activities connected with the war effort, they found securing qualified farm workers rather difficult. The situation became so bad in 1943 that nine local dairies went out of business that year.

However, the World War II years fostered considerable cooperation between local dairymen so a new era of relationship came into being.

In June 1945, several dairymen "pooled" their financial and other assets to bring into being the Perfection Cooperative Dairies. During its 22-year history, this milk processing and distributing cooperative pioneered several dairy plant innovations that were "firsts" for Central Florida and may be "firsts" for the state.

Their first innovation was the processing of homogenized milk and in 1948 the plant commenced using paper containers for milk. Other milk processing plants in the area followed suit and the "glass" milk bottle soon disappeared from the local scene.

In 1950, Perfection Cooperative Dairies started bulk handling of milk. They installed bulk milk holding tanks on members' farms and started transporting milk in tank trucks. This soon relegated the milk can to the agricultural museum.

Mr. Earl Tatgenhorst started the Perfection Dairy in 1938 when he moved to Orlando from Ohio and set up his dairy farm near Rio Grande Avenue and 35th Street. The Mo-Ho Trailer Park now occupies part of this former dairy farm.

In 1940, his son-in-law, Dick Lawrence, moved to Orlando to assist him in the operations. By that time he was milking 100 Jersey cows and was still unable to produce enough milk to supply his customers. As a result he bought milk from several other dairymen.

In 1945 B.W. Judge, Sr. of Conway, C.D. Hiatt of Bithlo and Fred St. Lawrence of the Union Park area formed a milk marketing cooperative and bought Mr. Tatgenhorst's milk plant and distributing business. They retained the original name but added the cooperative title. It operated until 1967 at which time Roberts bought out the plant and milk routes.

Dick Lawrence, the Plant Manager between 1948 and 1966, was responsible for getting the local milk distributors to use paper milk containers. He also started the bulk milk handling.

In August of 1945, Orange County dairymen and cattlemen participated in an agricultural "FIRST" of international importance This was the first large scale use of DDT to determine its effectiveness in the control of several cattle pests.

Because of its long residual toxicity DDT has since become a controversial insecticide. However, that fact was not known at that time and the experiment went down in the history books as a major breakthrough in the control of several insect pests of cattle.

Due to the historical significance of this agricultural "FIRSTS" by Orange County dairymen and cattlemen the complete rundown of this DDT demonstration should be recorded for posterity's sake. Agent Moore's report of this historical demonstration is as follows:

"Demonstration and Experiment In the Use of DDT For The Control of Insects Affecting Livestock

The greatest accomplishment of this year and perhaps of all of my years in service was a cooperative spraying program using DDT for the control of insects infesting cattle. This was done through the cooperation of the cattlemen and dairymen of a large section of Orange County. Mr. W.G. Bruce, Entomologist of the Bureau of Entomology and Plant Quarantine, with headquarters in Savannah, Ga., the E.I. DuPont de Nemours & Company and their representative Dr. Carl Peterson and myself.

In an attempt to get approval on the purchase of DDT for two of our dairymen and two beef cattle owners I was told that all the experiments on individual herds had been made, and information had been gathered. Mr. Bruce wrote me however that if I could arrange to spray all the cattle in the county or in a considerable area in the county he would assist in securing the DDT, and in making and supervising the plans.

From an experimental standpoint Mr. Bruce was interested in finding out whether horn flies in particular, could be eliminated in the center of this area and how long it would take for the flies to build up in numbers from outside the area. We were fairly certain that most flies and some other insects would be temporarily killed.

I contacted a number of livestock owners and met with such encouragement that the project was undertaken. Letters were written to all livestock owners in the county outlining the proposed program. Favorable response was received from the large majority of those in an area covering approximately 360 sq. mi. in which there was about 90% of all the cattle. We then decided to attempt a complete coverage of this area. A second brief letter was mailed to everyone in this area with further explanations of what we wished to do, and my opinion of the value of such a spray program.

I wrote to several firms asking quotations on their DDT product. Dr. Carl Peterson of the DuPont Company offered to donate one of their DDT products provided they might use some of the findings in their advertising matter. Authorization for this use of the information was obtained by me from the Extension Service Director, and by Mr. Bruce from the Department of Agriculture.

When our plans were well set a meeting of all dairymen and cattlemen was called for the evening of August 3rd. We had a *most* representative attendance. The plans were outlined and a schedule for spraying the cattle and the dairy barns was arranged at this meeting. I divided those live-stock owners present into four neighborhood groups (as I had secured the services of four spray rigs), and they got together and outlined the time schedule to be followed.

Several prominent entomologists and scientists addressed the meeting briefly, and it was announced that during the next morning, Saturday August 4th demonstrations of the proper method of application of this material would be held at the R.C. Macy Dairy, Tottles Dairy, Thomas's Dairy, and on the ranches of Clarence Datson, and L. B. McLeod.

Attending this meeting were Dr. W.E. Dove, Division of Insects affecting Man and Animals, of the Bureau of Entomology and Plant Quarantine, Washington, D.C.; Col. E.C. Cushing, formerly head of the Bureau of Plant Quarantine and Entomology of Washington D.C.; Mr. E.F. Knipling, Entomologist, Bureau of Entomology, Orlando, Fla.; Mr. W.G. Bruce, Entomologist and his assistants Mr. E.B. Blakeslee, Mr. C.C. Skipper, and Mr. A.L. Smith, all Entomologists from the Bureau of Entomology and Plant Quarantine, Savanah, Ga.

Dr. Carl Peterson, and Mr. Allen Perry of the E.I. DuPont de Nemours Company, Wilmington, Delaware; Dr. L.O. Gratz, Dr. R.B. Becker, Dr. A.N. Tissot, all Entomologists from the Experiment Station at Gainesville, Fla. Mr. Hamlin L. Brown, Dairy Specialist of the Extension Service, Gainesville, Fla., and Mr. June Gunn, County Agent of Osceola County, Mr. Paul Hayman, County Agent of Polk County, and Mr. A.M. Bissett of Polk County.

The methods and results of the first few days' work was closely observed by the following notable scientists who had done some pioneering work in the use of DDT. Their presence in this section was, by request, not given any publicity. Dr. Paul Muller, discoverer of DDT, Dr. R. Wismaun, first person to use it in Dairy barns, and Dr. Langer, all of Switzerland, Dr. Metysse and Dr. Froechlicter of New York.

There were about 50 persons at each of the method Demonstrations held on August the 4th. The material used was 50% Water Dispersable DDT Powder. The cattle were sprayed with a 2½ percent strength of this material applying approximately 2 pints per animal. The interior of the dairy barns were sprayed with approximately 1 gal. for each 1000 sq. ft. of surface of the same strength.

Before the spraying was done it was estimated that there were between 1000 and 3000 horn flies, house flies and other flies on each cow, and the barns were swarming with house flies. The cows were vigorously switching their tails and throwing their heads about to relieve themselves of these pests. After the spraying when the cows were released they walked away quietly with hardly a tail moving.

Within 9½ days 53 dairy barns and 14,192 animals had been sprayed within the 360 sq. mile area, and about 1000 head of cattle had been dipped in a 1/10 of 1% mixture. Two large herds of range cattle and two herds of dairy cattle together with the dairy barns, outside the 360 sq. mile area were sprayed.

Orchard spray equipment was used in addition to a small power sprayer owned by the Bureau of Entomology and Plant Quarantine. The pressure was reduced below 100 pounds and nozzles adjusted to produce a spreading stream to wet the animals and the interior barn surfaces, stantions, etc. The owners of this equipment did the spraying at cost. They were W.C. Champion, of Orlando, Roper Bros., of Winter Garden, and N.B. Watson of Orlando. Mr. E.B. Blakeslee of Savannah, Assistant to Mr. Bruce instructed the spray operators in the method of applying the spray material. R.W. Barber, rendered a valuable service in the operation of the outfit supplied by the Bureau of Entomology.

All the cattlemen and dairymen signed a realease of responsibility for the Bureau of Entomology and one for the DuPont Company. I have never experienced such full cooperation from any class of farmers at any time as was given by all these farmers in this area. Only a few family cows were missed in this spraying; however a large number of family cows were sprayed, the owners bringing these cows to the most convenient dairy. Several dairymen and stockmen had spraying equipment; and the DDT was furnished them and they did their own work after witnessing the demonstration.

Ever since the spraying was done favorable reports have been coming in. We have had no report of any damage done to any livestock or person. One characteristic report was made by Mr. C.S. Radebaugh. He sprayed his cattle on the afternoon of Ausust 4th, two weeks after that date he ran all of his cattle through the pen for checking on screw worms etc., and reported that he had not seen any kind of fly on any cow, but that there were 3 mosquitoes on one cow. (I had been on this place a few days before the spraying, and was run out by mosquitoes).

Six or seven weeks after the spraying was done Mr. Bruce and I inspected a great many of these dairies and the beef herds. Around the perimeter of the territory in which the cattle were sprayed there were 3 to 20 flies found on the cows inspected, but the cows were quiet and grazing or lying down peacefully. In the center of this territory we were able to find only ten or twelve flies in the dairy barns, and an occasional fly on some of the cows. Some of the Dairymen reported an increase of milk production, not withstanding the fact that this is the season when many of the cows were being dried up, and few are coming into fresh production.

In most of the Dairies large numbers of cockroaches were killed and mosquitoes were almost completely controlled for two or three weeks. One of the men remarked that a bushel of cockroaches had been killed in a certain diary; and another man in the group said 'Well you are behind, I saw them haul off 2 wheelbarrel loads of cockroaches'. Even after six weeks some Dairymen reported that mosquitoes were not pestering them and the cows at milking time.

In an experiment conducted at the Florida Range Cattle Experiment

239

Station about this same time 36 steers that were sprayed gained an average of 56.35 pounds each during 3 weeks after spraying. They had made an average gain of only 23.17 lbs. during the 3 weeks previous. This shows a 33.18 lb. increase per steer during the 3 weeks. Dr. Kirk stated that 'This difference in gain cannot all be attributed to the use of DDT in the control of horn flies'. However if we assume that half this gain can be attributed to the freedom from flies, and that the sprayed cattle in Orange County made a similar greater gain in weight the total gain in weight of the 10,500 head of beef cattle would amount to approximately 168,000 pounds. At a price of 8 cents per pound the value of our livestock men would amount to $13,440.00.

The 4570 head of dairy animals may have gained in weight, especially the calves, heifers and bulls, but milk production figures tell their story. A considerable drop in milk production is normal for August and September in Florida as the dairy cows are bred to give a maximum production in late fall and winter months. The Florida State A.A.A. office made summaries of production from reports sent in with applications for milk subsidy payments; and the following is their statement with reference to the State averages as compared to Orange County summaries. Two Orange County dairies where spraying was not done are included in Orange County figures.

The daily average production per cow in the State decreased 3.5 percent in August over average production per cow in July, but in Orange County this decrease was only 0.9 percent. In September the average daily production per cow further decreased by 5.8 percent whereas in Orange County the decrease was only 2.6 percent.

Following these conclusions in terms of gallons of milk produced over what would have likely been produced if spray had not been used it is indicated that 5.8 percent more milk was produced than which would have otherwise been produced which when converted means that an additional production of 28,216 gallons was gained by the 45 dairies in the county or in terms of money value about $11,850 for the period up to October 1, 1945. (subsidy payments not included).

Mr. Bruce states: 'This was the most extensive demonstration and experiment on insects of livestock that had ever been conducted up to this time, and a larger territory was covered. It was also the most successful control of flies, mosquitoes and cockroaches. It was the most convincing demonstration of which I have any knowledge.'

It is likely that during the next year we will get 100% cooperation among all the owners of livestock in a program to keep the cattle free of flies, mosquitoes and lice.

This great demonstration consumed an estimated 24 days. Preparations were begun early in July and second check-ups were completed in October. Many consultations, telephone calls, and trips were necessary. Some special nozzles, etc. for the spray rigs had to be made. After 10 days of intensive preparations I was still uncertain until our meeting on Friday night, August 3rd that the program could be carried out. We did not know whether the cooperating dairymen and ranchers would sign releases of responsibility of the Bureau of Entomology and the DuPont Company. All present signed. I took this as a vote of confidence and I cannot express my feeling of appreciation, and the boost this meeting gave me."

We are also indebted to Mr. Moore for listing the local dairy-

men, the number of cows, and the size of their barns, who participated in this historic study between August 4th-15th. These participants were:

DAIRY	NUMBER OF COWS	BARN SIZE (Sq.Ft.)
Bunch Dairy — Orlando	200	6,500
Barber, Henry — Orlando	53	3,000
Bandi, J. — Orlando	40	3,784
Belknap, A. — Gotha	40	1,000
College Park Dairy — Orlando	50	12,000
Calloway (Sunnyside Dairy) — Orlando	100	9,120
Cloyd, J.R. — Orlando	195	4,280
Datsons — Orlando	235	9,600
Dodd, B.C. — Winter Park	125	5,000
Eunice Dairy — Fairvilla	117	3,500
Granger Dairy — Orlo Vista	25	2,500
Hiatt, Chester — Bithlo	286	8,800
How-Ann Dairy (Kellie) — Orlando	90	2,100
Hammond, W.L. — Winter Garden	115	1,800
Judge, B.W. — Conway	160	4,000
Kates, J.J. — Orlando	122	5,000
Lee, T.G. — Orlando	520	30,000
Mole, Alex — Orlando	90	2,600
Macey, R.C. — Pine Castle	110	6,000
Nelson, Glenn — Orlando	109	4,000
Nelson, Mae — Orlando	65	2,000
Perfection Dairy — Holden Heights	123	14,400
Powers, J.F. — Clarcona	110	5,000
Roberts Dairy — Conway	42	3,000
Smith, Kirby — Conway	120	2,384
Shader's Dairy — Orlando	95	4,000
Sneed, Mrs. Fred — Orlando	21	3,000
Smith, H.E. — Plymouth	19	1,000
St. Lawrence, Fred — Orlando	80	4,000
Tootle Dairy — Pine Castle	60	3,000
Tyson, Howard — Orlando	120	3,000
Thomas, A.W. — Orlando	100	3,000
Winslow, Mrs. — Orlando	45	3,000
Withruk, John — Orlando	40	4,840
Ward, Carroll — Winter Park	140	4,800
Ziegler, Clarence — Orlando	200	18,000
Ziegler, Allen — Orlando	139	4,000

This head count of dairies and cows involved in this
result-demonstration provides us an insight to the fact there were 37
commercial dairies with 4,301 cows in Orange County at the end of
World War II.

Obviously the herds varied in size, with the smallest having 19
cows and the largest 520 cows. The number of square feet in each
barn also provides us with an insight as to size of barn facilities with
the various herds.

This was a most impressive demonstration in the use of this new insecticide. Both W.A. "Al" Smith and Stanley Shader said they remembered vividly the "kill" this insecticide accomplished at their respective dairy farms. Smith said it literally killed roaches by the wheel barrow load and Shader described it the same way with the housefly population.

After 20 years of outstanding service to Orange County dairy and other agricultural interests, County Agent Moore retired in August of 1946. Fred Baetzman, County Agent of Volusia County was appointed to this vacancy.

Agent Baetzman was familiar with local dairymen and their problems. As a matter of fact, he had worked closely with dairymen Lee and Ward in the Pioneer DHIA testing program and as Secretary of the Florida Jersey Cattle Club.

One of Agent Baetzman's first undertakings after coming to the county, was to organize the Orange County Aftificial Breeding Association. This was another agricultural "FIRST" in Florida.

Dairymen Lee and Ward, with Agent Baetzman and Extension Dairyman C.W. Reaves, drafted the Articles of Incorporation and By-Laws of the Orange County Artificial Breeding Association in August and September of 1948. At an organizational meeting on October 11, 1948 the association came into formal being and hired Elbert Cammack as the first technician. President and Directors of this first association of its kind in Florida were as follows: President T.G. Lee; Vice President Carroll Ward, Sr.; Secretary F.E. Baetzman, County Agent; Treasurer J.T. Raper. Directors were: B.W. Judge, Sr.; Howard Kellie; Glenn Nelson; Gordon Eunice; and O.D. Thompkins. A contract was made with the Southeastern Artificial Breeding Association of Asheville, N.C. Since it was the "FIRST" Artificial Breeding Association in Florida to provide this service for dairymen, it is only logical to assume it could also claim title to the first "test tube" dairy calf in the state. Technically however, Seminole County was the first county to rightfully claim this distinction because of unusual set of events.

The How-Ann Dairy, then owned by Howard and Ann Kellie, located across Highway #441 from the Ben White race track had the first cow to be artificially inseminated. However, because of a premature birth, a grade Jersey cow (Pansey) in the herd of the Forest Lake Academy "dropped" the first "test tube" calf on July 28, 1949. The sire was Brampton Wonderful X=401699.

Two years after the Orange County Artificial Breeding Association commenced operation several dairymen became dissatisfied with

242

Technician Cammack's activities in trying to organize a milk producers association.

This dissatisfaction "boiled over" into the Orange County Artificial Breeding Association and a special meeting was called on July 18, 1950 to determine whether the association wanted to continue the services of Technician Elbert Cammack. Directors present were — T.G. Lee, Carroll Ward, Sr., B.W. Judge, Sr., Howard Kellie, Gordon Eunice, Glen Nelson, and O.D. Tompkins. By secret ballot four "yes" ballots and three "no" ballots were cast and Mr. Cammack was retained. Several dairymen were dissatisfied with this decision and started another artificial breeding service, the Central Florida Breeding Association and hired their own technician. As a result Orange County had two artificial breeding associations, an agricultural distinction of dubious merit.

These two competing associations continued in operation for about a year and a half. Then in 1952 the two associations voted to merge their resources after Technician Cammack resigned. He decided to go into the dairy business himself by buying the Roberts herd in Conway. His resignation resolved the personality problem and the merger was an automatic reaction.

The magnitude of the response of dairymen to this service was reflected by the number of insemination services performed by the technician for several years as follows:

November 1948 to August 1949 . . . . .1,024 Cows Bred
November 1949 to November 1950 (Two associations' records unavailable)
November 1950 to November 1951 (Over) . . . . . . .2,000 Cows Bred
November 1951 to November 1952 (Approximately) . .3,000 Cows Bred
December 1952 to November 1953 . . . . .2,970 Cows Bred
December 1953 to November 1954 . . . . .2,863 Cows Bred
December 1954 to November 1955 . . . . .2,480 Cows Bred
December 1955 to November 1956 . . . . .3,101 Cows Bred
December 1956 to November 1957 . . . . .4,082 Cows Bred
December 1957 to November 1958 . . . . .4,189 Cows Bred

Records for succeeding years were unavailable except for a statement in the 1961 minutes which reported 5,307 "first" services performed during the 1960-'61 fiscal year and a grand total of 9,792 services. Not all of these animals were in commercial herds nor were they in Orange County since the association covered Seminole County and parts of Osceola and Lake Counties. Then too, owners of family cows could, for a special fee, acquire the services of the organization.

The season 1960-61 was perhaps the peak year for the association. After that, dairy farms and cow numbers declined sharply. Land values and big real estate deals began to take their toll and many dairymen began to sell out.

This decrease in number of cows signaled the beginning of the "countdown" for the local industry as well as the association. As this took place service calls dwindled until only one technician was needed. By April of 1967 the small number of cows bred and the number of miles of travel involved became such that the last technician John O'Steen, resigned and the Directors agreed to disband the association. The remaining dairy farms decided to go on a self service basis. After that each farm trained its own personnel, secured necessary storage facilities and equipment, and did business directly with the Breeding Association. So, after 17½ years the Orange County Association ceased operation.

One year after formation of the Orange County Artificial Breeding Association in 1948, another progressive dairy association was organized. It was the Orange County Dairy Herd Improvement Association with Carroll L. Ward, Sr. as its first President and George Baumeister as the milk tester.

TODAY'S MODERN MILKING PARLOR — T. G. Lee's dairy in the Conway area.

So, in the fall of 1949, Orange County dairymen had two organizations to assist them in upgrading the milk production of their herds. Under the Dairy Herd Improvement Association, dairymen systematically culled the poor milk producers. This program coupled with a program of breeding their top producing cows to proven sires

244

through the Artificial Breeding Association gave each succeeding generation a higher milk production potential. These breeding and culling practices along with better feeds resulted in a marked increase in milk production To appreciate the time factor in relation to higher milk production goals, the reader should remember that the pregnancy period of a cow is 9 months. Then it requires 2 years to bring this calf into production. Thus, 3 years is required before the dairyman can start comparing the production potentials of daughters and their mothers (dams).

The results of these two methods of upgrading milk production is best reflected in the production records of 22 herds in the DHIA program. Cows under test averaged 6,414 pounds of milk during the test period in 1950, whereas 22 years later cows under the same test averaged 9,679 pounds of milk! An increase of 3,265 pounds or 380 gallons of milk per cow per year. This expressed more graphically reflects an increase of a gallon of milk per day! This dramatic increase in milk production was the result of these two progressive dairy associations.

The 22 yearly average chart for Orange DHIA from October 1, 1949 through September 30, 1971, illustrates dramatically how local dairymen profited from increased milk production. See chart on page 246.

After the milk production of Orange County began to increase significantly, due to the ABA and DHIA programs, marketing problems and price wars developed in the mid 1950's. By 1956 milk producers were divided into "camps."

One "camp" wanted a Federal Milk Marketing Order. Others wanted no federal intervention of any kind. Those "opposed" to a Federal Milk Order won out, but the proponents said — "The time will eventually come when the Orlando area will be included under such an order" and on January 1, 1967 Federal Order #6 went into effect placing the Orlando area under a Federal Milk Marketing Order. A prediction that came true 10 years later!

Because of poor milk prices the first part of 1956 was rather bleak for local dairymen. However, the Martin Company's "blockbusting" announcement of September 14th changed the perspective. The Martin Company land purchase and land speculation brought on by an impending "building boom" indicated dairymen were *now* in the real estate business and that dairying was a side line!

As speculators bid up land prices, many dairymen could not "afford" to continue dairying on such expensive real estate. The "countdown" for the dairy industry of Orange County began at that time.

TWENTY-TWO YEARLY AVERAGES FOR ORANGE DHIA
FROM OCTOBER 1, 1949 THROUGH SEPTEMBER 30, 1971

Year Ending	Cows	Lbs. Milk	Average % Test	Lbs. Fat	Value of Product	Total Feed Cost	Value Above Feed Cost	Lbs. 4% F.C.M.	Feed Cost Per 100 lbs. 4% F.C.M.
September 30, 1950	1421	6444**	4.4	280	$422	$185	$237	6766	$2.74
September 30, 1951	1521	7115	4.5	320	$483	$197	$286	7646	$2.57
September 30, 1952	1714	7310	4.4	322	$507	$237	$270	7748	$3.06
September 30, 1953	1636	7019	4.5	313	$510	$220	$290	7502	$2.93
September 30, 1954	1668	6852	4.5	312	$503	$194	$309	7421	$2.61
September 30, 1955	1868	7232	4.6	333	$532	$201	$331	7888	$2.55
September 30, 1956	2182	7445	4.6	344	$537	$198	$339	8138	$2.42
September 30, 1957	2509	7670	4.6	353	$559	$198	$361	8363	$2.36
September 30, 1958	2737	7918	4.5	354	$573	$216	$357	8477	$2.54
September 30, 1959	3622	7892	4.4	348	$573	$224	$349	8377	$2.67
September 30, 1960	3723	8161	4.4	358	$592	$229	$363	8634	$2.65
September 30, 1961	3893	8443	4.3	367	$599	$243	$356	8882	$2.73
September 30, 1962	3932	9098	4.4	397	$646	$254	$392	9594	$2.64
September 30, 1963	4087	9221	4.4	403	$652	$275	$377	9733	$2.82
September 30, 1964	4497	9500	4.2	400	$665	$282	$283	9800	$2.87
September 30, 1965	4458	9601	4.2	401	$612	$283	$329	9855	$2.87
September 30, 1966	4882	9531	4.1	387	$595	$299	$296	9617	$3.10
September 30, 1967*	3243	9328	4.1	381	$641	$275	$366	9446	$2.94
September 30, 1968*	3183	9705	3.9	383	$665	$296	$369	9627	$3.01
September 30, 1969*	2995	9426	4.1	383	$690	$286	$404	9515	$3.01
September 30, 1970	4753	9591	3.9	374	$709	$320	$389	9446	$3.34
September 30, 1971	4342	9679**	3.9	377	$733	$348	$385	9446	$3.59

*T. G. Lee herd out of program

**Converting pounds to gallons, the 1950 production per cow 750 gallons and in 1971 the production rose to 1,122 or a net gain of 372 gallons.

Through the years herds have been located in several counties:
1971 — Orange DHIA herds are located in Orange, Lake, Seminole, and Osceola Counties.

One of the oldest dairy farms, Ward's Lakemont Dairy at Winter Park, was one of the first dairy farms caught in the Martin Company "building boom". The following residential subdivisions now occupy the site of that former dairy — Golf Side, Brookshire, Winter Park Pines, and the Winter Park High School.

Other urban developments that occupy dairy farm sites of yesteryear are:

URBAN DEVELOPMENT	FORMER DAIRY SITES
Colonial Plaza Mall	T.G. Lee Dairy
Winter Park High School	Lakemont Dairy (Ward's)
Golf Side Housing Development	Lakemont Dairy (Ward's)
Brookshire Housing Development	Lakemont Dairy (Ward's)
Winter Park Pines Housing Development	Lakemont Dairy (Ward's)
Sky Lake Housing Development (part of)	B.A. Brockbank Dairy
Northcrest Housing Development (Apopka)	Morton Tarte Dairy
Orlando Central Park (Industrial Site)	Clarence Ziegler Dairy
Conway Shores	Datson Dairy
Lake Conway Woods Housing Development	Al Hammond Dairy
Lake Conway Woods Apartments (section of)	Al Hammond Dairy
Nubar Industries (Industrial Plant)	Tommy Knight Dairy
Dover Oaks Apartment Complex	Sam Speer Dairy
Mo-Ho Trailer Park	Perfection Dairies
How-Ann Jersey Jug Dairy	Warehouse Site
Industrial Park (part of)	Eunice Dairy

While dairy farms decreased in number, the value of dairy products continued to increase until 1964. To summarize, one might say that fewer dairymen with larger herds and more productive cows were able to launch the confusing agricultural paradox of — "Fewer and fewer dairymen, milking more and more productive cows, producing more and more milk, for more and more people, for less and less profit!"

This "countdown" in dairy farms is well illustrated, as follows:

Year	Dairy Farms	Product Value
1925	85	not available
1930	51	$ 346,700
1940	93	$ 321,164
1945	51	$ 905,507
1950	61	$1,805,041
1954	42	$2,072,092
1959	36	$3,354,861
1964	20	$2,785,215
1969	13	$2,508,535
1974	6	???

The number of dairy cows in the "countup" stage, 1884 to mid 1950's, and the subsequent countdown stage are illustrated in the following account:

1884 — First dairy cow in Orange County.
1927 — 1,350 cows in commercial herds (Agent Moore's Report)
1945 — 4,301 cows in commercial herds (Agent Moore's Report)
1950 — Over 5,000 cows in commercial herds (Agent Baetzman's Report)
1951 — More than 6,000 cows in commercial herds (Agent Baetzman's Report)
1974 — Actual — 3,334 cows in 6 commercial dairy herds
       (Agent Swanson's Report)
1984 — Back to one dairy cow?

T-MINUS SIX AND COUNTING — As of July 11, 1974 there were only six dairy farms left in Orange County. Fathers and sons gather for industry picture. (Front row, left to right) Fathers; Jim Allen, Lawrence Hiatt, T. G. Lee, Jim Blackwell, J. S. Cloyd, Don Platt. (Back row, left to right) Sons; Stanley Allen, Larry Hiatt, Dick Lee, Albert Blackwell, Arthur Blackwell, Vincent Cloyd, John Cloyd, Kenley Platt.

As the population clock "ticked off" more and more urban growth, the dairy farms and dairy cows in Orange County continued to decrease. In November of 1973, the Jersey Jug and the Tyson dairies sold out. This left Orange County with only 6 dairies, the same number the county had around the turn of the century!

The 70-acre home of the Jersey Jug Dairy farm was probably the dairy in continuous operation the longest in Central Florida, and perhaps in the state as well!

The clock keeps on ticking and the countdown continues. As of May 25, 1974 only six dairies remain of the 61 operating in 1950. Their locations are as follows:

DAIRY FARM	LOCATION	NUMBER OF COWS
PLATT DAIRY	BITHLO	445
HIATT DAIRY	BITHLO	95
BLACKWELL	BIG ECON AREA	446
CLOYD	UNION PARK	445
LEE	CONWAY	1,603
ALLEN	BOGGY CREEK AREA	300

248

To list the names of all the men and women who operated dairies in Orange County is impossible. Perhaps we owe it to history to list as many as possible. To that end we have listed the names of all known to have been in business between 1945 and 1974. We apologize for names we may have overlooked.

JOEL ALBRITTON	OZZIE KIRTON
MISS ISABELL ALEXANDER	TOMMY KNIGHT
HOYT ANDERSON	RALPH MACY
ARNDT BROTHERS	ALBERT MARTIN
O.D. "POP" BALLARD	V.G. McKIBBEN
J. BANDI	MOLE BROTHERS
CARL BARBER	GLENN NELSON
IRA BARROW	KEN PATERSON
GEORGE & JERRY BAUMEISTER	RAPER DAIRY
S.F. BLODGETT	CLAUDE ROBERTS
MISS ESTHER BOWEN	S.O. ROGERS
B.A. BROCKBANK	A.J. RUSTERHOLTZ, JR.
J.A. BULLINGTON	LAWRENCE ST. JOHN
ELBERT CAMMACK	STANLEY SHADER
HANSON COLLINS	"STEW" SHADEL
DATSON BROTHERS	RALPH STACEY
TOMMY EMMONS	MORTON TARTE
EUNICE BROTHERS	EARL TATGENHORST
MRS. GEORGE FARLESS, SR.	HILTON TEAL
TOMMY FARMER	FRANK THOMPSON
OLIVER FENNEL	MRS. E.L. TOOTLE
R.C. HAILEY	J.C. TRICE
IKE HALL	J.H. TYSON
KENNETH HALL	CARROLL L. WARD & SON
AL HAMMOND	GEORGE WINEGARD
ALDEN & LILLIAN HAMMOND	MRS. EMMA WINSLOW
HIATT FAMILY	ALAN ZIEGLER
B.W. JUDGE & SON	CLARENCE ZIEGLER
FRED KEITH	CLAUDE YATES
HOWARD & ANN KELLIE	

In summary these overall landmark dates of the national dairy industry might be worth noting as one reflects what has transpired with the passage of time.

    1611 — Cows arrive for Jamestown Colony
    1865 — Pasteur experiments start
    1884 — MILK bottle invented by Dr. Harvey D. Thatcher
    1895 — Pasteurizing machines introduced
    1914 — Tank trucks used for transporting MILK
    1932 — Methods of increasing Vitamin D in MILK made practicable

CHAPTER VIII

History of the Poultry Industry

The history of Orange County's poultry industry is in many ways similar to its dairy industry. In the period before World War II both industries were based on the family unit. However, after the World War II period both became "geared" to mass production techniques and the "factory" concept. Poultry farms became known as "egg factories" and dairy farms became known as "milk factories". Mass production techniques and specialization also brought about a complete reversal of the pre-war marketing pattern.

CAGED LAYER OPERATION — Inside view of how today's poultry operations have become highly automated "Egg Factories". (Top) Exterior view.

The poultry business is typically a short term operation. The famous sayings about crop dusting pilots also applies to poultrymen — "There may be bold poultrymen but there are no old, bold poultrymen:" So, the story of Mr. M. W. Heatherington the Dean of Orange County Poultrymen is unusual. He came to Orange County in

1913 from Chicago, Illinois and selected Orange County in rather a round about way. Upon arriving in Jacksonville by train, he disembarked and looked around, but finding neither orange groves or the Florida landscape he anticipated, he boarded a train for Ocala.

At Ocala he looked around with the same result as in Jacksonville. There he was advised to try Tavares. However, while waiting in Wildwood for his connection to Tavares, Mr. Heatherington met a Mr. Wurst of Fairvilla in Orange County. Mr. Wurst mentioned that he had 10 acres of land that would make a nice home site if Mr. Heatherington wanted to try Florida farming in a citrus area. So Mr. Heatherington took up residence in a one room cabin on this 10-acre site in Fairvilla in 1913. He began by growing some vegetables and his beginnings in the poultry business consisted of two setting hens and two settings of eggs. Soon after that he ordered some white Wyandotte chicks. To supplement his income he drove a team of mules for a Mr. J. D. Henderson and later married his boss' daughter.

When Mr. Heatherington was drafted into the service in World War I he sold his chickens and some of his equipment. But in 1919 he was back and brought his brother, A. E. Heatherington.

Picking up where he left off M. W. bought back some of the white Wyandotte chickens he had sold in 1918.

By the early 1920's he entered a pen of his birds in the Alabama egg laying trials. At that time Florida had no such program. He also entered birds in the poultry show at the Central Florida Exposition in the 1920's and 30's. By the late 1920's Mr. Heatherington had established the egg laying ability of his white Wyandottes through trap nesting, and offered baby chicks from his strain of high producing birds. By increasing his incubator facilities he was able to hatch some 300 to 500 baby chicks a week. Mr. Heatherington's practice was to keep about 2/3rds of his hatch of baby chicks and sell the balance which made him one of the pioneer hatchery operators in Orange County.

His facilities for his birds were among the best in Central Florida with excellent housing, well fenced yards and automatic waterers.

Mr. Heatherington also mixed his feed to his own formula and continued this practice well into the 1930's before finally buying formula mixed feeds.

The New Hampshire breed of chicken appeared in Florida in the mid 1930's and impressed Heatherington favorably. This breed put on weight faster and could be picked more easily than the Wyandottes, so he converted to the New Hampshire breed. At the same time he scheduled his hatching operations on a year around basis so that he turned out 300 broilers weekly for the local market. By raising these broilers in batteries of wire cages and using special feeds, he produced premium broilers in a very short time.

Heatherington also raised turkeys for the local market during the holiday season which made him a pioneer turkey producer in Orange County. By co-ordinating his 3,000 egg capacity incubators Mr. Heatherington turned out baby chicks and poults on a year around basis.

The late A. E. Heatherington, former "Dean" of Orange County Poultry-men. Picture taken July 11, 1974.

For reasons of age and health Mr. Heatherington closed down his poultry operations in 1957 and ended 38 continuous years of poultry farming in Orange County. Mr. Heatherington passed away December 27, 1974 at the age of 84.

This is an outstanding record in a field of agriculture noted for its high rate of financial failures. As one poultryman expressed it, "Sure, the poultry industry has a lot of money in it. It was put there by people who lost everything in that business!"

Mr. Milford White came to Ocoee from Oklahoma in 1920 and settled on what became known as White Road. He began his poultry operation with white leghorn chickens and maintained that breed until the early 1940's. His 20 years of continuous poultry farming gives Mr. White the second longest record of operation amongst Orange County's pre-World War II poultrymen.

According to Carroll B. Terry, a neighbor, Mr. White's flock size varied from 300 to 1,000 birds. His birds were under range-type management, and often roosted in the yard trees. The fact that he had very little invested in housing and equipment helped Mr. White to survive the bad years when they came. He also had his own egg route including the nearby T. B. Hospital, which provided him a constant market. Nevertheless, in 1941 he gave up his poultry operations to devote full time to his citrus groves.

Another man who had a brief fling in the poultry business but finally decided on cattle and citrus instead, was George D. Livingston of the Conway area. Mr. Livingston, with his father and brother, came to Orange County in 1924 and after planting a small citrus grove on his grandfather's old home site, he bought some chickens to supplement the family income. He obtained these (white leghorns) from a party in Lancaster Park, who caught them at night as they roosted in the trees. In 1925 Mr. Livingston moved to Mexico and left the chickens in the care of his father and brother. When he returned in 1927, and asked his father how the chicken business was going, his father replied, "Fine, we are making about a dollar a day off of them." Mr. Livingston found that they had been selling the eggs to a local feed store and it took him less than six months to terminate that losing venture!

Another of Orange County's early poultry farms was located in the Lockhart area at approximately the site of the Rimar Drive-In Theatre. This poultry farm was in business for approximately 20 years although there were three name changes during this period. First, it was Bo-White Egg Ranch, then Dixie Farms and finally Riggs Poultry Farm.

In 1931 Mr. Alan Schryver and Mr. Elva Hedges came to the Lockhart area from New Jersey and located at Lockhart.

Schryver and Hedges acquired several homes and buildings and moved them to the site as dwellings and poultry houses.

Their poultry flock varied between 1,000 and 3,200 birds and was an open range setup. An egg route was established in the Orlando area.

About 1932, Schryver and Hedges along with O. A. Dearing, Herb Reiners, Joe Williams, and Buren Carroll, organized a poultry market on North Orange Avenue near Livingston Avenue in Orlando to handle their poultry products. Mr. Dearing became manager. However, by 1935 the market was handling more fruits and vegetables than poultry products so Mr. Schryver, with about 18 other poultrymen, created the Bo-White Egg Marketing Organization in 1936. This organization candled, packaged and distributed the eggs in special window type blue cartons.

When Mr. Elva Hedges died in 1937, his son Wilfred assumed management of the Lockhart Poultry Farm and changed the name to Dixie Farms. Wilfred managed Dixie Farms until 1945 when he was drafted into the service. The farm suspended operations until his return in 1946. He started operations again and continued it until 1948.

The Dixie Farm operation was strictly an egg farm up until the war but it was expanded into a broiler production during the war

254

years and continued until 1948 when a Mr. Riggs took over the farm and operated it until 1951 or '52 under the name — Riggs Poultry Farm. When Riggs discontinued operations in the early 1950's, the property reverted to a Dr. Vannatta of East Orange, New Jersey, who had been a silent partner since the farm's beginning in 1931.

In 1938 Mr. Schryver went to work for Consolidated Products Company and for the next 20 years he sold these products to poultrymen in five southern states. In 1958 he joined the Mid-State Mill at Kissimmee where he continues to work today with the poultry industry of Central Florida.

Mr. Wilfred Hedges, son of Elva Hedges, Mrs. Schryver's original partner, worked for Mr. Schryver as a Consolidated Product salesman in Florida in the 1950's. Today, he is associated with Musselwhite Farms and is still active in the poultry industry.

Several other pioneer poultrymen and their type of operations should also be recognized for their contributions to the industry.

Mr. Joe Williams, a Winter Park carpenter became a poultryman in the 1930's because of the "depressed" local building industry. Mr. Williams built up a flock of some 800 - 900 hens and maintained a retail egg route in Winter Park. Later he joined Mr. Schryver and others in forming the Poultrymen's Market on North Orange Avenue in Orlando. Mr. Williams was affiliated with the Bo-White Egg Marketing outlet in 1936 and for several years was President of the Florida State Poultry Producers' Association. When the building industry revived in the early 1940's, Mr. Williams returned to carpentry.

Herb Reiners of Apopka, was one of Orange County's most progressive poultrymen in the pre-World War II period. According to Mr. Schryver, Mr. Reiners' diversified poultry produced 2,000 to 3,000 broilers a month. This was a large operation for the 1930's since he hatched his own chicks and raised them to broilers in battery pens, dressed and marketed the birds in Central Florida under the Sunshine broiler label. In his early operations he was an egg producer and a founder of the Poultrymen's Market. Later he was affiliated with the Bo-White Poultry Marketing Association.

Mr. Reiners was the inventor of the egg turning device of the Mammoth incubator. Later he also developed the "grasshopper" lawn mower. However, in 1940 he sold his farm on Highway #441 to Tommy Cressler. Mr. Cressler operated a hatchery and a poultry farm at this site 'til the early 1950's when he sold out and moved.

Mr. E. B. Stocking of Gotha was another pioneer poultryman. According to Mr. Schryver, Stocking had a flock of about 1,000 white leghorns, raised 1¼ lb. "squab broilers" for the Orlando hotel trade, kept milk goats and operated several acres of citrus. Mr. Stocking dropped out of the local poultry scene sometime in the late 1930's.

One unusual feature of local poultry husbandry during the pre-World War II days, was the friendship between the poultrymen and the local feed dealers. According to Mr. Schryver there were enough poultrymen and feed dealers that a softball team for each group was organized and he frequently remarked about those friendly contests in the early 1940's. Z. N. Harvey, a former feed dealer of those days concurred. In today's hurried world it is difficult to visualize a friendly ball game between poultrymen and feed dealers. In fact, to find sufficient feed dealers in the state to "field" a team would be difficult.

In his 1928 Annual Report, Agent K. C. Moore reported that the Orange County Poultry Association had been operating some seven years but in 1926, Moore found the association in trouble and rolled up his sleeves to help. In 1927 he reported — "The association under loose cooperative plan and attained a very unenviable reputation on the poor quality of the eggs."

The poultrymen elected new officers in January and re-organized and incorporated the association. Mr. Moore served on a committee to draft new By-Laws and contracts. Once these had been adopted, he assisted the association in getting a Charter from the State. Mr. Moore accepted this assignment without the benefit of an attorney. However, he apparently "filed" correctly because he received the Charter after several weeks of correspondence with the State Attorney-General and the Secretary of State.

We have records of principal poultrymen of those early days in Orange County but the size of the poultry industry is difficult to ascertain. County Agent Charlie Kime's 1925 Annual Report rates the poultry industry as the 4th in agricultural importance in the county. Truck farming with 1,200 acres was in second place and dairy farming was third with citrus being first.

In July of 1927, the poultry population of Orange County was estimated at 103,658 birds and the number of poultrymen at around a hundred. By comparison, one Orange County poultryman in 1974 has as many birds on his farm as the entire country in 1925 and the 29 Orange County poultrymen of 1974 have more than 10 times that number of birds.

However, in 1928 the high price of feeds and the diseases, coccidiosis and paralysis, were taking their toll and the country poultry business was on the down swing. Agent Moore said — "The high price of feeds, which have to be shipped from the grain producing sections of the country were the cause."

YESTERYEAR POULTRY MANAGEMENT — Scene of the White Wyandotte flock of A. E. Heatherington of Fairvilla in the 1920's.

Exhibition shows and fairs were a popular activity among poultryment in the 1920's and early 1930's but as poultry husbandry became more businesslike, this activity fell from favor and only poultry hobbists could justify participation.

By 1929, the Orange County poultry industry was in dire straits. Moore reported assisting in the organization of the Central Florida Poultry Producers Cooperative Association. He said the poultrymen were discouraged, that several had sold out and others planned to do so. The old Orange County Poultry Association was proving unsatisfactory as a marketing operation but a new organization idea would be hard to put over.

At this time Mr. Julian Langner was passing through our city, and one of the greatest poultry enthusiasts, Mr. C. F. Batchelder got acquainted with him and his abilities as an organizer of farmer cooperatives. The Orange County Chamber of Commerce assisted in financing the beginning of this association. Apparently this new association for poultrymen aroused some interest in surrounding counties because Agent Moore reported people from Lake, Osceola and Volusia Counties also joined.

This appears to have been the first truly cooperative marketing agreement by Central Florida poultrymen and perhaps may have been the "FIRST" in the state as well? In those days agriculture was the basic industry of the area and the Chamber gave its complete support. Today, the Chamber is dominated by the downtown business men and couldn't care less about agriculture.

These "ups" and "downs" in the poultry industry of 1929 is typical of one of the most hazardous of agricultural endeavors. The citrus and vegetable industries have had their ups and downs but theirs can't approach the frequency and magnitude of problems of the poultrymen.

A humorous and interesting account of poultrymen's interest in a specific topic is recorded by County Agent Moore as having occurred in October of 1930. The following anecdote reflects the poultryman's point-of-view: Extension Economist, Frank Brumby was brought in to explain the value of keeping records and accounts and to analyze them for 78 local poultrymen. Mr. Brumby's report was based on a survey of 182 Florida poultrymen. The keen interest of the poultrymen kept the speaker on his feet over 2½ hours!

Whether Mr. Brumby was that good or whether the interest of the poultrymen of that era was greater than that of today's poultrymen, remains undecided!

Perhaps at the other extreme, was this "goodie" Moore recorded in 1930 — "One day a hermit-type man entered the office and wanted to know the feeding value of palmetto stems. This man had been cutting them up fine and feeding them to young chickens. I found that this was so when I visited his place. Although the chickens looked alright, I was never able to determine the feeding value of palmetto stems."

Such is the life of an Extension Agent. He can expect just about anything to "pop" up in the course of his duties. Since everything is not in the "book", an agent must always be ready to say to such inquiries — "I don't know but will try to find out!" In Moore's palmetto experience it's doubtful if the inquiry went any further.

In 1931, the Chamber of Commerce planned a 5-year promotional drive to secure 1,000 new farmers for Orange County. To help recruit these new farmers the Chamber asked Agent Moore to prepare special fact sheets on the various agricultural commodity areas. These were given to interested persons.

The 1931 fact sheet provides an interesting view of the poultry business of those days:

"The average egg production per bird on commercial egg farms in Florida is found by a three-year study of flock records to be just as high as in similar studies in other states and higher than many.

Six ways of maintaining high egg production profitably in Florida are:

258

1. Maintain 50 to 75 percentage pullets in the flock.
2. Secure chicks from vigorous high producing laying stock.
3. For high yearly and high fall and winter egg production secure one hatch in February and another in April.
4. Birds must average 30 to 35 eggs a piece as total for November, December, and January.
5. High egg production results from high feed consumption.
6. The white leghorn gives the highest egg production for the least feed cost.

It is easily possible to keep 1,000 laying hens on five acre farms and have abundant green feed if the soil type is suitable for growing green feed. If all feed is purchased, a smaller acreage is sufficient. Corn, grain sorghums, peas and sunflowers produce average yields on adapted Florida soils. Additional acreage will be needed for these field crops. Keep your total layout for real estate, poultry, and equipment as much below $8.00 per bird as possible. Secure a good location on high well drained soil and convenient to a market for eggs. Poultry farming can be made to work well with growing oranges, or with truck farming if yards are properly fenced."

These 1931 recommendations are interesting in light of today's technology and highly mechanized conditions.

In May of 1931 poultrymen found that young cockerals offered as broilers were not selling well, and that some 8,000 surplus broilers were on hand. County Agent Moore and Mr. Risher, Poultry Marketing Specialist of the State Marketing Bureau, investigated the possibilities of shipping a car load of poultry to another city. However, they found the markets elsewhere not as good as in the Orlando area. So in co-operation with local feed dealers, Moore appealed to the people of Orlando to consume more chickens. In a talk to the Orlando Rotary Club he proposed the slogan — "A Chicken a Day for May."

The Kiwanis Club invited Moore to talk to their group and the local paper printed the slogan between each editorial for two weeks. The City Chamber of Commerce and many civic clubs featured fried chicken on their menus for six weeks. The housewives also joined in the campaign. As a result of the promotion Orlandoans ate fried chicken that summer as never before and no cockerals were lost or shipped.

In 1931 Agent Moore reported the success that the Orlando Cooperative Poultry Association had in marketing eggs and poultry. This was the association Mr. Schryver and others organized on North Orange Avenue near the Livingston Street instersection.

However, many farmers in the county failed in 1931-32 and it was a crisis period for the local poultry industry. County Agent Moore believed that high feed costs and low egg prices in spring and summer were contributing factors and that lack of green feeds increased the costs and lowered egg yields. Freight, mixing charges,

259

advertising and "service" kept the price of mixed feed high even though grain prices were low where it was grown. Lack of cash to buy the ingredients for home mixing and variations in quality of ingredients when bought in small lots caused many to leave the poultry business.

In March of 1933, a new poultry association — Poultry Producers of Orange County was organized. Almost immediately it was given the job of curbing unfair competition of cut-rate shipped eggs, advertising "leaders", and evasions of the state egg law. According to Agent Moore the association received prompt cooperation from Nathan Mayo, State Commissioner of Agriculture, and the situation was corrected. The Association helped enforce the new state egg law by informing local poultrymen of its requirements and cooperated with the state association to develop a fair practice code for poultry products.

In 1934 the Orange County poultry industry produced $145,468 worth of products and ranked 4th in agricultural income.

Scandal surfaced in 1934 when Agent Moore reported that the cooperative association had, through mismanagement and extravagance, caused several poultrymen to fail and caused heavy financial losses to most of the others. This brought about the failure of the Poultry Cooperative less than five years after its formation. However, the Poultry Producers of Central Florida organization continued to operate during this troubled period and acted as a rallying point by keeping members informed of state marketing regulations and other matters of common concern.

Ten years after County Agent Moore arrived in Orange County economic conditions were entirely different from the 1926 period when he arrived. Because of the economic stagnation, administrative officials in Gainesville conceived the idea of "bringing all branches of agriculture together to work toward common goals at the county level". The idea was to create a super planning council that would diagnose related problems, establish common goals and somehow develop programs that would improve the overall agricultural situation. To comply with this administrative mandate, Agent Moore selected 25 progressive individuals from all areas of the county to represent all facets of agriculture to act as the County Agricultural Planning Council. Representing the poultry industry on this Council were Allan Schryver, Lockhart; C. F. Ellers, Rt. #1, Orlando; and Joe Williams, Winter Park.

As might be expected this attempt to whip up enthusiasm for vaguely defined objectives among a group of widely diverse interests was a 'mission impossible'.

Eighteen of the 25 committee members showed up for the first meeting. Mr. Moore summarized this meeting as follows: "Since there was no definite thing presented as a guide or suggestion on which to begin work; and since these are busy men of large interests, I believe they left the meeting with a sense of disappointment." Mr. Moore commented further — "The types of farming in Orange County and the economic status of these enterprises make a problem of just what problems to take up with a probable hope of accomplishing anything. No one of our farming enterprises has got into a plight which has aroused the community's interest. Men do not like to delve into statistics til they must. One very intelligent man's attitude was reflected by the remark — 'Why worry about overproduction of citrus. You can't stop plantings and promotions, and anyway, we might any year have another freeze which will adjust matters'. Still fewer attended the next meeting and when a third meeting was called in connection with the Soil Conservation referendum, only two of the committee appeared!" Similar nebulous concepts continued to emanate from administrative circles, concepts that failed again and again over the years.

Consequently, Moore found it difficult to develop an Extension poultry program in 1936 and devoted his time to consultation rather than to promote meaningless programs among local poultrymen. Nevertheless, Moore enrolled five poultrymen in the Florida Calendar Flock program and 14 in the Grow Healthy chick program, so his efforts to help the industry did not fall on deaf ears. Moore also served as advisor on economic conditions for the local poultry industry.

In the summer and fall of 1937 many "new" potential poultrymen arrived in the county. Moore advised the newcomers as follows: "We have as good flocks in the county as can be found except where breeders have high priced, trap-nested, pedigreed birds. We also have good hatcheries and hatcherymen who will set only eggs from blood-tested and accredited flocks. I advise that chicks be purchased from these local hatcheries."

Looking back at the poultry industry of that time, I believe the industry was beginning to specialize and the need of a "generalist" type County Agent was disappearing.

When the clouds of World War II began to appear on the horizon, Moore devoted much time to locating supplies of scarce items such as feed and labor for the industry. When the war ended the industry was ready for expansion and specialization in the factory concept.

The post war period brought a complete re-building of the local poultry industry with new people except for a few old stalwarts. M.

W. Heatherington of Fairvilla was now beginning his 32nd year of operation. Clyde Wiggins of the south Winter Garden area returned to the poultry business after working for the railroad for two years during the war — 1943-'45 and there were a few others. However, the majority who started in the poultry business in Orange County after World War II were newcomers with little or no previous poultry experience.

One progressive newcomer was Mr. Roy Seckinger. He came to Maitland in 1945 from Ohio after a successful career as an insurance executive. Mr. Seckinger intended to continue in the insurance business but more or less "backed into" the poultry business.

After acquiring a home and some citrus acreage north of Lake Minnehaha in 1947 he decided to raise some poultry on the side. To that end he built pens and houses for a range flock of leghorns. Being research minded Mr. Seckinger read everything available on poultry raising including a California publication on raising poultry in wire cages. He ordered several thousand cages and in late 1951 established the first wire caged layer operation in Central Florida. This rather progressive step was regarded by many as a crazy idea and contrary to all sound principles of poultry husbandry. However, it was the beginning of the egg factory concept of poultry operations in Orange County. Mr. Seckinger ultimately increased his caged layer operations to 10,000 birds before retiring from the poultry business in 1957.

Mr. Seckinger was a charter member of the Central Florida Poultry Cooperative organized in 1951 and located on Edgewater Drive behind the Ben White horse stables. During its first year of operation, the Coop handled 300 cases of eggs a week. By 1952 this cooperative had 25 members and did nearly a quarter of a million dollars worth of business. The 2nd year of operation a $2,600 egg cooling room was added to provide storage for four hundred and fifty cases of eggs. In 1953 the Cooperative had 32 members and handled about 1/3 of a million dollars worth of eggs. The years 1953 and '54, were good for Seckinger and other poultrymen in and out of the Cooperative. In fact, six caged layer operations were started in Orange County in those two years.

The numerous inquiries about the poultry industry prospects prompted Agents Baetzman of Orange County and Norris of Lake County to sponsor a joint six weeks poultry school in the Winter Garden area. Over 80 people enrolled. However, by 1954 overproduction had set in, egg prices declined and the interest of out-of-state folks in the Orange County poultry business cooled considerably. Several caged layer farms closed down and of those still in business many were unable to purchase replacement stock.

Among other problems that caged-layer operators experienced was the difficulty of disposing of cull birds. The Cooperative investigated the possibility of building a dressing plant to dispose of surplus birds at better prices.

Overproduction in the local poultry industry had brought marketing problems. To find answers to such problems, the Orlando Area Poultry Association was organized in 1956 with Roy Seckinger as President; Bernard Radford, 1st Vice President; J. C. Huggins, 2nd Vice President; Frank Stephens, Treasurer; and Kathleen R. Johnson, Secretary. When Mr. Seckinger found that his feed costs equaled his egg returns in 1957 he saw no alternative but to sell out. Seckinger had pioneered the caged layer type of operation in Central Florida and also helped organize the Egg Cooperative which helped poultrymen market their eggs in that period of mass production.

H. S. Musselwhite, Jr. was a newcomer to the local poultry scene in the immediate post-war period. Whereas Seckinger's poultry operation was unable to survive the disastrous egg prices of the late 1950's, Mr. Musselwhite succeeded and today he is the most successful and diversified poultryman in Central Florida.

When Mr. Heatherington and Mr. Seckinger retired in 1957, Mr. Musselwhite's poultry farm became the oldest continuously operating poultry farm in Orange County. In an agricultural endeavor where the mortality rate is so high, that is quite a record.

Mr. Musselwhite arrived in Orange County in 1945, the same year as Mr. Seckinger and similarly "backed" into the poultry business. He tried several small businesses before purchasing a small produce hauling route from Ira Hawthorne in 1946. With his brother-in-law Elwood DeMott, they bought poultry, eggs, and other produce in Georgia and distributed these products all over Florida. Then in 1947 Mr. Musselwhite sold his interest in the produce hauling business to his brother-in-law and started a flock of about 1,000 Rhode Island Reds on the Wekiwa Springs Road near Highway 426. The experience gained through marketing produce proved valuable in marketing poultry products. By 1958 he had nearly 30,000 birds under a closed house type of management, a very large operation for that time in the poultry industry.

In 1960, he moved to a new site a little northeast of his old site on Wekiwa Springs Road. He also acquired the franchise for the DeKalb strain of white leghorns and established a hatchery in addition to his egg operations.

Diversification was always a key ingredient in the many successful management decisions made by Mr. Musselwhite early in his operations. For example, he was one of the first to convert ·his layer operation from a closed house to a caged system. In 1966 he established his own feed mill in Zellwood, and in 1969 he acquired the old Central Florida Poultry Cooperative on Edgewater Drive to facilitate his marketing operations.

Mr. Musselwhite was one of the few producers not associated with this egg cooperative. At a time when the majority of local producers were pooling their talents in a common marketing venture he worked tirelessly to maintain his independent egg route. Years later, all the charter members had gone out-of-business, but Mr. Musselwhite was still going strong!

REMEMBER WHEN? — Allan Schryver (left) H. S. Musselwhite, Jr. (center) and Wilfred Hedges (right) "recap" poultry operations of a bygone era. April 23, 1974.

The Musselwhite farms today are highly successful diversified poultry business with a hatchery, breeding flocks, contract producers, feed mill, and an elaborate marketing outlet that covers the Central Florida area.

Nowadays, most of today's Orange County poultrymen are contract producers. Consequently this type of operation should be discussed briefly. The originator of this management arrangement in Orange County, Mr. Jerry Watson was for many years associated with the Ralston Purina Company. Through him we have the history of this development.

In 1959 Mr. Watson, Manager of the Poultry Products Division of Ralston Purina, encouraged the expansion of the local poultry industry through producer contracts. Under this arrangement, Ralston Purina Company agreed to certain pooling agreements provided the producer did likewise. Thus the poultryman and feed dealer became partners in an egg merchandising venture.

The identity of the first person to pioneer this type of arrangement is uncertain but Mr. Watson believes that Ray Goolsby of Apopka was first and that Marvin Moore of Apopka was second. The first contract was let in 1959 or early 1960. At that time, it was next to impossible for an individual to secure a production loan from a lending agency such as the Central Florida Production Credit Association, mainly because financial failures in the poultry industry were notorious and it was considered a poor credit risk. Mr. Watson remembers that Ray Goolsby was the first to establish the fact of his previous poultry experience with the credit association. This was possible because a member of his family had once been enrolled in a 4-H Poultry Project!

When the contract poultry arrangement proved successful, the credit rating of the poultry industry acquired a respectable reputation with lending agencies. Thanks to this new financial soundness, in more recent years poultry veterans of 10 years or more experience are more numerous.

Because the egg producer relied on the feed company to market his eggs, some critics of the program claimed that the producer had lost his identity and was virtually an employee of the feed company. Actually the arrangement proved economically sound and the managerial ability of local producers made this contract arrangement so successful that many poultry business men from other areas came to study the merits of this operation.

Some broiler agreements were also fostered but they were mostly of short duration and generally less profitable.

However, with the exception of H. S. Musselwhite, Jr., and perhaps one or two others, most Orange County poultrymen started in business after this new management concept began.

The various poultry farms, size of operation and type of operations as of May 1974 are as follows:

BRONSON FARM CONTRACTS		INDEPENDENTS	
Bryant	30,000	Hillcrest	106,000
El Rancho	22,000	Bay Ridge	30,000
Spring Grove	30,000	Pine Oaks	55,000
Twin Lake	25,000		
Eva Suggs (Pullets)	14,000		

CAL MAINE FOODS CONTRACTS		MUSSELWHITE FARMS CONTRACTS	
John Talton 1 — (Pullets)	34,000	Chaudoin & Musselwhite	51,000
John Talton 2 — (Pullets)	34,000	Harrelson	30,000
John Talton 3 — (Breeder)	11,000	Talton Estate (Breeders)	24,000
John Talton 4 — (Breeder)	11,000	Marden	30,000
Alex Dewar	30,000	Miny	50,000
Ponkan	40,000	Slover	20,000
Riffle (Pullets)	16,500	Delvich	60,000
		Blackwelder	82,000
		Dorset	26,000
		H. S. M. Pullets	80,000
		Millhouse	80,000
		Millhouse	50,000

Unfortunately the future direction of the local poultry industry can only be downward. County-wide zoning just about makes it impossible for any new poultry farms to begin operating. As urbanization and industrialization creep across the county like an octopus, zoning officials look upon poultry farms with more and more disfavor. On the other hand, poultry farms already in existence are constantly being harassed by health officials and neighbors concerning flies and odors or other undesirable aspects of their industry. Increasing land values resulting from urbanization also make the purchase of land for agricultural use economically impossible.

NO TURKEY — For over 24 years John M. Myers raised annually between 8,000 and 10,000 Turkeys at his Avalon Turkey Farm. He sold out his turkeys in 1973. The reason why, in 1949 feed cost $3.00 a hundred and he received 55¢ a pound at the farm for his turkeys. In 1973 feed cost $14.00 a hundred and he received 21¢ a pound for turkeys shipped to North Carolina.

In November of 1973, the Avalon Turkey Farm in the rural southwest corner of Orange County, ceased operations after 26 years. During their best years, Mr. John Myers, the manager, sold 8,000 to 10,000 turkeys from the premises to people who came from a 75-mile radius. Since this site is close to Walt Disney World and fronts on S.R. 545 some developer would doubtless offer a good price to convert it to a housing development.

The dynamic changes that have taken place in the local poultry industry may be summarized as follows:

In 1974, one poultryman can handle a volume of business that required 110 poultrymen in 1926. Today's "egg factory" operation is the result of specialized marketing. However, the greater concentration of birds per farm has intensified the manure disposal, flies, odors, and related problems. These are problems that troubled yesteryear's poultrymen very little. Now, the industry trend is toward a reduction in number of birds per farm as well as in number of farms.

Reflecting on changing farm and bird numbers, some of the following statistics about an industry that will soon pass from the local scene are of interest.

```
1926 — 110 Yards — Kime's Report
1927 — 103,658 Poultry Population — Moore's Report
1934 —                — Value of Poultry Products Sold — $  145,468 (4th Place)
                        Moore's Report
1940 — 108 Farms — Value of Poultry Products Sold — $  100,292
                — Census Report
1944 —                — Value of Poultry Products Sold — $  295,012
1949 —  61 Farms — Value of Poultry Products Sold — $  456,861
1954 —  60 Farms — Value of Poultry Products Sold — $  448,009
1959 —  47 Farms — Value of Poultry Products Sold — $  581,856
1964 —  67 Farms — Value of Poultry Products Sold — $2,760,349
1969 —  38 Farms — Value of Poultry Products Sold — $5,801,070
1974 —  26 Farms — Value of Poultry Products Sold —      ??
                — 1,076,500 Birds
```

As land becomes too valuable to farm or use for agricultural purposes, the land moves into a "higher" use category. As more and more higher-use category developes around the remaining farms trying to ride out the urbanization pressures, pollution abatement restrictions will in turn intensify.

CHAPTER IX

History of the Cattle Industry

Those who think it strange that cows are "holy" in India don't know their early Florida history, for cows once had "holy" status in the open range era of Florida. In fact, the rights and privileges enjoyed by cattlemen without let or restraint staggers the imagination today! Those special rights are well remembered by people who lived through the "open range" era.

When the open range concept prevailed in Florida, cows roamed the countryside at will in search of vegetation. This "pursuit of grass" was the inalienable right conferred by the open range law and could not be challenged by anyone, including the mighty railroad barons! To cope with the situation, railroads maintained specially trained section foremen to patrol sections of railroad track and to identify and report all "kills" found. "Kills" were posted on the bulletin board, at the nearest train depot, so cattlemen could learn of any losses. According to a pioneer cattleman, the late Walter Bronson, cattlemen often claimed the dead cow was one of his better cows and requested payment of 12 dollars instead of the eight or ten that was the going rate during that period. According to R. I. "Bert" Wetherbee, another pioneer cattleman of the open range era, the railroads were seldom "fooled" on the value of the killed cow. Section foremen knew the difference between a cow, bull, steer, or heifer, were knowledgeable about marks and brands and were sharp cowmen themselves. Furthermore, the railroad found and reported the dead cows, so it seems doubtful that cattlemen would push their claims too far. That railroads were liable for cows killed on railroad property seems inconceivable in light of the laws and court decisions of today.

The rules for railroads also applied to motorists of those days. After all, cows had the right to search for greener pastures and in so doing, they frequently crossed highways. In which case, the motorist was required to yield the right-of-way to the cow, night or day! Readers familiar with those days remember only too well that during cold nights, cattle and horses sought out the warm pavement on which to sleep. If the motorist hit a cow and survived, he was still liable for damages regardless of his injuries and the damage to his car. Some motorist charged for damages by the cattleman perhaps originated the famous remark — "Holy Cow!"

At times, communities took exception to range cattle roaming the town square. To correct this problem the public pound came into being. Whether the community could legally fine cattle barons in those days is uncertain. However, the pound still exercises such authority today although it deals primarily with stray pets rather than cattle. R. I. "Bert" Wetherbee says he remembers that in the early 1920's, an irate cattleman released some stray cattle one dark night from the Taft community pound.

Impressive as were various "cow rights", the "property rights" of cattlemen were even more so. This is especially so, since cattlemen found it more advantageous to "use" land rather than own it. The "use" practice imposed no tax burden on the cattleman and at the same time gave him more legal rights than the owner of the land, just because he owned cattle. Al Smith, told us of Mr. Joe Daley a pioneer cattleman of the 1930's, who subscribed to the theory of "own no land" cattle-type operation. Daley owned several hundred cattle and "used" land in Eastern Orange County. By not owning land Daley did not have any tax liabilities and the open range concept afforded him grazing rights and privileges to operate under! For example, people living in the country who wanted to keep cows out of their yards or gardens, were required to "fence out" the cows. It was not the cattleman's responsibility to fence them in!

Cattlemen literally took possession of the land they used and often fertilized it with a match! Since it required some 50 acres of native pasture to support a cow, cattlemen burned off the woods in the spring to provide new grass for his cattle. This burning practice constituted his pasture improvement program and no one, not even the landowner had a right to challenge it! The open range era fostered an unusual golden rule agreement between cattlemen. Because their cattle "shared" common ground, cattlemen observed strict respect for each other's marks and brands. The ears of the animal were notched for identification purposes and a special brand was imprinted on the animal's hide. Cattle were doubly identified under this system of ear marks and hide brands which were recorded at the County Court House. In those early days the county recommended to the Governor a person to supervise the administration of the marks and brands program within a county. In 1945, House Bill #819 transferred the recording of marks and brands and the inspection of marks and brands of live and slaughtered cattle to the jurisdiction of the Commissioner of Agriculture.

E. L. "Red" Yates, pioneer cattleman of Taft, was Orange County's last appointed marks and brands inspector before this responsibility was turned over to the Commissioner of Agriculture. Mr. Yates' investigations of rustling activities in the early 1940's led to the conviction of several people for violation of the marks and brands law. We are indebted to "Red" Yates, Cecil Tucker, and Al Smith for information regarding marks and brands.

270

In those early days a running iron was used to brand cattle. It consisted of a piece of automobile brake rod about 30 inches in length, with a curve or slight hook at one end and a handle at the other end. When this rod was heated, cattlemen could burn into the hide almost any kind of a design, numbers, or combination. Twice a year, once in the fall and once in the spring, a cooperative roundup of cattle called a "cattle drag" took place in the open range area of the county. The purpose was twofold, to pair (mammie) the new born calves with their mothers so they could be marked and branded alike and to castrate the young bull calves. Also, any unbranded yearlings missed the year before were picked up.

Log books were kept on these operations and cattle owners that were members of the community "cattle drag" made appropriate notations in their books. If the cattle checked were not owned by a member of the community "cattle drag", the information was passed on to him which revealed exactly how many new calves he had, how many were marked and branded, and how many were castrated. This point is mentioned to let the reader know that thievery was rare because "news" traveled fast. Furthermore, the honor code functioned well because of common interest and committments.

Wild hogs as well as cattle fed on the open range. For instance, E. L. "Red" Yates, remembers helping his father, around World War I round up two carloads of razor back hogs for which they received $3.00 a head. During the days of the open range, animals primarily steers, were sold directly to buyers and without middlemen. When a cattleman sold all of his cattle, the new owner assumed the marks and brands as his own. The "news" of a new acquisition soon made the rounds so everyone quickly "knew" who owned these cattle now. Perhaps a description of the typical cow of those open range days will interest the reader. There are several versions of this animal. Some say that they were originally cows that escaped from the early Spanish conquistadors and survived three hundred years of wandering through the wilds of Florida. Dr. Monroe Lynn, Orange County's pioneer veterinarian, called them "pole and china" cows. When asked the meaning of the expression "pole and china", Dr. Lynn responded —— "Poor emanciated cows you have to prop up with a pole to keep them from falling down so you can milk them in a china cup!" Al Smith, a native of Orange County and a third generation cattleman said that native Florida cows generally weighed between 400 and 600 pounds, were English type in appearance, had "Devon-type" horns, were short-haired and were all colors and combinations of colors.

Perhaps a description of the cattleman of that period is in order too. While the hazards of the open Florida range scarcely compared with the old west, nevertheless the cattleman of that period were

271

"hardened" individuals who used their "heads" rather than their "hearts" in their occupation. They loved the open and working with cows but needed their heads to make a living. This called for hard decisions.

Men who "roughed" it in the woods for days and weeks at a time were considerably less glamourous than today's TV cattleman. In the open range days cattlemen were more like their cows, oriented to survival rather than beauty. Rustlers, rattlesnakes, red bugs, cattle ticks, and screwworms, were all part of his daily fare. The horse was his transportation and today's glamorized TV commercials of air-conditioned pickup trucks or helicopter roundups were not part of the "cracker" cowboy's equipment! Such was the situation of cattle operations in Orange County during the open range era.

Many people credit Governor Fuller Warren with ending the "open range" type of cattle business in Florida. Furthermore his 1948 campaign pledge to get cattle off the Florida Highways was fulfilled by passage of the "No-Fence Law" in 1949. (Chapter 588 of the Florida Statutes). However, in Orange County a different sequence of events occurred. These events began with the introduction of the Texas fever tick into Orange County around 1918, although pinpointing the beginning of the tick problem is difficult.

Robert W. "Bob" Barber, son of a pioneer cattleman, vividly remembers the impact that the tick eradication campaign had on his life. While "dipping" cattle on July 24, 1920 at a community vat at the intersection of Dixie Bell Drive and Pershing Avenue in the Conway area, Bob's father Joseph A. Barber suffered a stroke and died shortly thereafter.

Since no County Agent reports or records are on file covering this period, available information is quite limited. The earliest such report during this period was County Agent Charlie Kime's Annual Report for 1925. In that report Agent Kime wrote he "handled" 75 gallons of arsenical cattle dip for tick work

OLD CATTLE DIPPING VAT — (left to right) County Agent Henry Swanson and cattleman W. A. "Al" Smith inspect old dipping vat built on Barber place in Conway area around 1910

which was provided by A. L. Wright of the County Road Depart-

272

ment. From this statement it would appear the program was being funded by the county.

C. L. Campbell, D.V.M., State Veterinarian and Director of Division of Animal Industry, Department of Agriculture, Tallahassee also provided information on the early phases of the tick eradication program. Dr. Campbell wrote —

"I have been unable to find any difinitive information with respect to your particular county. Generally, cattle fever tick eradication in Florida first began shortly before World War I on a spasmodic basis so it is not unreasonable to assume that some of the old-timers in Orange County were correct in their recollections that fever tick eradication might have begun there in 1919.

Sometime between 1921 and 1923 a systematic eradication program was started in the state in Escambia County, progressing eastward through the panhandle, then south until eradication was achieved throughout the state in the 1940's.

It was not uncommon in those early days when cattle owners were resisting dipping efforts in arsenical solutions on a two-week basis to have dipping vats blown up by objectors. As a result of this, it often became necessary to station National Guardsmen with machine guns at a given vat vicinity wherein all cattle in that area would be driven for dipping on a two-week basis. The guardsmen with their machine guns acted as a deterrent to dynamiting that particular vat.

The foregoing is, of course, history which was related to me and about which I have read as I personally did not become involved in dipping campaigns until early 1947, following the discovery of cattle fever ticks in Okeechobee County in December of 1945. This was a new infestation of cattle fever ticks and involved the species *Boophilus microplus*. In previous years the cattle fever ticks involved was *Margaropus annulatus*. The finding of the tick in 1945 brought about an eradication campaign involving most of the counties south of Okeechobee, as well as a few northern Florida counties, such as Volusia and Seminole, and lasted until November of 1949. Since then we have had limited findings of the tick in 1957 and 1960.

I realize that the preceding is generally rambling in nature, and with a lot of research in the Minutes of the old Florida Livestock Sanitary Board over some four decades, a more complete history could be developed; however, I hope that this will be of some benefit to you."

This brief summary of the tick program by Dr. Campbell does not mention the deer eradication program which took place from 1937 up into the 1940's. It will be covered later. Some personal insights on the tick campaign as it was conducted in Orange County were provided by L. A. Albritton former inspector in Orange County and agent for the Federal Bureau of Animal Industry from 1935 to 1941.

According to cattleman "Bert" Wetherbee, Orange County financed its own tick eradication program during the first outbreak and County Agent Kime's report that he handled 75 gallons of arsenical cattle dip tends to substantiate this. The intensive tick eradication programs of the late 1930's and early 1940's were the primary factors that forced cattlemen to "fence". Governor Fuller Warren only voiced the demand of the cattlemen in ending the no-fence law.

For a more detailed chronological report of the origins of the local cattle industry we must call upon reports of former County Agents and pioneer cattlemen of Orange County. In 1925 County Agent Kime reported "range cattle becoming less plentiful as land is fenced and resold in large and small tracts." One of the "boom" time real estate inroads on open range territory in east Orange County was the creation of Bithlo community. According to B. C. Dodd, pioneer cattleman of South Seminole County, an S. P. Bailey of Orlando "staked out" some four square miles (2600 acres) in 1922 and started a campaign to make the area a metropolis that he called Bithlo. Bonds were issued in 1924 to help establish this new city in the heart of the open range territory of east Orange County. The Legislature blessed the project on November 30, 1925 but soon after that the "boom" had "bust". This and other land speculations of that period together with tick problems severely depressed the fledgling cattle industry.

In 1926, K. C. Moore replaced Charlie Kime as Orange County Agent. Moore's first mention of the local cattle industry was the statement in his 1928 report that "The Eastern half of Orange County is still an open range county, and is utilized, in so far as it is made use of at all, for grazing of the ordinary nondescript range cattle. One large ranch owned by M. McCrory, of McCrory chain store fame, dominates the beef cattle industry. They are improving the strains of cattle by the use of some purebred beef type bulls and some of the Brahman bulls of India. The Superintendent of this large estate has consulted with the county agent with reference to planting of tame grasses in some of the pasture lands, and I am planning for the coming year to do a great deal of work with him in pasture development." Elsewhere Moore wrote "looking to the day when the state will be free of the cattle ticks, I have tried to promote the planting of pasture grasses. In 1927 a number of pastures were planted, but because of the extreme dry weather, and poor quality of seed, especially the Dallis grass seed, most of these pastures were complete failures." As a matter of fact 1927 with rainfall of only 33.84 inches is still (as of 1974) the "driest" year on record.

Moore's aims for pasture development in 1929 were thwarted by another problem, however. In April 1929 the Mediterranean Fruit Fly was "discovered" in Orange County and all Extension programs changed drastically! In fact, it was 1931 before Agent Moore returned to the cattlemen and their problems. However, the year 1929 saw a record established in the local cattle industry. Carl Barber, Orange County's largest cattleman shipped 500 steers out-of-state, an unprecedented record for those days. According to his daughter, Mrs. Margaret Vickery the cattle were loaded at Wewahootee and shipped to Wichita, Kansas.

In 1931 Moore reported holding special meetings with the Extension Specialist regarding East Orange County problems. The purpose was to emphasize keeping the best cows for breeding purposes, and to "dip through". The depression and the cattle tick contrived to scuttle Moore's 1932 hope of getting purebred bulls for breeding purposes. That same year the Chamber of Commerce launched a program to secure "1000 Farmers in Five Years for Orange County". To help in this program Moore was asked to prepare "fact sheets" on each agricultural industry that the Chamber could mail to interested parties. That Moore failed to prepare a "fact sheet" on the cattle business for the local Chamber of Commerce in 1932 suggests that the cattle business was in trouble.

More trouble for the local cattle industry "surfaced" in 1933. Texas fever ticks were found in the Eastern part of Orange County and since it was supposed to have been cleared up, it made Agent Moore uncertain about the merits of trying to get cattlemen to upgrade their herds by getting purebred bulls. Since there was very little he could do for cattlemen in general, they were not included in the Farm and Home Institute program that was held at the Magnolia school building in Orlando in August of 1933.

In 1934 the Orange County cattle industry was evaluated at only $20,528! Granting that the dollar was worth more in 1934 than today, other fields of agriculture were evaluated on the same basis and only the ornamental plant industry had a lower dollar value. Prior to 1934 the agent did well to mention the cattle industry once or twice in his annual reports. However, 1934 was a turning point for the Orange County cattlemen and the 1934 report devoted more space to cattle activities than in the previous 10 years! For example, in describing his work on Flood Relief for the Agriculture Adjustment Administration Moore wrote as follows: "This is my valued single service in the county this year, most of our cattlemen use the low prairies and marshes of the St. Johns and Kissimmee River Valleys for summer pasturing. The unusually heavy spring rains covered or ruined the grasses in these areas. All cattle began to lose flesh rapidly. Some became sick from eating grass that had been submerged. They were driven to the high lands that are usually reserved for winter grazing. Fear was felt that over grazing the winter ranges would mean cattle starving next winter and even on the higher pastures still lost flesh. Scores of them became too emaciated to drive to the dipping vats as was required in some sections and many died."

Agent Moore, cooperating with F.E.R.A., the Drought Relief section of the Agriculture Adjustment Administration, reported the flood relief for cattlemen in seven flooded counties operated on the same basis as drought relief in the Western States. On July 24, 1934, County Agents were instructed to arrange the sale of some of the cattle to relieve the situation. In this regard Moore reported — " I called a meeting of all cattle owners for August 1st. At this meeting the proposition was explained by State Director W. J. Sheely, and the cattlemen selected Messer, E. O. Tanner and Walter F. Bronson as county appraisers and E. C. Bass alternate." Later Moore received instructions from Washington that only Tanner and Bronson would be given authorization.

The 30 cattlemen involved in this program sold a total of 1542 cattle which brought to them $19,628. Some 960 cattle, two-years old and over were shipped, 148 were condemned and killed; 98 yearlings were shipped and 38 condemned; 210 calves shipped and 100 condemned. The two-year old and over cattle averaged $14.81 each, yearlings brought $11.32 each, and calves were $5.92 each. According to Moore's summary of these actions no one was dissatisfied with the way the appraisers and he handled the operation.

These statistics give us the going price of cattle during that era and pretty well explains why so few people pursued this agricultural endeavor.

This activity apparently increased Moore's exposure to this agricultural commodity group and led to his assisting them in organizing a county association of cattlemen early the following year. Later Moore helped the association prepare resolutions and petitions for relief from dipping requirements that were still in force after three years. These had been extremely costly to men in the quarantined territory and some would have gone bankrupt except for the flood relief sale.

Another new threat appeared on the cattlemen's horizon in 1934 when the screwworm was found in neighboring counties. Moore sent a circular letter on control and detection methods to every person owning even one livestock animal. No cases of screwworm had been reported in Orange County at the end of 1934 but in 1935 the screwworm appeared. To expedite matters, Moore funished a desk and office facilities for the local screwworm control worker and in November arranged office space for the District Supervisor. He also arranged for distribution through the local feed and fertilizer merchants of the pine tar oil and benzol used in the program.

That year Moore reported twelve screwworm infestations. To disseminate control information he demonstrated the method of infection to many cattle and hog owners and held two meetings to explain the worm's life history and the type of damage to be expected.

Other items of importance in 1935 were Clyde McKenney's purchase of six purebred Angus bulls from a ranch in McIntosh, Florida and conferences with cattlemen on marketing their cattle in a local auction, and on their need of a locally regulated abattoir. Two bulls were sold to small operators to upgrade local herds. That same year Walter Bronson, pioneer cattleman, moved to an area south of the present Martin Company site, with his new bride. There he eventually expanded his operation to several thousand acres of land carrying many hundred head of cattle.

In December 1935 L. A. Albritton came to Orange County to supervise inspectors concerned with Texas fever tick eradication in Orange, Brevard, Seminole, and Osceola Counties. Under his supervision a rigorous bi-monthly "dipping" program was set up. This program continued until December 1941 when the last Orange County herd (Carl Barber of Christmas) was dipped and pronounced clear of further quarantine restrictions.

That the tick eradication program developed a different attitude on the part of the local cattle industry which was reflected by Moore's statement in 1936, as follows: "This industry is making more progress than most any line of our agriculture throughout the state. However, only six or seven Orange County cattlemen are keeping abreast of this progress. These men are buying registered bulls of Hereford and Guzerat Brahma breeds." and Guzerat Brahma breeds." Pasture improvement also took on new interest when Clyde McKenney and V. H. Conner seeded their pasture tracts with carpet grass in 1936.

An overall County Agricultural Planning Council was established in 1936. At that time W. L. Wetherbee, of Taft; Louis Ziegler, of Pine Castle; E. C. Bass of Christmas; and Walter Bronson, of Windermere volunteered to represent the cattle industry. The increased interest and awarenesss of cattlemen was reflected in Moore's 1937 report, as follows: "Within the past three years, beef cattle owners have made more strides in improving their herds and ranges than for years previously. It seems no longer necessary to urge men to get better bulls. They are buying them as fast as they are able, and conditions warrant."

Another problem that received attention at this time was "salt sickness" a disease caused by the deficiency of certain minor elements. Moore undertook an educational program to get cattlemen to supply these important minor elements to their animals but had some difficulty in convincing some cattlemen of its merits.

Of all the pest control programs the Mediterranean Fruit Fly Campaign of 1929 and the early 1930's was perhaps the most discussed and cussed eradiation program ever conducted in Florida. The great destruction of crops and plants made it of "pocket book" concern of a great many people.

In retrospect, the deer eradication aspect of the cattle tick eradication program of 1937 through the early 1940's, could have been equally controversial had the public been as "conservation oriented" then as they are today. A brief inspection of this program is important from an historical point-of-view and from a "soul-searching" point as well. The Resolution and Quarantine passed by the State Live Stock Sanitary Board of Florida at Tampa on October 7, 1936, affected Orange County as follows:

RESOLUTION

Whereas, It has been determined by the U.S. Bureau of Biological Survey, The U.S. Bureau of Entomology and Plant Quarantine, The U.S. Bureau of Animal Industry and the State Live Stock Sanitary Board of Florida that deer, as well as cattle, carry and propagate the cattle fever tick, *Boophilus annulatus australis,* and

Whereas, It has been determined by the U.S. Bureau of Animal Industry and the State Live Stock Sanitary Board of Florida that cattle fever ticks, *Boophilus annulatus australis,* exist in the following described area of Florida, Therefore,

BE IT RESOLVED, By the State Live Stock Sanitary Board of Florida, in regular meeting assembled, that Townships 23 and 24 South, Range 32 East, and Sections 14, 15, 16, 17, 18, 19, 20, 21, 22, 23, 24, 29, 30, and 31 Township 23 South, Range 31 East; Townships 23 and 24 South, Range 33 East; and those portions of Townships 22, 23, and 24 South, Range 34 East, lying west and south of the St. Johns River, the properties of the McCrory Land, Timber and Cattle Company, the Peavy-Wilson Lumber Company and the Tosohatchee Game Preserve, in Orange County, Florida, also that part of Sections 34, 35, and 36, Township 22 South, Range 33 East, lying south of Cheney Highway and east of Taylor Creek road be, and the same is hereby placed under quarantine for the purpose of conducting tick eradication work in said area, and, during the existence of this quarantine no horses, mules, oxen, cattle, cattle hides, deer, deer hides, or other animals or things which are or may be subject to infestation with cattle fever ticks, *Boophilus annulatus australis,* shall be transported or moved through, into or from the above described area, except in accordance with the regulations of the State Live Stock Sanitary Board, and no hay, straw, moss, timber, pine straw or similar materials, wild shrubbery and plants on, in, by or to which cattle fever ticks may become attached, carried or transported, may be moved from the above described area, except in accordance with the regulations of the State Live Stock Sanitary Board.

That this quarantine shall be in full force and effect from and after the 20th day of November, A.D. 1936.

DONE AND ORDERED By the Board at Tampa, Florida, this the 7th day of October AD 1936.

NOTICE OF QUARANTINE

TO ALL WHOM IT MAY CONCERN:

Notice is hereby given that under and by authority of Chapter 9201, Laws of Florida, Acts of 1923, and Chapter 17273, Laws of Florida, Acts of 1935, and in accordance with the provisions thereof the State Live Stock Sanitary Board of Florida has placed under quarantine Townships 23 and 24 South, Range 32 East, and Sections 14, 15, 16, 17, 18, 19, 20, 21, 22, 23, 24, 29, 30 and 31 Township 23 South, Range 31 East; Townships 23 and 24 South, Range 33 East; and those portions of Townships 22, 23 and 24 South, Range 34 East, lying west and south of the St. Johns River, the properties of the McCrory Land, Timber and Cattle Company, the Peavy-Wilson Lumber Company and the Tosohatchee Game Preserve, in Orange County, Florida, also that part of Sections 34, 35 and 36, Township 22 South, Range 33 East, lying south of Cheney Highway and east of Taylor Creek road.

In official action, the Board on January 5, 1937, at its meeting in Tallahassee incorporated all the various county resolutions regarding sections of Brevard, Orange, Collier, Highlands, Osceola into a state wide campaign.

Entered into the official minutes of that January 5, 1937 meeting was the notation that "Mr. Edgar Bass of Christmas, Florida, County Commissioner of Orange County, appeared before the State Live Stock Sanitary Board and presented a copy of a resolution adopted by the Board of County Commissioners of Orange County, directed to Governor Fred P. Cone, soliciting support of the deer reduction program in Orange County. The resolution was read by the Secretary and, upon motion of Doctor Wilbanks, seconded by Mr. Barley and unanimously carried, the Secretary was directed to file the resolution and write a letter of appreciation to the Board of County Commissioners of Orange County."

Then on August 9, 1937 at a joint meeting of the State Commission of Game and Fresh Water Fish and the State Live Stock Sanitary Board at the San Juan Hotel, the following Agents, representatives and employees of the State Live Stock Sanitary Board were commissioned, as authorized by the Special Laws of 1937, to participate in the deer reduction program to complete tick eradication as carried on by the State Live Stock Sanitary Board:

ORANGE AND OSCEOLA COUNTIES

G. M. Townsend	C. H. Clark
Steve Hunter	John D. Canada
Alfred Raulerson	Floyd Cox
H. B. Sapp	Walter Yates
Alex Hendry	W. H. Lanier
Gay Story	M. M. Raulerson
Everett Yates	Kenneth Hancock
Bill R. Brown	John T. Cox

Those interested in the controversy this program stirred up concerning the proposal to exterminate the deer of the Seminole Reservation would be interested in reading Commissioner Collier's Report for the office of Indian Affairs Washington to Secretary of the Interior, Harold Ickes, January 15, 1940. In brief, Collier recommended that the State of Florida and the Bureau of Animal Industry be invited to construct a fence around the Seminole reservation and the deer be left unmolested. The program having cost $5,389,546 up to this time (1940) the proposed fence would cost approximately $40,000 or 3/4's of one percent of funds already expended!

Looking back in sort of a Monday morning quarterbacking analysis, if cattlemen had not operated under the open range concept then but had been required to "fence" their cattle, would a deer "reduction" campaign been instigated?

Returning briefly to 1937, at that time Agent Moore served on a committee of the Cattleman's Association seeking to secure adequate holding pens for cattle shipped from Orlando to cattle markets. Previously, local cattlemen sold direct to slaughter houses or custom slaughtered for the butcher trade. However, in 1937, the marketing of cattle began to move in a new direction. The Atlantic Coast Line Railway enlarged their holding pens, and the Cattlemen's Association installed scales on a lease arrangement. The new pens were equipped with water troughs and electric lights and were adequate to accomodate three or four carloads of cattle.

Also that year a special cattle sale was the subject of a conference between representatives of three meat packing houses and H. L. Lewis of the State Marketing Bureau. As a result of all of these increased activities concerning marketing of cattle, the Kissimmee Livestock Market came into being in 1938.

Regarding the opening of this new market, Agent Moore wrote the following letter to Orange County Cattlemen:

"June 24, 1938.

To: All Cattlemen and Dairymen

Dear Sirs,

It is likely that from time to time you may be wanting to offer some of your cows, calves, steers, etc. for sale at the Kissimmee Auction Market. This market seems to offer an outlet for some of the cull dairy animals, as well as beef animals.

I am writing to call your attention to the fact that this county is still under quarantine, on account of the ticky deer in the Southeastern part of the county.

If you plan to carry any cattle to this market you will have to have a permit from the State Livestock Sanitary Board. Dr. J. C. Jeter 1518 Greenwood Avenue, Orlando, whose Post Office Box is 54, will inspect your cattle and give you a certificate, which you are supposed to file with the auction people.

Yours truly,

K. C. Moore
County Agent"

Another important item in 1937 was the discovery by Dr. Jerry Ruble, a local veterinarian, that *Crotalaria spectabilis* an important leguminous cover crop, is poisonous if eaten by cattle. Moore notified all livestock owners of this new discovery by special letter.

In the years 1938 through 1940 local cattlemen and dairymen sought to improve their pastures by planting improved pasture grasses. Previously, only a few small plantings of improved pasture had been made. Several demonstration pastures were planted but there was little incentive towards large scale pasture improvement.

However, the cost-assistance provided under the A.A.A. program encouraged pasture improvement programs. During the 1939 - 1940 period, Agent Moore reported that 7,583 acres of wild land was prepared by destroying the native vegetation and seeded to improved grasses. Some 242 acres of this total were sodded or planted with cuttings of bermuda and para grasses. The remainder was planted mainly to carpet grass.

In 1940 a new pasture grass was available. The Experiment Station had developed a disease immune variety of Napier grass that made some of the old strains obsolete. As a result of these improved pastures and the use of better bulls for breeding, many cattlemen were moving away from the open range, scrub cattle type of cattle industry.

In the quarantined, cattle tick areas, cattlemen had to dip their cattle every two weeks. A stiff penalty of $1.00 per animal was charged those who failed to comply with the dipping program. "Dipped" cattle were painted appropriately and special range riders periodically checked to see that the law was complied with. These new conditions left little incentive to continue open range type cattle raising.

Moving cattle over considerable distances to the dipping vats every two weeks interferred with their grazing. So the rigors of the dipping program and the constant disruption of grazing kept the open range cows in rather poor condition. According to L. A. Albritton, a former inspector for the tick eradication program, there were 12 different vats located in Orange County. Some of these were located and named as follows: Tootoosahatchee game reserve, Forks of Taylor Creek, "Barber" Vat, Claude Partin Vat, "Canada" Vat, Turkey Lake Vat, "Ziegler" Vat, north of Taylor Creek, and Wetherbee Vat near Lake Ramsey.

More and more land was fenced in the late 1930's and the open range cattle business became more and more marginal. In 1939, Edgar B. King, a pioneer cattleman in the Apopka area, claimed that he was "forced" out of the cattle business by this trend. He ran a herd of about two hundred cattle in the area known today as the Errol Estates, an exclusive housing development. During the spring months he grazed these cattle on the Apopka marshland but during the fall and winter months they "wintered" on the high ground where Errol Estates is now located.

Rationing of meat and gasoline during World War II and the scarcity of all farm supplies from barbed wire to fertilizer, produced serious problems for cattlemen. In 1943 the Agricultural Conservation Program reported 245,000 acres of fenced, non-crop, open pasture land in Orange County. This is the first and only estimate we could find of the acreage in pasture in Orange County. That same year, Moore reported on a new pasture grass, as follows: "We have now about three acres of this digitaria grass planted in the county. We are studying it with interest and high hopes." This is the first test planting of pangola grass reported in Orange County. In 1948, several old timers told me that Orange County was one of the first counties in Florida to have a test planting of pangola grass and that Agent Moore's efforts to introduce this grass were responsible. According to the "official" account, *Digitaria decumbens stent* (pangola grass) was not released to Florida livestock producers until 1945! If so, we can conclude that Orange County was "first" in the state with extensive plantings of the new pasture grass.

In 1945, Moore wrote "I have been emphasizing the superiority of pangola grass for pasture in the county. About 64 acres of this grass was planted. Although this may seem small it must be remembered that it is a new type of grass, and no seed is available, and labor is scarce and costly for setting sprigs of this grass. One cattleman cut hay from a small plot before the rainy season and again after the rainy season. Two cuttings of cured hay from the same measured plot were weighed and he estimated that the yield was almost 10 tons per acre. The last cutting was made early in October. Since then this pangola grass has made more growth and he will have good winter grazing on this area."

Agent Moore failed to mention the name of the pangola grass pioneer and since he is no longer here to speak for himself, I will report that Walter Bronson was responsible for "pioneering" this new pasture grass in Orange County. Mr. Bronson told me this before his death in 1971 and corroborated his story with a clipping from the Orlando Sentinel of September 25, 1944 which stated "Mr. Bronson is listed as the first rancher in the county to plant a considerable acreage to carpet grass or any other tame pasture grass." R. I. Wetherbee also verified that Walter Bronson was the first to successfully grow this new pasture grass. This historical record is important because pangola grass was a major factor in increasing the carrying capacity of pastures, and gave the cattle industry a strong "push" toward improved pastures. It should be noted that not every new pasture grass was so highly recommended. In fact in 1944, Moore opposed the planting of "torpedo grass because of the likelihood of its spreading to groves and cropland, and because we have other grasses which I believe to be equally good."

The late Carl E. Barber

283

The year 1943 witnessed a change in the holder of the "Mister Cattleman" title of Orange County. After 30 years of ranching, Carl E. Barber had become Orange County's largest cattleman and had clearly earned the title "Mister Cattleman". However, in 1943 that title fell to George Terry.

In his 1943 report, Moore says, "Quite a lot of time was spent with our newest and largest ranch operator Mr. George Terry. We have assisted him in pasture plans, in directions for growing forage crops, in securing building permits, etc. to properly get his ranch into food production."

Mr. Terry's Magnolia Ranch was the largest in Orange County and would accommodate approximately half the cattle in the county. Consequently some mention of this man from an historical as well as human interest point-of-view seems justified. On one of his many trips to Florida Mr. Terry decided to buy some land and go into the cattle business. His first Florida venture occurred in 1930 when he bought 1/3 of Venice, Florida. At that time he was offered 100,000 acres for 25 cents an acre! In 1941, Terry bought a tract of land near Englewood in Sarasota County. He had big plans to expand his holdings there but soon found out he was "locked in". About this time he talked to Sarasota lawyer, Otis Radebaugh, a brother of Orange County cattleman and lawyer, Cushman Radebaugh. From Otis Radebaugh Terry heard that the McCrory tract in Orange County was for sale. This tract, formerly owned by the McCrory chain store magnate, consisted originally of some 100,000 acres of game preserve in Orange and Osceola Counties. An area of approximately 50,000 acres, located in Osceola County, had been sold. Mr. Terry was favorably impressed with the tract for cattle raising and bought the remaining 56,000 acres in March of 1942 for $2.00 an acre. He was also offered two sections, not part of this consolidated tract, for $10.00 an acre. Since the latter tract was a considerable distance away from the main parcel, Terry decided it was no bargain at that price. Today, these sections are adjacent to Highway #50 in a highly urbanized section of Orlando!

Shortly after Terry bought the McCrory tract, he bought another 10-12,000 acres to increase his pasture acreage to 62,000 acres. Within the purchased area, Carl Barber owned a 10-acre tract which Terry said he also bought to consolidate his holdings. He said this was necessary because under the open range concept Barber would have been permitted to graze his cattle within his (Terry's) property. Terry named his ranch "Magnolia" and started building up his herd with native cows. He contracted with Ross Beason of the "Hi Hat" ranch in Sarasota County for his foundation herd. Beason's herd was built up from cattle originally obtained from Osceola County cattleman Irlo Bronson. Beason had decided to sell his herd

284

because his son had been recently killed in a training flight in military service and he no longer was interested in maintaining his ranch. So Terry's herd had its beginning in nearby Osceola County, was transferred to Sarasota County and now was back in neighboring Orange County!

Over 2,000 head of cattle was transferred from Sarasota to Orange County. They were transported by rail from Sarasota to Narcoossee in Osceola County. Terry contracted with Carl Barber, another pioneer cattleman, to "herd" them the last 15 miles from the Narcoossee railroad siding to the Magnolia Ranch. Two separate drives of about 1,000 cattle each were made. This was probably the last large cattle "drive" in Orange County or Central Florida because soon after that the No Fence Law placed the liability responsibility on the cattleman when cows got on the highway.

At the close of World War II, Orange County cattlemen and dairymen participated in an historical field demonstration of the new wonder insecticide D.D.T.'s effectiveness in controlling horn flies. Thanks to Agent Moore's detailed records we know the cattlemen who participated in that experiment and the number of cows they entered in the program. The Orange Countians who participated in this program, August 4-15, 1945, and the number of beef cattle involved, were as follows:

Bunch Dairy	200
Bronson, Walter	810
Bronson, W. H. — Winter Garden	30
Britt, T. M.	32
Champion, W. C.	140
Datsons	450
Doughtery, G. T.	100
Dease, Luther	45
Watson, J. W. (Dease, H.E.)	230
Henson, Glenn	850
Hamrick, Wilson H. & Carroll	625
Hansell, E. W. — Apopka-Orlando	25
Hodges, A. C. — Taft	20
Johnson, L. E. — Taft	15
Johns, Mrs. Thelma	16
Livingston, G.D.	116
Macey, R. C. — Pinecastle	100
McLeod, L. B. — Orlando	450
Purcell, B. E. — Orlando	120
Price, W. K.	44
Phillips, George — Christmas	500
Radebaugh, Cushman	300
Redditt, Jim	100
Row, Mrs. Marie (Smith) — Pinecastle	35
Smith, Kirby	145
Seef, H. M.	75
Salas, Mrs. Louis C.	30

Swope, Sid	65
Stone, Guy	44
Terry, George	3500
Tucker, C. M. — Oakland	110
Tucker, Cecil — Christmas	65
Wetherbee, Bert — Taft	200
Warren, Sam — Orlando	78
Yates, E. L. — Taft	300
Total	9965

The benefits of this D.D.T. spraying program were evaluated and reported in a special letter the following year as follows:

"May 16, 1946

TO ALL DAIRYMEN and CATTLEMEN of Orange County

Dear Sir:

The DDT spraying of cattle in this county last August was worth while.

By spraying the dairy cattle and barns Orange County cows produced about 28,200 gallons of milk more than they would have if they had not been sprayed. This figure was arrived at by comparing the decline in production of the state average of cows during the months of August and September.

If Orange County beef cattle gained half as much in weight after the spraying as some cattle at the Ona Experiment Station did, it would amount to about 200,000 pounds the first week. The cattle at Ona were sprayed July 30th, and they were weighed every week during last season, both before and after the spraying.

If you have not controlled the insects by the use of DDT this season, I am sure it would be worth your while to spray them. I know a number of cattlemen and dairymen have sprayed.

I am writing to suggest that we try to get all the cattle sprayed the first two weeks of June. If we could get them all sprayed during that time, we would have no trouble with insects coming in from the neighbors for several weeks afterward.

Mr. Bruce thinks that one pound of 50% water dispersible DDT powder in four gallons of water should work about as efficiently as what we used last year, which was one pound in two and one half gallons of water. For dipping, it was one pound in 25 gallons of water.

However, as we had no injury from using one pound to two and one half gallons of water, this might be used if you prefer.

Yours truly,

K. C. Moore
County Agriculture Agent
Orlando, Florida"

By 1946 pasture improvement had become the most important agronomy project in Orange County. The reason for this according to

286

Moore was the presence of "a growing beef cattle industry, and need of dairy expansion, requires better pastures because improved cattle require better grazing, pasture is the cheapest feed, we have large soil areas not adapted to most other uses, and all concentrate and roughage feeds are imported in this county."

Since Cattlemen were "forced" to fence their cattle, because of the cattle tick problem, more and more cattlemen began improving pasture tracts. Also, more cattlemen owned their land instead of "renting" or leasing as before.

It should be noted that the tick problem was not ended. Moore noted in his 1946 report, that: "A meeting of the Central Florida Cattlemen's Association Directors was called to plan ways in which our cattlemen could help in the control of cattle fever ticks, soon after the infestations were discovered in the Lake Okeechobee section."

On August 31, of that year Agent Moore retired and was succeeded by County Agent Fred E. Baetzman of Volusia County. Baetzman, an animal husbandry major in college, began an active program of pasture improvement, especially emphasizing White Dutch Clover.

Another sign of the times was one of the last Orange County cattle drives which was conducted almost within the city limits of Orlando by pioneer cattleman Kirby Smith and his son Al. In 1948, they "herded" some 50 cattle from the Hansel pasture on South Kuhl Avenue (now South Orange Avenue) through the community of Pine Castle and east along Hoffner Avenue to their pasture adjacent to Highway 15 near the present Bee Line Expressway.

In 1948, pioneer cattleman, R. I. Wetherbee of Bobby Creek, decided that "orange trees stayed inside fences better than cows". Wetherbee and his father had been in the cattle business continuously for almost 30 years. Nevertheless, Wetherbee dropped out of the "cow business" and devoted full time to growing citrus. The problem of keeping cattle penned up together with labor problems forced him to this decision. Up to that time cattle on the highway were the responsibility of the motorists, now the responsibility had come home to the cattleman. This and other factors stimulated the departure of Wetherbee and others from the cattle business.

A cold winter followed by a dry spring in 1947 and 1948 convinced Terry of the merit of Baetzman's recommendation of White Dutch Clover in his carpet grass pastures. One of the first pasture tours was the one held in 1949 to see this combination of White Dutch Clover and carpet grass combinations at the Terry Magnolia Ranch.

Terry soon realized that to insure sufficient moisture for a good stand of clover, irrigation was required. Conservationist Hutchinson of the local U. S. Conservation Service helped him design a seepage irrigation system for his improved pasture. Ten deep wells of varying sizes (10" to 16") were drilled in various locations in his pasture so water could be pumped in open ditches to all parts of his pasture. This extensive seepage irrigation system was one of the first of its kind in Central Florida. In the early 1950's, Terry inaugurated another new practice in cattle ranching. This consisted of seeding and fertilizing some of his large isolated pasture tracts by airplane!

At this time (1950's) the cattle population probably reached its peak in Orange County, an estimated 45,000, although no accurate figures are available. Also at this time, Orange County cattleman, Cushman Radebaugh, was elected President of the State Cattlemen's Association.

The increased cattle population stimulated the opening of two cattle auctions in the county within weeks of each other! Interviews with old timers, suggest that the Orlando Livestock Market at 3600 South Orange Avenue (then Kuhl Avenue), opened first, probably around the end of August in 1950 and that the Bithlo Livestock Market opened a week or two later. Cattleman and citrus grower, W. C. Champion, Sr., was the "spark plug" who organized the Orlando Livestock Market. He owned an old fertilizer plant adjacent to the railroad and just off South Orange Avenue and this became the site of the Orlando Livestock Market. B. C. Dodd, Seminole County cattleman helped establish the Bithlo Livestock Market. He owned an old fertilizer plant adjacent to the railroad and just off South Orange Avenue and this became the site of the Orlando Livestock Market. B. C. Dodd, Seminole County cattleman, helped establish the Bithlo Livestock Market by providing six acres of land on the south side of Highway #50 in Bithlo. He also put up capital and co-ordinated the organization efforts.

However, both markets experienced financial difficulties soon after opening which led to foreclosures and re-organizations. The Bithlo market opened and closed several times and finally went out-of-business in 1954. The Orlando Livestock Market closed once for several weeks and after re-opening operated continuously until it was closed down October 1, 1973.

A brief examination of the highlights of these two livestock auctions is of interest from an historical as well as a human interest point-of-view. In 1954, the name of the Orlando Livestock Market was changed to Mid-Florida Livestock Market, and the sale day originally Thursday was later changed to Monday.

B. C. Dodd soon found that the members of the Bithlo market

288

did not support it very strongly and were also selling cattle at the Orlando Market on Monday. Some of these cattle were re-sold at the Bithlo market on Wednesday. During this period "cow speculators" did a lot of "cow swapping". To avoid competition the slaughter buyers quickly selected one market as best and closest for their purpose.

After six months operation the Bithlo market found itself in financial trouble and was sold before the end of the year. The new owner quickly realized that the odds were against him and sold out after about eight months. The next owner tried to use the market facilities for selling and buying dairy cows only but after a few short months this venture also failed and the market closed down completely in 1954.

However, the Orlando Livestock Market also had problems. It seems the manager misappropriated funds and left town with somebody else's wife. As a result of the former fact the market closed down after operating a couple years. However, under the leadership of pioneer cattleman Carl Barber, the market was re-organized and re-opened in April 1954 under the name, Mid-Florida Livestock Market. In May 1958, cattleman Al Smith, and Brevard cattleman Gilbert Tucker bought the market and ran it until October 1973. Smith had several interesting facts to relate about the market's first sale day in 1954 and its first six months of operation.

On the first sale day 498 cattle were sold, $33,451.55 changed hands and the market realized a net profit of $472.06! At the end of six months (28 sale days) a total of 11,001 cattle had been sold, approximately 393 head of cattle per week. According to Smith before the market closed in the fall of 1973 it was doing three million dollars per year in gross sales and had a $60,000 yearly payroll. This was an outstanding record considering the market operated only one day out of the week.

By the mid 1950's local people considered the cattle business routine and expected few surprises. However on September 15, 1956 a "bomb" went off! On that morning the headline read — "Martin Aircraft comes to Orlando". Because the Martin Company paid $1,950,000 for 10 square miles of pasture land in Southwest Orange County, the cattlemen found themselves in a new ball game. New dimensions in land values and land leases had been created. Local land could no longer be considered as merely holding the world together. As buyers began speculating in land prices, the cattlemen found their leases cancelled or written up for short terms only. As land values rose so did taxes. This in turn created higher lease agreements for the cattlemen. As the "squeeze" increased, many found the economic returns of the cattle business diminishing.

In retrospect, there is little question but that this historic announcement by the Martin Company signaled the end of the cattle business as a major enterprise in Orange County. The industry had learned to live with the cattle tick, screwworm, and the "No Fence Law" but these new factors of sky-rocketing land values and taxes, were too much. Not even the most efficient cattlemen were able to cope with this new situation. Mr. Radebaugh sold his 3,000 acres of land in Orange County that year and moved his operations to St. Lucie County. Today, his former ranch land makes up 2/3rds of the Major Reality Company, of Tangelo Park, and a portion of the I-4 Highway and Florida Turnpike!

Although the Martin Company was getting the lion's share of the newspaper publicity in 1956-57, a special pilot plant operation was being conducted in Orange County that would later produce more benefits for the Florida cattle industry than any previous man-made achievement.

Agricultural Research Service Entomologists of the U.S. Department of Agriculture's Livestock Insect Laboratory of Kerrville, Texas had established a substation at the laboratory for Insects Affecting Man and Animal in Orlando and were developing procedures for mass-producing and distributing laboratory-reared sterile male screwworm flies in hopes of eradicating this devastating livestock pest from the state. The entomologists had successfully demonstrated this method on the Caribbean Island of Curacao in 1954 and now researchers were evolving procedures and techniques for a massive scale eradication involving thousands of square miles. It was this pilot-plant operation in 1956-57 which provided the necessary "know-how" to move out in an all-out campaign to wipe out the screwworm in 1958.

In July 1957, the cattle expert Agent Fred E. Baetzman retired and was succeeded by Henry F. Swanson. Assistant Agent Albert F. Cribbet was placed in charge of Extension programs for cattlemen. In his 1958 report on the Orange County cattle industry, Cribbett wrote as follows — "The beef cattle industry is definitely declining in total cattle numbers due to extremely high land values and taxes and low market price of cattle. In order for a cattleman to get into the business his inital investment in land is more than he can gain back from the investment. With low cattle prices cattlemen cannot ranch on $300 to $500 acre land and make reasonable returns. Rapid suburban expansion of housing developments is cutting into many developed ranch areas. Large ranch lands are being held on land speculation deals. The local cattle industry is serviced by the Central Florida Cattlemen's Association and one small market. Many larger markets are readily available within a hundred mile radius."

The Central Florida Cattlemen's Association was made up of cattlemen from Lake and Orange Counties. Donald Rybolt of East Orange County was President and W. A. Smith of Orlando and R. W. Maxwell of Lake County were Vice-Presidents. The association actively co-operated with federal and state officials in the screwworm eradication program.

The winter of 1957-58 brought five severe freezes that severely damaged citrus groves in the county. In addition many cattlemen required supplemental feed for their cattle but found it difficult to obtain. After five or six comparably mild winters the cattlemen had grown to believe their cows could "rough it" through the winter months. However, the freezes in December of 1957 and January 1958 completely destroyed what little pastures there was and many found their cows at the point of starvation. Feed was available but prices were so high, that cattlemen looked for ways to feed their cattle on the range.

Good quality hay seemed the best feed that could be supplied these range cattle until new spring growth appeared. The main problem was to get the hay. Transportation costs to Central Florida were high but there was a man to "solve" this problem for the cattlemen, the late A. H. Whitmore, Secretary-Manager of the Florida Citrus Production Credit Association of Orlando. Whitmore came to the County Agent's office to work on plans for a new Agricultural Center and "happened" to see the cattlemen meeting in the adjoining office. After a casual "hello" to several men he knew, he asked what they were doing. They told him they were trying to figure out some way to get reduced freight rates on hay for their starving cows. This proposal required that someone high in the Federal Government certify that an emergency due to a natural disaster existed in Florida. Once this fact was established, the I.C.C. could then authorize the railroads to bring hay to the disaster area at reduced freight rates. Whitmore immediately placed personal phone calls to Senators Holland and Smathers and to Congressman Herlong in Washington. Walter Bronson and other cattlemen listened to his telephone conversations on an extension and added appropriate remarks. These calls to interested Congressmen provided the persuasion required to get the necessary action.

After emergency tariff rates were approved, a county disaster hay committee was organized on February 18, 1958. It was made up of two cattlemen, two dairymen and Agent Cribbett and was organized to process over 100 requests by cattlemen and dairymen for hay shipped at reduced freight rates. The first 12 cars of hay arrived in Orlando March 1st and were distributed to ten cattlemen. After the necessary procedures were worked out on a group basis for this

291

first shipment, each individual ordered and financed his hay requirements through local brokers. In the summer of 1958 a state-wide campaign was instigated to eradicate the state of the dreaded screwworms.

Summarizing the Orange County cattle situation for 1958, Agent Cribbett reported: "Beef cattle numbers and ranch numbers have continued to decline, although not as rapidly as in the past reporting period. Market prices on all classes of cattle have been very steady and strong since late January 1958. The majority of the feeder and stocker cattle in this county have been sold through the local Kissimmee livestock market or by private treaty to feed lots in the mid-west, southwest and parts of the southeast. The quality of cattle running through the local market has been about the same as previous years. Although land prices and taxes have continued to rise, a few people are jumping back into the business on a relatively small scale because of strong prices. The larger ranching sites are largely held by a few land syndicates.

The severe winter this year was nearly disastrous to some cattlemen in the county and few cattlemen were prepared for continued freezing periods that occurred. Heavy driving rains made the winter more of a drain on the new calf crop. Losses for the county, as a whole, averaged 10% above normal. Cattlemen are now giving more consideration to winter supplemental feeding, winter green feed, and winter hay supply."

In the year 1958, the cattlemen's interest was directed to the brucellosis (contagious abortion) program. Every opportunity was taken to encourage cattlemen to vaccinate their young animals and test for brucellosis. A county Brucellosis Committee was asked to serve and work toward accrediation. Members of the committee were:

Dr. L. A. Scribner, Public Health — Chairman
A. F. Cribbett, Assistant County Agent — Secretary
Fred Roper, Commercial Cattleman — Member
Cecil Tucker, Commercial Cattleman — Member
Donald Platt, Commercial Diaryman — Member
B. W. Judge, Sr., Commercial Diaryman — Member
Dr. M. E. Legge, USDA Veterinarian — Advisor

Bulletins were sent periodically to all cattlemen on brucellosis testing, calf vaccination, and livestock board regulations.

Agent Cribbett's 1958 records show that the Central Florida Cattlemen's Association (Lake and Orange Counties) had 76 paid members representing 42,000 head of cattle. When the membership and numbers of cattle declined, the Directors asked for a reduction in the State Cattlemen's Association assessment against the Central

Florida group. This reduction was approved at the Florida Cattlemen's Association's state meeting in Cocoa on June 18th. There is a universal joke that cattlemen never know how many cows they own, so it is noteworthy that in this case the association "knew" they didn't own as many cows as the state association claimed.

In 1959, Agent Cribbett summarized the Orange County cattle situation as follows: "Beef cattle number and ranch numbers have continued to decline, although market prices have been the best since the break in 1951. Market prices on all classes of cattle, particularly stock and feeder calves and yearlings, have been strong and very steady all year. The decline in cattle numbers has been due to urban, suburban and rural industrial and residential expansion and land speculation. Many large acreage plots have been tied up by speculators, who will not rent or lease grazing rights to cattlemen. A number of large grazing areas have been sold because of high land values and taxes." Cribbett noted in his report that county screwworm inspection records showed 78 cattlemen owning approximately 18,000 to 20,000 cattle. Since early 1959, no screwworm infestations had been reported and dropping of sterile flies ceased November 14, 1959. That year the Central Florida Cattlemen's Association declined to 76 paid-up members. The officers and directors were:

PRESIDENT — Al Smith, Orange County
VICE-PRESIDENT — George Terry, Jr., Orange County
VICE-PRESIDENT — A. C. Lockwood, Lake County

DIRECTORS FOR ORANGE COUNTY
E. L. Yates, Sr.
George Terry, Sr.

DIRECTORS FOR LAKE COUNTY
Zera Giles
Dick Whittington

STATE DIRECTORS
Donald Rybolt, Orange County
Robert Maxwell, Lake County

Since the brucellosis program became such a prominent topic among cattlemen it is well that Agent Cribbett's summary of 1959 activities be listed in their entirety. Cribbett reported that every opportunity was taken to encourage cattlemen to vaccinate calves. Reminders of the value of calf vaccination and recent information on the program were disseminated periodically through circular letters, radio programs and personal contacts.

In May of that year the County Brucellosis Committee, the CFCA Directors and representatives of the Central Florida Milk Producers Association met to reach a common understanding on the brucellosis problem. Cribbett's report shows that the CFCA Directors voted to support the Central Florida Milk Producers' Association for

293

continued use of the ring test, once a year test under Plan A. The Central Florida Milk Producers' Association pledged to support a compulsory calf vaccination law with no test and slaughter for range herds.

In September the County Brucellosis Committee was re-organized as directed by the Florida Agricultural Extension Service Director's Administrative Directive. The re-organized committee consisted of the following persons:

A. F. Cribbett, Assistant County Agent, Chairman
Dr. J. Harland Paul, County Health Officer
Hanson Collins, Farm Bureau Director
E. L. Yates, Sr., Central Florida Cattlemen's Association
A. J. Rusterholtz, Jr., Central Florida Milk Producers' Association
Dr. H. E. Caton, D.V.M., Private Practioner

The cattle industry was declining in 1959 but it was a long way from defunct. That year the imaginative and enterprising George Terry came up with another agricultural "first" for the entire state. At his Magnolia Ranch in southeastern Orange County, Terry constructed a pellet mill to utilize home grown hay as a base for mixing with other feeds to form pellets. This development foreshadowed big changes in Mr. Terry's cattle operations. In January 1960, he converted from a cow-calf operation to a feed lot operation.

By the following November his feed lots had a capacity of 900 steers. He also acquired a ranch in Palm Beach County to round out his Florida cattle operation. The steers were grown off at the Magnolia Ranch and the stockers were shipped to their Palm Beach County ranch for grass fattening. The higher grade animals were then returned to the Magnolia Ranch for a 60-90 day period at grain feeding. The majority of the steers were sold to slaughter houses by private treaty. Terry developed his feed lot operation to the point where it was among the largest in the state before it closed down in 1973.

Rainfall was another problem for cattlemen. The 12.4 inches of rainfall above normal in 1959 was followed by a record 17.37 inches of above normal rainfall in 1960. These two "wet" years back to back created serious problems for the local cattlemen. Among other things, it created a problem in scheduling their annual field day activities. According to Agent Cribbett, the County Beef Cattle Advisory Committee met in April, 1960 to plan a cattlemen's field day for May. They proposed to show cattlemen the type, weight, grades and breeds of stockers and feeders were looking to buy. Because the Florida Ranch Lands were extremely wet and the pastures were behind in growth, the field day was postponed until August. When it was obvious in July that the situation was even worse that site was cancelled. The advisory committee suggested holding the field at

Terry's Magnolia Ranch and set the date for late September. However, Hurricane Donna arrived on September 10th so the field day was moved to November 17th. So, on that day cattlemen were conducted on a tour of Terry's feed mill, feed lots, work pens and other items of interest.

In 1960 it was estimated that the 78 cattlemen in the county owned between 18,000 and 20,000 head of cattle. The officers and directors of the Cattlemen's Association were:

President: Al Smith, Orange County
Vice-President: Dick Scovill, Lake County
Vice-President: George Terry, Jr., Orange County
Secretary: Extension Agent A. F. Cribbett, Orange County
Treasurer: E. L. Yates, Sr., Orange County
State Directors:
    Don Rybolt, Orange County
    R. W. Maxwell, Lake County
Directors:
    George Terry, Sr., Orange County
    Dick Whittington, Lake County
    Zera Giles, Lake County

In June of 1960, T. M. Deal of the Bar D Ranch of Pine Castle, adopted a program of production testing as follows: During September a group of weaned calves were weighed and graded by J. E. Pace, Extension Animal Husbandman and Agent Cribbett. The second group of weaned calves were weighed and graded in November. However, W. T. Champneys of Apopka discontinued his production testing program on his small Hereford herd because he believed that the information obtained was not worth the cost.

In his 1961 report Agent Cribbett noted that the number of cattle and full time cattlemen had declined to a new low. At that time there were approximately some eighty cattle owners and 16,000 head of cattle in the county. Only four full time cattlemen were residents in the county. It is obvious from Cribbett's statement that land speculation and Orange County's burgeoning urban population were taking their toll of the land formerly devoted to cattle. Brucellosis was also becoming a top level problem.

The Florida Range Cattle Brucellosis Committee met in August to discuss the new program and ways that it might be implemented. The committee decided to: (1) Request that the Central Florida Cattlemen's Association to set up an association brucellosis committee to promote calf vaccination. (2) Plan a campaign program during the spring of 1962 featuring calf vaccination. Unfortunately, the results of this 1962 program were not reported.

The burning of native pastures and a trespass law with teeth were two more items of special interest to cattlemen.

During 1961, the Florida Forest Service had developed a new procedure called "Fire Danger Alert". Under that procedure, land owners could receive no help while burning their property. In February during an "alert", several cattlemen burned their native pasture and in so doing requested help. The fires got out of control onto another person's land and as a result the cattlemen were arrested for illegal burning. In order to arrive at a solution, the cattlemen could live with, Agenty Cribbett arranged a meeting between the County Forest Ranger and Cattlemen's Association Directors. The Forest Ranger agreed to notify all land owners of the new procedure and work with them as much as possible. This problem was also brought to the attention of the Florida Cattlemen's Association to prevent similar happenings in other areas. Local problems that had developed in the 1961 hunting season involved complaints of trespassing and shooting of cows, etc. To prevent recurrence of these problems in the 1962 season the local cattlemen's association sponsored a newspaper educational program concerning Florida's trespassing laws which was endorsed by the County Sheriff and the Sportsmen's Association.

According to Cribbett's report, the Sheriff gave his endorsement to the special educational campaign. The Sportsmen's Club and Cattlemen's Association agreed to co-sponsor an educational fund of up to $300 on a matching fund basis. However, after much discussion by the Board of Directors (Cattlemen's Association) it was decided to abandon the idea of paid advertisements. Instead Agent Cribbett contacted news columnists, radio and TV commentators and secured considerable "free" coverage on this trespassing concern connected with hunters.

In 1962, former Orange County cattleman Cushman Radebaugh became the first Floridian to become President of the American National Cattlemen's Association! What was Orange County's loss became St. Lucie County's gain!

In July of 1962, A. F. Cribbett resigned to become County Agent in Pasco County and Assistant County Agent R. Bruce Christmas was transferred from 4-H activities to conducting adult programs in the fields of: cattle, dairying, poultry, and agronomy. As cattlemen departed from the local scene so did Extension Agents charged with educational programs for cattlemen. Agent Christmas who replaced Cribbett in August 1962 to work with cattlemen, resigned in 1966 and was replaced by Agent John C. "Jack" Lester. Lester stayed for one year and was replaced by O. J. Hebert in 1967.

After his arrival, Hebert quickly became involved with the brucellosis testing program. At a meeting of local cattlemen on September 1967, a program was set in motion to test the majority of the beef cattle in Orange County. Cattleman W. A. "Al" Smith was chairman of the advisory committee. They divided the county into nine geographical areas. A cattleman from each area was appointed as · co-ordinator for that area to assist USDA Veterinarians in locating herds and securing cooperation of the cattlemen. Cattlemen Coordinators were as follows:

T. L. Smith, Plymouth
Richard Risser, Clarcona
W. M. Teal, Winter Gardne
E. L. Yates, Sr., Taft
George Livingston, Conway
Leo Faurot, Lake Hart
Theodore Vickery, Christmas
James O. Phillips, Christmas
Donald F. Rybolt, Lake Pickett

During the ensuing nine months 35 herds comprising 9,729 cattle were tested and 99% of the cattle in 95% of the herds tested, were found to be free of brucellosis. On May 16, 1968 the state issued to Orange County a modified certified brucellosis area designation.

A further decline in cattle numbers resulted from the building of Disney World, the Florida Technological University and othe;- urban developments in 1968. On June 18, 1973 the Cupboard News printed the following article: "At that time the cattle population of Orange County had declined to 50% of the 1942 population. Raw land southeast of Orlando that in 1942 was bought for $2.00 an acre was reported sold last week for $750.00 an acre. A group of Palm Beach investors, calling themselves the Heminway Corp., purchased 16,000 acres of pasture and grove land in Magnolia Ranch for $12 million. George Terry, Sr., Orlando cattleman was the seller. Indicated he would lease the property from its new owners for grazing. E. G. Green, the real estate operator, who handled the purchase for the Palm Beachers, termed it for investment."

The land was originally part of a 55,000 acre tract that Magnolia Ranch pruchased in 1942 for $111,000. In 1968, Terry had offered to donate 200 acres to the Orange County Commissioners, for construction of a sports stadium, but they declined the offer.

In September 1973 the Mid Florida Livestock Market announced that it would close as of October 1st.

The continued decline of the cattle population together with traffic congestion and other problems brought cattle sales in Orange County to a halt. By January of 1974 the number of cattlemen had dropped to approximately 30 with some 11,000 cattle. At this point the number of horses was about half the cattle population. This indicated that a new era had arrived in Orange County.

Within a very few years the Orange County cattle business and dairy industry will doubtless be things of the past. As one travels about the county today, many major urban developments occupy pasture tracts formerly used by local cattlemen. Several major ones which can be listed for the record are — The Martin Company, Major Reality Complex, Disney World, Florida Technological University, Tangelo Park, Rosemont, Azalea Park, Bonneville, and Orange Wood to mention just a few.

CHAPTER X

Agricultural Custodians

I. AGRICULTURE – THE COUNTY AGENT

Passage of the Smith-Lever Act by Congress in 1914 brought into being a cooperative educational endeavor in agriculture and home economics between the United States Department of Agriculture, State Land-Grant Universities and local county units of government. This three-way educational partnership was both unusual in design and revolutionary in concept.

First, the agents charged with disseminating practical and helpful information in agriculture and home economics were to be "off-campus" faculty members in that their "teaching" would be off-campus. This "off-campus" approach required that certain academic requirements of the university be met but the nature of their work requires that the agents live and work in non-academic surroundings.

Their classrooms would be the homes, farms and public meeting places of the people. In fact, the county would become their classroom. Their method of instruction would be entirely different also. For example, participants in these practical and helpful informal learning sessions would attend on a strictly voluntary basis. This "freedom of choice" learning atmosphere called for an entirely different type of faculty member, one who would use methods of teaching quite different from conventional classroom instructions.

This meant that off-campus teachers must first win the confidence of the local people by being "one of them". Next, educational material must be presented at their level of use and free from the usual academic trimmings of big words and "do-it-my-way or else" attitude.

To reach people of all educational levels and all backgrounds and attitudes, teaching was primarily concentrated around the demonstration method. Hence, in the early days they were often called County Demonstration Agents and Home Demonstration Agents. However, with the passage of time the Agricultural Agent became generally known as "County Agent".

The County Agent was usually housed in the Court House complex and being charged with the overall well-being of the local agricultural economy, people in and out of agriculture sized up his job responsibilities as that of a custodian or keeper of the agricultural industry's well-being. He was expected to provide the leadership and

299

"know-how" to help farmers prosper. This entailed assistance in both production and marketing. The County Agent had contact with and was often the go-between the Experiment Stations and the farmer. Consequently, he was charged with keeping the farmer up-to-date on the latest research findings in all agricultural fields. If he did not have ready answers for their questions, it was his responsibility to find out this information.

With this background, the County Agent concept of carrying agricultural information to the farms of America came into being in 1914. Some counties entered into this educational partnership earlier than others because they saw the merits of such a program and because they had the finances to fulfill their part of this new concept. Orange County was in this position and acquired its first County Agent in early 1914.

By 1960, six different County Agents had served Orange County. During this 56-year period the county population grew from less than 20,000 to over 350,000.

LOOKING BACK — (left) County Agent Swanson and Myer Shader citrus grower look at picture board of Orange County Agents. Shader had a working relationship with all six while Swanson with five.

Not many present day (1975) residents of Orange County knew all of these six County Agents! However, Judge Don A Cheney knew each of them on a casual basis and Myer Shader, through his agricultural endeavors, knew each County Agent on a working basis. Also, I personally knew and had a working relationship with these agents, all but the first one, Charles Henry Baker. It was also my good fortune to be able to interview each of these men concerning his personal experiences and to record them on a firsthand basis.

Some knowledge of the period in which each County Agent served Orange County is helpful because it gives the reader some appreciation of the problems each County Agent encountered and the nature of his response to those problems. Sometimes his response must be judged in light of administrative edicts from his supervisors. These considerations are important because his clientele as well as the reader may wonder why did the agent do — "such and such".

By law, each agent was required to report his activities annually in a statistical and a narrative summary. However, that type of report was eliminated after the 1961-'62 Extension reporting year. The computer age dictated a report more statistically comprehensive than the long narrative reports that agents formerly spent days writing in long hand. With these narrative reports went a page of history because these extensive reports provided historians with a report of what happened, when and by whom.

The narrative reports for County Agents Charles Henry Baker and Ezra Franklin DeBusk are not in the files. Only the 1925 annual narrative of Agent Kime is on record with the other five reports missing. All of Agent Moore's twenty years of narrative reports are on file as are the six years of annual reports for Swanson. Several are on file for Baetzman's years of tenure as agent.

Personal interviews with DeBusk, Kime, Moore and a close working relationship with Agent Baetzman provided opportunities to gather historical information on the several periods when these agents served the county's agricultural industries.

CHARLES HENRY BAKER
The first County Agent
February 23, 1914 to July 31, 1917

No information is on record concerning Orange County's "first" County Agent that would provide some background on his training or his programs. The county had just lost a portion of its area to create Seminole County when he arrived on the scene. At that time Myer Shader was a young man (17) and lived with his family on a small dairy farm at Fairvilla. He remembers Agent Baker visiting their farm in a buggie. Judge Don Cheney remembered Agent Baker as a tall, well dressed man with grey or white hair. He often wore a sun helmet and this along with his mannerisms and dress gave him the appearance of an English gentleman.

With the clouds of World War I on the horizon Baker resigned. What the reason and where he went are both unknown. Our interview with former County Agent DeBusk in the summer of '71 shed no light on these matters. DeBusk said — "He met with Baker to learn what he had been doing and gathered that he was primarily interested in ornamental plants and that his training had been in the field of botany." DeBusk mentioned that Baker seemed unknown to the farming interests of the county and had not established any particular educational program with the local people.

So, the clues we have on Orange County's "first" County Agent are few indeed.

EZRA FRANKLIN DeBUSK
The 3 F County Agent
October 1, 1917 to October 31, 1919

Orange County's second County Agent was a native of Tennessee who graduated from Lincoln Memorial University of Lexington, Tennessee in 1910. DeBusk's desire upon graduation was to come to Florida to work with the fabulous citrus industry. Towards that end

he came to Florida in 1911 and obtained a job with a real estate company in Polk County that was selling grove land to northern investors. DeBusk soon realized he had a lot to learn about insect control and fertilizer programs for citrus so in 1913 he applied to the University of Florida for a course in citriculture. However, at that time no such course was available. Next. he went to Hillsborough County to teach science courses in the high school and in the summer of 1916 he worked with the State Plant Board in the citrus canker eradication program in Hillsborough and Pinellas Counties.

County Agent E. F. DeBusk

In 1917 DeBusk was offered the job of County Agent in Orange County, replacing Charles Henry Baker who was resigning. DeBusk reported he did not know where Baker had come from or where he went from Orange County. DeBusk had a brief conference with Baker when he arrived in Orange County. He wished to learn what programs had been started and what should be continued but could learn very little about what Baker had been doing. Apparently Baker's interest was mainly in gardening and ornamental plantings around homes in and near Orlando and according to DeBusk few farmers knew Baker.

302

DeBusk said he was influenced to come to Orange County because the USDA had established a research station in Orlando and the county had considerable citrus acreage. Since citrus was his first love, he believed that he could learn a great deal as County Agent in these surroundings. Then too, his salary as a science teacher in Hillsborough County was only $125.00 a month whereas Orange County offered him $154.16 2/3rds cents per month! The "clincher" was the 2/3rds of a cent which fascinated DeBusk. He bought a Ford sedan for $425.00 and reported to Orange County on October 1, 1917 to become the county's second County Agent. Before long DeBusk encountered some of the frustrations that are so typical of Extension work. The job as he visualized it was entirely different from the way it was administered by Extension supervisors!

For example, World War I was creating a demand for increased food production. In response to that need, the administrators at the Federal level conceived the "Food, Feed and Forage (F.F.F.) program for Extension workers to "push" nation-wide to help the war effort. No consideration was given to the fact that agriculture, soils and climate might differ from one part of the country to another. The campaign was conceived as a national effort and that was what it would be, regardless!

All kinds of directives started coming his way. DeBusk was told to build up the local cattle industry by securing better breeding cows as well as purebred bulls. He was directed to increase the local production of corn, peanuts and field crops in the county. To push for forage programs he was told to encourage farmers to construct concrete silos. One of the concrete monuments to DeBusk's efforts was constructed at the Marshall Farms near Ocoee where it stood vacant in memory of that campaign for over 40 years!

Dr. Monroe Lynn, DVM, who had laid the foundation for federal hog cholera work in Orange County was called into the Service. This program then became another responsiblity for Agent DeBusk. In one month he remembers having had to vaccinate 3,000 hogs! Also, to help improve the local hog industry. DeBusk located and bought 300 bred sows in Wisconsin for Orange County hog raisers and after they arrived, he vaccinated them.

He was also ordered to see that all the cattle in the county were dipped for the control of the splenic fever tick. This called for building dipping vats all over the county and trying to secure the cooperation of cattlemen to go along with this unpopular program. This program alienated many cattlemen against the County Agent because he was a "party" to the "feds" in this unpopular program.

However, one individual today still remembers a service DeBusk performed for him that had a lasting effect on his life. DeBusk put up an argument that kept Myer Shader of Fairvilla from going into the Service during World War I. His older brother had already enlisted and Myer was needed at home to help run the dairy farm. DeBusk contended that Shader's need on the farm was greater than any contribution he would make in the war effort.

Shortly afterward DeBusk received the same advice. He had become tired of all the directives and thought that he would enlist in the Service. He met with Dr. Rolfs at the University of Florida, who was then in charge of all agricultural work in Florida, to discuss his plans. Dr. Rolfs told DeBusk he was performing a service for the country in his work and not to quit.

In 1919 DeBusk's desire to do citrus work became too great and he accepted a job with a fertilizer company in Polk County to get away from the diverse agricultural work associated with Extension endeavors. However, this new job proved to be more one of selling the product than working with citrus, so when he was offered the County Agent's job in Lake County in 1920 he accepted. He remained in Lake County 'til in 1923 when he was offered the position of State Extension Specialist in citrus at Gainesville. He accepted this offer and became Associate Plant Pathologist with the Experiement Stations and Extension Citriculturist.

In 1931, Arthur S. Rhoads and E. F. DeBusk co-authored Bulletin 229 — "Diseases of Citrus in Florida". This extensive 213 page bulletin on Florida citrus diseases was the handbood for the industry for almost 20 years. At last, DeBusk was busy doing the work he loved best and feeling that he was making a contribution to the rapidly expanding citrus industry.

This enjoyment was to last but a few short years when along came World War II and a new series of work directives for DeBusk. He was placed in charge of supervising the construction of Farm Labor Camps and recruiting some 20,000 farm laborers during the war. By 1947 he was both physically and mentally tired and decided that the time had come for him to retire. So on June 30, 1947 he resigned from Extension work and was replaced by Fred Lawrence who held the Extension Citriculturist position from June 1947 to June 1974. Mr. DeBusk died in Gainesville on March 28, 1974 at the age of 90.

Although his direct service to Orange County as County Agent was the shortest time of all (2 years), he served Orange County as a state specialist for 24 years making many contributions in grove management practices. He was a pioneer in citrus irrigation methods, helped in developing citrus fertilizing practices, promoted the use of zinc sprays as soon as it was discovered that zinc eliminated the disease known as "frenching". DeBusk also established grower demonstrations proving the value of copper sulphate in the elimination of "ammoniation".

So, Orange County's loss really became the state's gain because his talents were spread over a larger area and benefitted more people than if he had chosen to remain in Orange County doing work he was neither trained to do or liked!

CHARLES D. KIME

The "Boom-Time" County Agent
July 1, 1919 to July 15, 1926

County Agent Kime, known to most people as "Charlie", was Orange County's third County Agent and the first with previous experience as a County Agent. He had been County Agent in neighboring Brevard County from 1917 to 1919, when he received the offer to fill the vacancy created by the resignation of E. F. DeBusk.

Kime's tenure of six years was a rather peaceful era and could well be referred to as the "good ole days" of Extension work. World War I had ended and the country was going through a period of re-adjustment and mechanization was beginning to change the way of life as well as its pace. The cattle tick was the major problem of Orange County cattlemen and dipping had become a compulsory but rather spasmodic activity. The fernery business in the Apopka — Zellwood and Conway areas was increasing in activity with the addition of many

County Agent Charlie Kime

small ferneries and new citrus groves were being planted throughout the county. Also, there was a rather strong push in the Avalon area of West Orange County to encourage northern investors to become citrus growers.

Because of water management problems, the vegetable industry had moved from the Apopka marshlands in the northern end of the county to the flatwoods soils of the Oakland — Winter Garden and Ocoee areas of West Orange County.

Some 80 small dairy farms were scattered about the county and over 100 poultry flocks of varying sizes were located in various sections of the county.

The most inaccessible area in the county was Christmas. In fact Kime had to go through Oviedo to get there. However, in the early twenties the Old Cheney Highway (later State Road 50) opened up the eastern portion of the county.

County Agent Kime's headquarters were in the old brick Court House where the new Court House Annex stands, and he shared a secretary with Home Demonstration Agent Nellie Taylor. Kime said he was not bothered with home owner calls for assistance and could visit the farmers as the need arose.

Retired Extension Citriculturist Fred Lawrence remembers, as a boy at Gotha in the late teens and early twenties, that he assisted County Agent Kime when he visited their grove at Gotha. Among other things, he carried Kime's La Mote soil testing kit as he went about their grove making soil tests.

The main administrative edict that came down to Kime during those years was "to organize agricultural clubs" in the various communities for the purpose of creating a forum to disseminate timely information on agricultural topics. Kime said he organized some 10 to 12 agricultural clubs in the county and Zellwood had the most active club in the county.

When the real estate "boom" developed in the mid 1920's Agent Kime's activities changed considerably. In 1925 Kime reported a decrease of 3,000 acres of citrus due to "subdivisions". He continued as follows: "Citrus and truck gardening have fallen off because of the immense real estate development causing frequent changes in property ownership. Dairy and poultry have received an immense impetus and expansion is rapid, though even here the dairy industry is tending to drift toward the cheapest and obtainable. The small farm tract of three, five, 10 or 20 acres is putting in an appearance in vastly increasing numbers." However, with the "boom" creating "paper millionaires" over-night, Kime figured he should get in on part of the action so he resigned in July of 1926 to go into private business.

Later, in an interview (July 9, 1971) he said, "that was a sorry mistake on my part". The boom was soon over and he found himself on the outside looking in. Before long he was assisting County Agent K. C. Moore in a special capacity with the newly discovered Mediterranean Fruit Fly Campaign in the 1929-'30 period.

In 1930 he became Southeastern Agricultural Representative, of the Tennessee Coal, Iron, and Railroad Company. In 1943, he again became associated with the Florida Agricultural Extension Service by becoming County Agricultural Agent in St. Lucie County. He served in this capacity 'til in 1960 when he retired. He now lives in Ft. Pierce.

306

KINGMAN COLQUITH MOORE
"The Depression County Agent"
October 1, 1926 to August 31, 1946

Outside his family, few people knew the meaning of Mr. Moore's initials because nearly everyone addressed him as "K. C.". Moore was a native of Georgia and a graduate of Mercer University in 1897. He also took some courses at Cornell University in 1905. His background consisted of being a school teacher, farm supervisor, County Agent and District Agent in Virginia, a Marion County, Florida, County Agricultural Agent from 1921-'25, a Florida District Agent (Duval County-South) for a while before resigning to become Orange County Agricultural Agent on October 1, 1926. Moore said the Orange County position paid more than the District Agent position! He received $450 a month until 1930 when the salary (because of the depression) was reduced to $180.00 a month. Finally, in the fall of 1934 it was raised to $220.00 and when he retired in September of 1946 it had climbed to $377.50 a month.

County Agent K. C. Moore

Moore's 20 years as County Agent was "plagued" with one crisis after another, plus all kinds of extra administrative responsibilities to go with these various crises. Upon reading Moore's narrative reports for this 20-year period, one is amazed how one man accomplished so much with so many interruptions. He was quite philosophical about his County Agent's work and responsibilities. He frequently bared his soul with occasional insights to his role as he saw it in his annual reports.

A couple of "goodies" that Moore revealed are recorded for reader interest and as "lessons" for future Extension workers. In his 1927 report, Moore described how hundredes of people had inquried about land-use possibilities, sources of plants and seeds, requests for information on insects, diseases and troubles of all kinds. He complained that, "we do not always have the information and do not know where to find it. Much of it is not available and the agent had to reason and advise by analogy, explaining that this is only his theory!!"

Frustration was revealed in his 1928 report when he wrote — "Our college, experiment station, and Extension Division, employ

307

specialists for special phases of work, sometimes six to ten men in one department, consequently one county agent in a county with the diversity that we have has a heck of a time trying to keep posted on production, marketing, and statistics so as to be able to assist specializing farmers, and carry on demonstrations and secure reports on these from busy men."

In another report Moore wrote about his service calls and revealed his philosophy in this regard by writing — "Some days when I have no positive engagements, but still a trip planned, office callers will keep me in the whole day. At other times, urgent requests and calls prevent a regular round of planned visits. This seems particularly true here where so many new people are continually getting up against new difficulties. An agent can hardly refuse to go and help a man giving as an excuse that he must go out elsewhere to start or see a demonstration." It was Moore's opinion that this kind of advisory service in the office and in the field seems to be "what the people want and need; and it is my opinion that it is accomplishing as much good as much fewer definite set demonstrations."

Writing an annual narrative report of an agent's activities for an entire year, plus a statistical report, is a frustrating experience. Taking time from a busy and overloaded schedule to do this administrative detail automatically compounds the agent's problems.

In this regard it is interesting to note that Moore was so impressed with the new guidelines that came out in 1934 that he wrote in the foreword of his annual report — "This page is dedicated to the man or men who devised this latest form for statistical yearly report. It is by far the best I have seen in seventeen years of report making in the Extension Service." Since he had been with Orange County only eight years at that time, Moore evidently went back not only to the time he was Marion County Agent but also included the years he was in the Extension Service in Virginia!

However, on his 10th anniversary in Orange County, Moore took time to reflect on his activities for this period in his 1936 report by writing — "I completed 10 years of service as county agricultural agent in Orange County on October 1, 1936. During all these years there has not been a day when calls for information, or personal service calls did not fill my working time. It has been impossible to seek out farmers who might want to cooperate with me, because I have usually not been able to keep up with calls which I am asked to make, with arrangements for meetings with letters, with news articles or radio talks, with motorcades, etc., etc."

Moore really bared his honest soul in 1939 when he wrote — "I regret the small amount of poultry work done, but I do not like chickens. The poultrymen must sense this, but I can't see how. However, I do like all the poultrymen and always stand ready to serve."

In 1943 Moore wrote, "With the conclusion of this report I will have spent a total of twenty six weeks — six months — a full half year of time on annual reports!"

In closing out his career in 1946, Moore summarized his philosophy on his work, as follows — "I have always tried to explain the reasons for advice that I have given farmers of all classes. Demonstrations have aroused their interest and desire to know why. And I have tried to inspire them with the desire to seek out the best that was known rather than to use me or anyone else as a service man."

Lewis Maxwell, who served with Moore briefly as a special Assistant County Agent in conservation practices in 1937, said he picked up two philosophies of Moore's that he still uses today. He remembered that Moore warned him against trying to "oversell" an idea. He and Moore had visited a poultryman whom Maxwell wanted to switch from Leghorns to New Hampshires because the New Hampshires were a promising new breed with many desirable traits. Moore told Maxwell afterwards it was alright to point that out but not to oversell because the man could resent it.

Maxwell remembered another observation that Moore made on another poultry farm visit. The poultryman was rather cantankerous but Moore systematically answered the gentleman's various questions point-by-point. Upon returning to the office, Moore immediately wrote him a letter again laying out the various points raised and the appropriate answers. Maxwell said to Moore, "You told him all of that so why write him?" Moore replied — "You know it and I know it, but I want everybody to know it."

Moore's time as County Agent was not a "happy one" for he had to contend with several crises such as — the Mediterranean Fruit Fly Campaign, screwworm outbreak, cattle tick, the 1934 and 1940 freezes, the depression, new agricultural programs such as the Agricultural Adjustment Act (A.A.A.), Farm Credit Administration and lastly World War II with the various emergency boards such as the USDA War Board (Draft Deferments for agricultural workers), Emergency Farm Labor Program, Farm Machinery Rationing Committee, County Farm Transportation Committee, War Meat Committee, Emergency Seed and Fertilizer Loan Agency, Regional Agricultural Credit Corporation loans, plus special Victory Garden Campaigns!! These were followed by special counseling programs for returning veterans in '45 and '46 concerning agricultural careers.

When Moore became County Agent in 1926, he inherited the educational programs connected with cattle tick eradication. This controversial program placed the County Agent in bad light because he was part of a program that cost the cattlemen financially and also inconvenienced him in many ways. Compulsory programs, especially when administered by out-of-town folks are never popular! However, this was mild compared with the Mediterranean Fruit Fly eradication campaign in Orange County. Moore wrote — "Hundreds of thousands of boxes of perfect fruit and vegetables were destroyed as well as hundreds of acres of vegetables not yet harvested. My job was to attempt to keep up the morale of our people and to educate them as to the fly's habits and destructiveness. In the course of this effort I made the following contacts: four talks to 5,460 school children, I proposed and assisted in the organization of a committee of leading citizens of the county for the purpose of lending voluntary assistance to the Plant Quarantine and Control Administration and State Plant Board in matters relating to the public's attitude and unofficial connections with these regulatory bodies."

Moore noted this later in his report by pointing out this lay committee did a lot in softening bitterness of the uninformed people toward the State Plant Board and the Federal Plant Quarantine Control Administration. This organization sent the first delegation of Florida citizens to Washington to present Florida's case to the President and Congress.

The stock market "crash" in 1929 also triggered several crises for Moore and materially altered his work in the years that followed.

RETIREMENT PARTY -- AUGUST 1946 — A group of friends honor retiring County Agent K. C. Moore after serving 20 years as Orange County Agent. First Row — George D. Livingston, Mrs. Alice Ballentine, K. C. Moore, Inez Furrea Santry, Lenora Conroy Sloan. Second Row — James Rolfe, Mrs. Ralph Boswell, Ruby Goodman, Dorothy Johnson, James D. Pounds. Third Row — Ralph Boswell, Neil Dale, Ibera Dickensen, A. H. Repphard, E. F. DeBusk (Orange County's 2nd County Agent). Fourth Row — Ralph Macey, Bob Barber, Myer Shader (the only agriculturist to know every County Agent from 1914 - 1975), Dwight Freeman, A. H. Whitmore.

First of all Moore suffered a salary cut. From $450.00 a month in 1929 his salary was reduced to $180 a month in 1930. The secretary he shared with the Home Demonstration Agent was put on half time and Moore's office was closed half of each day, at the same time requests for services were multiplying. As emergency loans of various kinds became available to farmers in the spring of 1932, Moore was beseiged with inquiries concerning who was eligible and details of these programs. In April of 1932 Moore's office efficiency was further reduced when his secretary was fired. As a result Moore worked one or two nights per week and parts of most Sundays to keep up with correspondence, and other office chores. He also personally paid for some work that was done privately for the county. Then in May of 1932, Moore lost his private office and was moved to a space in a larger room occupied by the Orange County Chamber of Commerce. Moore reported this arrangement was satisfactory but keeping up with office callers and bulletin requests was an impossibilty. During this period Moore worked with the Orange County Unemployment Relief Committee to encourage special home gardens which he referred to as "subsistence gardens". Seed, fertilizer, and technical assistance was given those who desired to produce home vegetables. Moore conceived and put into effect a Farm and Home Institute for Orange County folks to substitute for the Farmer's Week Program that the Agricultural College abandoned due to economic conditions in 1933.

In 1934 Moore found himself involved in three emergency programs. This time it was the Drought Relief Section of the A.A.A. Program which had put seven flooded counties on the same disaster basis as drought areas of the western states. A total of 1,542 cattle were sold for 30 cattlemen who had cattle on the flooded marsh area of the St. Johns River in Eastern Orange County. This special program required much paper work and supervision by Moore.

In 1935 Moore found himself involved in two other emergency programs. The severe freeze in December of 1934 brought hundreds of inquiries on how and when and where to prune the hundreds of acres of citrus trees damaged by the cold. Special programs were set up to meet these demands.

Discovery of the screwworm in Orange County in 1935 found Moore arranging office space for a local screwworm control worker, arranging for the distribution of pine tar oil and benzol from various sites accessible to farmers and conducting demonstrations on how to treat cattle and other animals for screwworms.

Moore also arranged for the meetings and located observation stations for the newly created Federal-State Frost Warning Service.

The newly created Agricultural Adjustment Program was just

311

getting started and Moore found it difficult to keep himself and the members fully informed on all the regulations and requirements. Moore found it necessary to write stories and make radio broadcasts concerning the corn-hog contracts and related matters. Moore also assisted Florida residents who owned farms in other states to properly sign contracts, fill out and sign receipts, etc. Several emergency crop loan associations were functioning in Orange County and Moore had to assist growers in making applications for the various kinds of loans. For example, in December of 1935 and January of '36 he assisted 77 farmers who had signed up under the Potato Adjustment Act. Moore mentioned that six lots of stamps had been issued to five small producers so no special help was required to facilitate this aspect of the program.

The State Agricultural Extension office issued a special administrative directive in 1936 to create a County Agricultural Planning Council. Twenty-five leading citizens representing all segments of agriculture agreed to serve on this planning group. With considerable effort they were gotten together to discuss broad goals and objectives. After the committee disintegrated Moore reported that these were busy men and unless specific and attainable goals were laid out these men felt it was a waste of their time. Moore subscribed to that opinion. However, the directive came from the state office and he did his best in organizing the committee to help formulate attainable goals.

In May of 1936 Moore laid the ground work for implementing the Soil Conservation Program which later became known as the A.A.A. Program. A County Committee was organized, a full-time senior stenographer, a part-time assistant and typist were hired. Three desks, filing equipment and other items were added to Moore's already crowded office facilities. However, only six of the 1,268 properties involved, qualified for diversion payments. To check for compliance, measuring land, etc. Moore asked three committee members to handle the most "complicated" properties. Moore found the three men unable to finish the work in a reasonable time, and employed three others who primarily assisted those three. He kept six crews of two men working 'til the order came to stop measuring and map making. The six supervisors finished checking the 255 remaining properties in 4½ days. These "sketchy" accounts clearly indicate how he was bogged down with paper work and supervision with this new program that pulled him away from other County Agent activities. By the end of 1936, Moore had completed about half of the necessary paper work. However, by 1937 the Agricultural Conservation Program was well organized and beginning to function according to federal guidelines but no full time office manager had yet been authorized. Consequently, Moore performed all of the administrative responsibilites.

In 1938, the Agricultural Conservation Program hired Barney Sullivan as county performance supervisor, three assistant performance supervisors, and three office secretaries. It was now pretty much on its own with Moore acting mostly as an advisor to the program. In 1937 some 1,041 work sheets on 1,800 farms were prepared. In 1938, 1,424 work sheets on 2,500 farms had been prepared.

With these countless regulations, guidelines and financial audits snowballing as a result of this new agricultural program, Moore no doubt breathed a sigh of relief when he was able to shed the direct responsibilities of this additional time-consuming program. However, Moore's relief was only short-lived after the various emergency programs — A.A.A., Farm Security, R.E.A. and others when they acquired their own staffs. The severe 1940 freeze required another round of emergency programs to meet these problems!

With the start of World War II, all heck broke loose as new programs, new board responsibilities and new directives for Extension programs and activities descended on Moore.

In 1943 Moore wrote —"I look back on this past year's work with more satisfaction than I have experienced in recent years. The statistical summary indicates little accomplished in actual Extension Service. The jobs which had to be done were filled with trying and tiresome experiences. But in cooperation with the farmers on the various boards and committee I have rendered service. And now I am glad that it has been hard.

Because of the great value of their helpful work, I want to report here, rather than later under the heading 'other Programs', that the members of Orange County's War Board, Farm Machinery Rationing Committee, County Farm Transportation Committee, War Meat Committee, and Farm Labor Advisory Committee, regularly and willingly gave their valuable time and counsel to these projects. I am greatly indebted to them."

How did Moore evaluate his job after inheriting all the various extra curricular activities and directives through the years? In his 1943 narrative report after having been an Agent and District Agent in Virginia, County Agent in Marion County four years and now some 17 years in Orange County, Moore wrote "I used to think that a County Agent could not accomplish much in an office. I still hold that demonstrations are the most forceful means of teaching, but so many more contacts can be made in the office with people who have specific problems to solve, most of whom put our advice into practice, that I have had to change my opinion on office calls. After all,

313

most of the time farm visits do not mean demonstrations. I believe that farmers who evince their confidence and make the effort to come to the office for information will usually put it into practice. If it proves helpful they will tell their neighbors."

These insights into some of the crises Moore experienced during his tenure as County Agent and his philosophies should provide the average lay person a better insight as to the custodial role a County Agent performs on behalf of agricultural interests in his respective county.

Agent Moore retired August 31, 1946 and died March 9, 1968 at the age of 91.

FREDERICK ERNEST BAETZMAN
"A County Agent With Assistants"
October 1, 1946 to June 20, 1957

Fred Baetzman, a native of Chicago, Illinois, came to Florida to study agriculture because his father owned a grove at Howey-In-The-Hills. His original desire was to study pharmacy but his parents convinced him an agricultural background would be helpful to his father in his grove operations. At the University of Florida, Baetzman preferred animal husbandry rather than horticulture and majored in that subject. After graduation in 1928 he became a salesman for a national feed company and was assigned the Central Florida territory. In this capacity he made friends with many people he would later work with in a County Agent's role.

County Agent F. E. Baetzman

In 1934, Baetzman was appointed County Agent of nearby Volusia County and shortly thereafter became Secretary to the Florida Jersey Cattle Club. This position like, his former salesman role, provided him an opportunity to meet many people in Orange County, especially dairymen. He organized a Dairy Herd Improvement Association (Pioneer DHIA) for Volusia County dairymen and encouraged Orange County dairymen to become affiliated since Orange County had no such organization. Dairymen T. G. Lee and Carroll Ward became affiliate members.

With such a close working-relationship with so many Orange County cattlemen, it was only logical that Baetzman be selected to

314

succeed K. C. Moore as County Agent for Orange County. Moore retired August 31, 1946 and Baetzman became Orange County's fifth County Agent October 1, 1946. However, after all these cattlemen contacts with Orange County, his first requests for assistance came from rabbit producers and beekeepers. The meat and sugar shortages and resultant rationing of these commodities during the war years had created unusual prosperity for these two agricultural groups.

However, with the war and rationing both things of the past, the marketing position of rabbit producers and beekeepers had changed drastically. As Baetzman described the situation — "both groups were camped at my door when I moved to Orlando in the fall of 1946." He found himself working toward a common goal for two totally unrelated agricultural commodities. Also, both were of minor economic importance as compared to some other Orange County agricultural commodities. Nevertheless, they were people with problems and what they lacked in numbers they made up in persistence!

Baetzman helped the rabbit producers to acquire a site and a building adjacent to Fairview Park (Ben White Raceway) where they could establish a cooperative marketing outlet for their rabbits. However, the producers soon began to squabble amongst themselves and the organization disbanded and each went his own way.

His efforts with the beekeepers were more successful and their cooperative venture persisted over many years. The beekeepers were of a different temperament than the rabbit producers and they were from several Central Florida Counties. Baetzman tried to secure some old buildings at the abandoned army air field at Pine Castle for their use but the group decided that a site at Umatilla (Lake County) was more suitable to their needs.

Before long other groups called on Baetzman for help. In the late 1940's the Orange County citrus growers asked for help in organizing a growers organization that was being called Florida Citrus Mutual. It was on his way home from the trip to the organizational meeting of Florida Citrus Mutual that Baetzman was involved in a serious automobile accident. The complications resulting from this accident, Parkinson's disease, ultimately necessitated his retirement in 1957.

Next, however, the poultrymen asked for assistance with their marketing problems and in 1955 he helped them organize the Central Florida Poultry Cooperative with headquarters on Edgewater Drive behind the Ben White stables. Another group that asked for assistance were the dairymen. It was this group that caused him the most anguish. He had so many close friends in this field and they were so sharply divided on the issues that he found it extremely difficult to remain totally neutral. So, it was Assistant County Agent Swanson's duty to call a public meeting to hear the "pros" and "cons" of a proposed federal milk marketing order for the Central Florida Milk Shed.

Several administrative changes in Extension policy began to surface during Baetzman's tenure which are worth noting because work responsibilities for agents started to specialize at that time. For example, in October of 1948 the state office and the Orange County Commissioners agreed to fund two new Extension staff positions for Orange County.

An Assistant County Agent position was created and funded for a full time person to conduct Boys' 4-H Club work and a similar position in Home Demonstration work was created to work with girls enrolled in 4-H Club work. These two new county Extension positions in Orange County were the first to occur in 34 years! Prior to this time the County Agent and Home Demonstration Agent handled both the adult as well as youth work, although Lewis Maxwell was employed for approximately seven months to assist Agent Moore with the recently started Conservation Program in 1938. However, this program of the newly instigated Soil Conservation work was specially funded and was not an Extension position.

Additional funds for staff specialization within broad program areas were secured in 1954. Because of his horticultural training Swanson was placed in charge of adult programs in horticulture. This included citrus, ornamental horticulture and vegetables. A. F. Cribbett was hired to fill the Boys' 4-H Club position. County Agent Baetzman, in addition to being administratively in charge of the Boys' 4-H Club work, the adult horticultural program areas, also became the program leader for all adult work in animal industry fields of dairy, poultry, beef, and swine.

This horticultural staff position for Agent Swanson was the first county staff position in the state to move in the direction of subject matter specialization. Prior to this time, the Assistant County Agent positions were only responsible for Boys' 4-H Club work.

The state Extension office had recognized specialization within agriculture and the rate at which new research information was becoming available. The day of the County Agent as a generalist in all agricultural subjects was disappearing and Extension Agents would now have to become specialists like their counterparts on the state Extension staff. Professional improvement and the need to keep up-to-date on the latest research findings in more specialized program areas marked the beginning a of a new type of Extension worker in the mid to late 1950's.

316

Meanwhile new Federal pilot-programs were launched to bring about closer working relations between the Home Demonstration Agent and the County Agent. One such was the Farm and Home Development Program. This involved selecting several farm families in a county where the Home Demonstration Agent and the County Agent, as a team could assist the family in its planning of farm and home budgets. The concept had merit for certain areas of the country where general farming was practiced. Here in Florida, especially Orange County, several shortcomings existed in this farm and home concept. For example, a general farm family does not exist in our highly specialized agriculture. A wife of the owner of a specialized Florida agricultural endeavor did not fit the mold of a wife of a general farmer in the midwest. Few Florida agriculturists actually lived on their farms and those who did are highly mobile. Husband and wife interests were not so closely knit and interrelated as those on general farms. In many cases the Florida agriculturist's wife was not a participant in the local Extension Homemakers Clubs or activities. Likewise, women active in Extension Homemaker Club activities, often had husbands who were not associated with an agricultural business for their income. In summary, this Farm and Home Development Program instigated at the Federal level was applicable to only a very few pilot families in Florida, and in Orange County only a very limited attempt was made to implement the program.

The overall shortcomings of the Farm and Home Development Program and the accompanying directives repeated some of the problems encountered by County Agent DeBusk in 1917 with the Food, Feed and Forage Program.

Baetzman's retirement because of physical disabilities June 30, 1957 occurred before job responsibilities, titles, and the Agricultural Extension Program underwent the most traumatic and unprecedented changes possible. He died January 29, 1967.

HENRY FREDERICK SWANSON
Orange County's "Last" County Agent

COUNTY AGENT
August 1, 1957 to June 30, 1963

COUNTY CHAIRMAN
July 1, 1963 to June 30, 1969

COUNTY EXTENSION DIRECTOR July 1, 1969 to ----

Henry Frederick Swanson, sometimes called "the agent of many titles" became Orange County's sixth County Agent before becoming a full Agent. He was also the first Orange County Agent to have

317

participated in Extension programs as a boy. He enrolled in the Boys' 4-H Club Program in 1937 when R. E. (Bob) Norris was Assistant County Agent in Lake County. These experiences and associations with various Extension workers motivated him to pursue a career as an Agricultural Extension Agent.

He enrolled in the University of Florida in 1941 and dropped out in 1943 to serve three years in the Hospital Corps of the U.S. Navy during World War II. He re-entered the University in 1946.

County Agent Henry F. Swanson

Upon graduation from the University of Florida he became Assistant County Agent in Charge of Boys' 4-H Club work in Orange County, October 1, 1948. Six years later he became a specialist for adult programs in several subject matter fields, the first Assistant County Agent in the state to do so. Because of his horticultural training, he was made Program Leader for Extension Programs in citrus, vegetables and ornamental plants and served in this capacity until 1957 when he was promoted to County Agent.

Swanson's title changed several times during his tenure as Extension Agent in Orange County. These title changes make him technically Orange County's "last" County Agent because the title "County Agent" has been replaced by more "high toned" names.

By the late 1950's it was evident that policy changes were in the making. Dr. Ralph L. Miller, Orlando Citrus Consultant, former USDA Entomologist, and a member of the Board of Control, 1954-1962, recognized that Extension policy changes were imminent when he reviewed budget requests for the Florida Agricultural Extension Service. New demands were being put on Extension Agents by urban residents and Dr. Miller recognized that demands for environmental protection was going to require program emphasis by Extension Agents.

However, the magnitude of the changes in the Extension Service, between 1963 and 1973, was far greater than Dr. Miller or the Extension Agents thought possible. Extension Service titles were changed and area of program emphasis as well. In fact, the Extension Service was literally turned inside out as though to completely eliminate anything from the past, as a new Extension image was pushed. It is important that these policy changes be documented because the

318

custodial role of the Agricultural Agent changed with them. Past and future clients of the Extension Service should be appraised of the custodial role the Agent has played if for no other reason than for the historical records.

Before discussing the changes that have occurred in the County Agent's position, recognition should be given to a Federal Program which proved most helpful to Orange County Extension activities just before and during the policy changes.

In 1958, Ezra Taft Benson, then Secretary of Agriculture, directed that certain USDA employees in counties all over the country act as committees to inventory Conservation Needs. These (CNI) Committees were to record the number of acres devoted to various agricultural endeavors in their respective counties and how much was in urban use. Upon completing these inventories, the committees were then asked to project the changes in population and land-use that might take place by the year 1975. This 17-year "look ahead" projection was to be reviewed by a special state-wide CNI Committee. When the county reports were completed, they were to be forwarded to the U.S. Department of Agriculture for use in future program policies.

The County USDA Conservation Needs Inventory Committee in Orange County consisted of — County Agent H. F. Swanson, District Conservationist Albert H. Swartz of the U. S. Soil Conservation Service, the late Neil Dale, Office Manager of the Agricultural Stabilization and Conservation office and Charles Chellman, Farm Forester. In 1958 this committee totaled acreage devoted to various agricultural endeavors with little difficulty. However, determining the Orange County population by 1975 and its impact on local land-use, proved most difficult. No professional planning bodies existed at that time (1959) in Orange County. The area was undergoing a post-war building boom although the Martin Company development and related "spin-offs" were about the only big thing taking place at the time.

The telephone company appeared to be the only qualified long-range planner in the community who could hazard a guess about future population so they were contacted in this regard. Telephone company officials said the greater Orlando area population 17 years hence (1975) would have a population of 850,775 people for the three county area — Seminole — Orange and Osceola.

Projecting this population forecast on a map of Orange County, it was quite obvious a "Big Countdown" in land-use would occur in Orange County during the next 17 years! The Orange County CNI 1958 situation and 1975 esitmates that were submitted were as follows:

1958 SITUATION		1975 ESTIMATES
Orange County Population	237,000	3 County Population 850,775*
Citrus Acreage	68,505 Acres	43,190 (36% loss)
Vegetable Acreage	9,000 Acres	9,000 (no change)
Pasture & Range	185,686 Acres	141,352 (23% loss)
Forest & Woodland	213,494 Acres	148,157 (30% loss)

The CNI Committee estimated perhaps 65% of this growth (562,000) would be in Orange County.

Now that 1975 has caught up with these estimates, how close were the "Countdown" projections for land-use and population in Orange County?

	1958 SITUATION	1975 ESTIMATE	1975 ACTUAL
Population	237,000	562,000	462,000
Citrus Acreage	68,505 Acres	43,190 Acres	56,320 Acres
Vegetable Acreage	9,000 Acres	9,000 Acres	14,000 Acres
Pasture & Range	185,686 Acres	141,352 Acres	147,844 Acres
Forest & Woodland	213,494 Acres	148,157 Acres	169,983 Acres

These 17-year projections of land-use, prompted the County Agent to launch an educational program in 1960 to inform agricultural interests, community leaders and others of the implications revealed in the CNI Report.

An educational campaign was developed around a series of Kodochrome slides of California "before" and "after" scenes along with "people problems" such as pollution, traffic, taxation, crime, etc. that would result as the "countdown" progressed. This awareness program fit in well with the changes in the Extension Program and the new administrative responsibilities delegated to the County Agent. Many of his custodial responsibilities related to production activities were being re-directed because of increased land values. During this countdown period agriculturists were being caught up in zoning disputes, higher land assessments, vandalism problems, etc.

The 1958 Federal directive that focused attention on possible changes in land-use was scoffed at by some Agents, but it proved to be a most useful guideline for Extension Programs in Orange County. Whereas the Federal Food-Feed-Forage Campaign of World War I (during Agent DeBusk's tenure) was not timely or appropriate for Orange County, the CNI Report of 1958 was a blessing in disguise!

The first change in the County Agent's role occurred in 1963 when the County Agent title was changed to "County Chairman". About this time the state office recognized the need to coordinate county budgeting at the local level and decided on one unified budget to cover the Home Demonstration Agent, and the County Agent for secretarial help, office supplies, and salary supple-

*Telephone Company's Estimate

ments. On July 1, 1963 the state Extension Director designated the County Agent as County Chairman and made him responsible for combining requests for funds of the County Commissioners as a single budget request. Thus, the County Agent acquired another responsibility and a change of title.

Specialization of Extension Agents and the resulting increase in county staffs brought other changes in titles. For example, Home Demonstration Agents became "Home Economists".

Furthermore, the Civil Rights Act passed by Congress in 1964 brought de-emphasis of sex in relation to job titles and started a new reclassification of Extension activities. For example, the Boys' 4-H Club programs and Girls' 4-H Club programs became a unified program of 4-H work with no designation as to sex. The Agent in Charge of this work became known as the 4-H Co-ordinator.

However, by the mid 1960's it became obvious to state administrators that administratively all county Extension programs had to be unified to implement all of these new policies concerning regulations under the Civil Rights Act. After considerable ground work the merger of all county Extension programs — Commercial Agriculture, Home Economics, 4-H Work and Urban Horticulture was accomplished on July 1, 1969 at which time the County Chairman title was changed to County Extension Director.

About the time these "in house" re-organizations had simmered down to job responsibilities, and job titles and areas of program emphasis finalized, another bomb shell exploded. The administration changed the name of Florida Agricultural Extension Service to Florida Cooperative Extension Service. Some old timers considered this the straw that broke the camel's back. They believed that the administration wanted to totally eliminate any tie with the past to make the new image complete.

Citriculturist Fred P. Lawrence, now retired, believed his patience had been tried to the point where he should speak out. He wrote as follows:

"March 19, 1970

Dear Dean Busby:

The mornings mail brought your March 17 memo stating FES is now simply ES. What is your best estimate of when we will be taken over by HEW or some other similar 'progressive' department or non-agricultural agency?

Sincerely, I am becoming concerned for agriculture's future, and particularly about the Extension Service's apparent desire to associate itself with non agricultural activities.

Admittedly the State and County Governments do, in instances, put more money into the program than does the Federal

321

Government. It is, therefore, only natural to give them some credit but why disassociate ourselves from agriculture completely, as we did earlier this year?

The latest change in name could very well be the beginning of the end. I'd hate to see the SCS, ASC, Farmers' Home Administration or some other agency replace us in the field of agriculture.

Very truly yours,

Fred P. Lawrence"

Extension position openings now must be publicly circularized stating the requirements the applicant must meet to fill such a vacancy. Requirements for County Extension Directors have been greatly broadened in recent years because of the many policy changes in employment practices and the job responsibilities now required. As of January 1975 County Extension Directors' vacancies exist in Duval, Highlands, Manatee and Charlotte Counties. Requirements for these vacancies are advertised as follows:

"Master's degree required; major in agriculture, home economics, or related area required. Cooperative Extension experience required. County Extension Director of similar administrative experience preferred. Must have administrative and/or Extension program responsibility experience. Candidate must possess ability to organize and motivate people, establish and maintain positive relationships, and be of excellent health and character. Thorough knowledge of the program development process, cognizance of the principles that motivate people to help themselves improve their economic and social status".

No doubt the academic background and training of future custodians of Orange County's agriculture will vary as the "Countdown" goes on for agriculture and for Extension Agents.

Extension Agents serving Orange County through the years are as follows:

ORDER	POSITION	SERVICE PERIOD	
	County Agent	From	To
1st	Charles Henry Baker	2/23/14	7/31/17
2nd	C. F. DeBusk	10/ 1/17	10/31/19
3rd	C. D. Kime	7/ 1/19	7/15/26
4th	K. C. Moore	10/11/26	8/31/46
5th	F. E. Baetzman	10/ 1/46	6/30/57
*6th	Henry F. Swanson	8/ 1/57	7/ 1/63
	County Chairman		
1st	Henry F. Swanson	7/ 1/63	7/ 1/69
	County Extension Director		
1st	Henry F. Swanson	7/ 1/69	–
	Home Demonstration Agent		
1st	Miss Harriet B. Layton	1914	1916
2nd	Mrs. Nellie W. Taylor	1916	1944
3rd	Miss Elizabeth Dickenson	1944	1952
*4th	Mrs. Marjorie Ludeman Williams	1952	–

*Title Changed

ORDER	POSITION	SERVICE PERIOD	
	Home Economics Agent — Program Leader		
1st	Mrs. Marjoire Ludeman Williams	1969	--
	Assistant County Agent - Boys' 4-H Club Work		
1st	Henry F. Swanson	10/ 1/48	10/ 1/54
2nd	Albert F. Cribbett	10/ 1/54	10/ /57
3rd	Shelby Brothers	10/ /57	10/ /58
4th	Robert B. Christmas	1960	1962
5th	Kenneth L. Rauth	1962	1966
*6th	Ernest Cowen	1966	1971
	4-H Co-Ordinator		
1st	Ernest Cowen	1968	1971
2nd	Lester C. Floyd	3/ 1/72	--
	Assistant Home Demonstration Agents — **Girls' 4-H Club Work**		
1st	Miss Sammie Kilgore	10/ 1/48	1951
2nd	Miss Nancy Watlington	1951	1953
3rd	Mrs. Mary Moore	1954	1956
4th	Mrs. Joyce McDonald Rine	1956	1960
5th	Miss Janet Davidson	1960	1964
6th	Mrs. Deloris Wilkins	1965	1968
*7th	Mrs. Linda Luman	1968	1969
	Extension Home Economics Agent - 4-H		
1st	Mrs. Linda Luman	1969	--

SPECIALIZATION

ORDER	POSITION	SERVICE PERIOD	
	Assistant in Soil Conservation Program		
1st	Lewis S. Maxwell - 7 months employment	1938	
	Animal Industries		
1st	Albert F. Cribbett	1957	1962
2nd	Robert B. Christmas	1962	1966
3rd	Jack Lester	1966	1967
4th	Oscar J. Hebert	1967	--
	Horticultural		
1st	William E. Colburn	1959	1961
2nd	Bruce A. Barmby	1961	1966
	Commercial Horticulture		
1st	Bruce A. Barmby	1966	--
	Urban Horticulture		
1st	Kenneth L. Rauth	1966	1966
2nd	Dr. S. E. Tamburo	1966	1971
3rd	Thomas J. MacCubbin	1972	--
	Home Economics		
1st	Mrs. Mary Moore	1956	--
**2nd	Mrs. Leala Collins	1963	--

*Title Changed
**First Negro Agent to join County Staff

The several County Extension positions in Orange County as of 1975 with the various academic ranks of present individuals holding these positions are indicated by the following symbols:

I — Instructor
II — Assistant Professor
III — Associate Professor
IV — Full Professor

County Extensic Director IV
Extension Agent III — Ornamentals & Vegetables
Extension Agent II — Livestock Multi-County
Extension Agent II — Horticulture
Extension Agent I — 4-H Co-Ordinator
Extension Home Economics Agent III — Program Leader
Extension Home Economics Agent III
Extension Home Economics Agent II
Extension Home Economics Agent II — 4-H

II. ORANGE COUNTY FARM BUREAU

Because of mutual concerns and goals Trade organizations within the agricultural commodity area have a long history. However, attempts to unify the diverse interest of all agricultural commodity groups under one banner has seldom been entirely successful. In an attempt to unify the diverse groups into a single industry-wide organization the Farm Bureau came into being and coined the slogan of "Voice of Agriculture".

ORANGE COUNTY, FARM BUREAU OFFICE —, 2750 West Washington, Orlando, Florida.

In Florida, the Farm Bureau campaign to secure "one voice" for all of agriculture was launched in 1941 under the leadership of John Ford. Trying to put together a state-wide organization while building county organizations was a paradoxial situation that raised the question of — "which came first, the chicken or the egg?" The eruption of World War II added to the organizational difficulties and created new problems. Even to establish with certainty the date when Orange County's Farm Bureau unit was organized, appears to be impossible. Records are not available concerning this date and conversations with Farm Bureau Directors and officials only added to the confusion. For example, Art Karst, President of the 1944 Board of Directors, said he was the 2nd President and the organization had come into being in 1943 with Vern L. Bullis as first President. A letter from the latter's son, A. L. Bullis regarding this fact is quoted in full because of the points of historical significance it raises. "I am sorry that I have been this long in answering your letter of October 30th, but I have been trying to find the answer to some of the questions you asked. My father, Vern L. Bullis, moved to Orlando, in 1919 from Montana. He was very active in citrus activities until he had a stroke in 1943 and passed away in 1948. He planted his first citrus in the Bear Lake section in Seminole County in 1922 and also owned a grove in the Avalon section of Orange County.

He was a director and very active in the Orlando Citrus Growers Association on Concord at the railroad in 1931 when Ken McCall was manager.

He helped found and was a director of the Florida Citrus Production Credit Association in 1933 and helped obtain the services of Al Whitmore, who later became manager. He also helped found and was a director and Charter member of the Soil Science Foundation in Lakeland.

I know that Dad helped with forming the Florida Farm Bureau and was an Orange County Director, but I can't say if he was ever President, as I had joined the Navy about this time."

Between Bullis' leter and Karst's memory of events, it seems possible that the organization could have occurred in 1943. If so, it would be natural to expect County Agent Moore to report such in his annual report for 1943. Then again Moore may have been so involved with many new wartime boards and responsibilities he could have overlooked this small new organization for that year. However, in his 1944 annual report he wrote — "Upon request I attended the meetings of the Board of Directors of the Orange County Farm Bureau as 'agricultural advisor'." These statements plus the picture of the Board of Directors taken in November of 1944, confirms that Orange County's Farm Bureau was an active organization at that time.

It should be noted for the record that the state-wide Florida Farm Bureau Federation had its headquarters in Orange County from 1941 until 1956. Their headquarters were located in the Washington Street Arcade building in Orlando from 1941 until 1947 and from 1947 to 1956 their offices were located in the old Aloma Country Club at the corner of Lakemont and Aloma Avenues in Winter Park.

However, in 1956 the headquarters of the Florida Farm Bureau Federation were moved to Gainesville.

This fact is important because while the state offices were located here in Orange County from 1941 through 1956, local County Farm Bureau activities were at a rather low level. However, in 1957, the county organization took on the major project of securing an Agricultural Center for the agricultural interests of the county that would house the Agricultural Extension staff. This project is one of the organization's major accomplishments and has helped the local industry more perhaps than any other singular endeavor.

In 1957 the County Agricultural Extension staff was housed in an old three story residence on Wall Street across from the telephone company and behind the old Orlando fire station. This facility also housed the Visiting Nurses Association. These old run-down dwellings had neither meeting facilities nor adequate parking for office visitors. Also, the County Agricultural Extension staff was judged by "the house it kept" and this poor image reflected the poor public relations of the county's important agricultural industry.

In recognition of this critical need at the time of his appointment in 1957, County Agent Swanson instigated a project to correct the problem. He contacted A. H. Whitmore a local Farm Bureau member and the Secretary-Manager of the Orlando based Florida Citrus Production Credit Association. Whitmore, a friend of agriculture and a willing worker on its behalf, undertook this project. He went before the Board of Directors of the Orange County Farm Bureau in early 1957 and appealed for their "VOICE" and support in securing a center for the agricultural interests of Orange County. The Board adopted such a resolution to that end and President Charlie Root appointed Whitmore Chairman of the Farm Bureau Building Committee.

With this endorsement in his pocket, Whitmore embarked on a campaign to get recognition for Florida's second agricultural-income producing county. The first phase of Whitmore's campaign consisted of pointing out the need for such a facility through a special brochure. Pictures of Agricultural Centers in Polk, Brevard, Palm Beach, Osceola and Sarasota Counties were attached to Farm Bureau stationery. Under these pictures were statements of the cost of these facilities and the value and rank of that county's agricultural industry. The fact was emphasized that the multi-million dollar agricultural industry of Orange County was surpassed only by Polk County.

This awareness campaign prompted the Orange County Commissioners to tell the Farm Bureau Building Committee to come up with a building site and they might become more actively concerned.

Whitmore actively sought the public donation of a site for an Agricultural Center but the land speculation craze set-off by the Martin Company's activities at that time left no one willing to donate land for such a cause. Since no funds were available to purchase a site, the search for property narrowed down to parcels already owned by the county or city.

After careful consideration of all aspects, including public transportation to and from the proposed Center, the location that best met these various needs, was the county-owned property at the intersection of Bumby and Michigan in southeast Orlando.

Farm Bureau Directors had been hoping for a site either north or west of Orlando as being nearest to the major agricultural areas of the county. When Whitmore made it known that the Agricultural Center would have to be constructed at the other end of Orlando, some of the Directors not only became less enthusiastic but almost decided to oppose the project! Whitmore got those opposed to promise not to jeopardize the project by publicly revealing their displeasure with the proposed site.

Whitmore next secured the county's approval for the Michigan and Bumby location. With a site question now settled, he launched a campaign to get public funds committed for the construction of the Agricultural Center. He knew the state had matching funds available under the provisions of Senate Bills 302 and 488, to construct exhibit buildings about the state for educational purposes. He reasoned that if the county knew the state would put up $20,000 toward the construction of a building, the county would commit itself to matching this amount or more.

With this strategy in mind, Whitmore contacted T. K. McClane, Executive Vice President of Florida Farm Bureau and a member of the State Fair Committee for approving requests for constructing exhibit buildings under the provisions of this Act. McClane and other members of this State Fair Committee visited the Michigan and Bumby site to see if it met the state's criteria for accessibility to the public, size, drainage and other aspects. The committee agreed that the proposed site qualified for the state's $20,000 if the county would commit matching money and would dedicate the property accordingly. With these state commitments in his pocket, Whitmore asked for a financial commitment from the county for matching funds. The county requested architect Richard Boone Rogers to draw up plans for an exhibit building to meet the state's specifications. When these plans were submitted for public bid and a construction estimate of $65,000 was obtained, this cost suggested a 1/3 state and 2/3rd's county investment.

Once the contract for the exhibit building was let, Whitmore immediately launched a campaign for the county to construct an office-auditorium complex nearby. His approach was — "You must finish the job you can't leave an exhibit building without a supporting office complex." The Commissioners were not enthusiastic about building a complex that they would have to finance entirely out of county revenue. To build and equip such a facility would cost approximately $125,000. This fact, along with other pressing construction needs for the county would require an increase in county millage to raise such funds. Raising taxes is never popular and as a result the Commissioners voted three to two to support this request! Thus, the package deal of constructing the office-auditorium complex, the exhibit building and equipping the facilities came to approximately $200,000 in 1959.

ORANGE COUNTY AGRICULTURAL CENTER — 2350 East Michigan Avenue, Orlando, Florida.

On February 24, 1959 approximately 500 county and city leaders, agriculturists, homemakers, etc. were on hand to hear and see Dr. J. Wayne Reitz, President of the University of Florida formally dedicate the Orange County Agricultural Center. Dedication plaques on both buildings summarize the purposes for which both facilities were constructed. The dedication plaque on the wall of the office facility reads as follows:

ORANGE COUNTY AGRICULTURAL CENTER
A.D. 1959

DEDICATED TO THE PEOPLE OF ORANGE COUNTY, FLORIDA, TO SERVE AS A CENTER OF INFORMATION, FOR ADVISING AND INSTRUCTING THE PUBLIC CONCERNING THE LATEST KNOWLEDGE AND IMPROVEMENTS DEVELOPED IN THE SCIENCE OF AGRICULTURE AND HOME ECONOMICS AND ITS USE, WHICH CONTRIBUTES TO BETTER LIVING AND COMMUNITY GROWTH.

BOARD OF COUNTY COMMISSIONERS
ORANGE COUNTY, FLORIDA
John H. Talton, Chairman

John T. Murdoch, Jr.
A. D. Mims

Jack W. McDowall
James T. Cooper

Henry F. Swanson
County Agricultural
Agent

A. H. Whitmore
Chairman-Building
Comm., Orange Co.
Farm Bureau

Marjorie Ludeman
Home Demonstration Agent

Richard Boone Rogers
Architect

Henry B. Stephens
General Contractor

The dedication plaque on the wall of the exhibit building reads as follows:

AGRICULTURAL EXHIBIT BUILDING
ORANGE COUNTY
A.D. 1959

THIS BUILDING IS DEDICATED TO THE PEOPLE OF ORANGE COUNTY AND THE STATE OF FLORIDA TO HELP IN THE FULFILLMENT OF AN ABUNDANT LIFE BY PROMOTING THE SCIENCE OF AGRICULTURE THROUGH EDUCATION, EXHIBITS AND DEMONSTRATION. IT HAS BEEN ERECTED BY JOINT COOPERATION OF THE STATE OF FLORIDA, THROUGH PROVISIONS OF SENATE BILLS NUMBERS 302 AND 488 AND THE BOARD OF COUNTY COMMISSIONERS OF ORANGE COUNTY, FLORIDA.

STATE OF FLORIDA

Leroy Collins — Governor

Nathan Mayo — Commissioner of
Agriculture
and Chairman of Committee

FAIR SHOW COMMITTEE

T. P. Chaires, Jr. — Pres. Fla. Federation
of Fairs
T. K. McClane — Exec. Vice President
Fla. Farm Bureau

M. O. Watkins — Director of Agr.
Extension Service
Neill Rhodes — Commissioner of
Markets

L. H. Lewis, Director, State Farmers Markets

ORANGE COUNTY COMMISSIONERS
John H. Talton-Chairman

John T. Murdoch, Jr.
A. D. Mims

Jack W. McDowall
James T. Cooper

and

A. H. Whitmore
Chairman-Building Committee
Orange County Farm Bureau

Henry F. Swanson
County Agricultural Agent

Marjorie Ludeman
Home Demonstration Agent

Richard Boone Rogers
Architect

Henry B. Stephens
General Contractor

Another important "voice of agriculture" project in the late 1950's was the re-evaluation of citrus groves that were damaged by the severe freezes of December 1957 and January 1958. Whitmore and a special delegation of Farm Bureau members appealed to Tax Assessor Helen Bennett for a re-appraisal of groves because of the tree damage caused by excessively low temperatures in the '57-'58 season. As a result of this formal request, Tax Assessor Helen Bennett arranged for a special citrus survey crew to re-appraise all Orange County citrus groves in the spring of '58. Thanks to this action tax bills in November of that year reflected a considerable saving to growers. Again the "voice of agriculture" was heard! Orange County was the first and only Florida county to experience such a special tax concession. However, this concept set a precedent that Tax Assessors followed when the disastrous freeze of '62 hit the industry. At that time all Tax Assessors reassessed citrus groves in accordance with tree conditions.

30-YEAR REUNION OF FARM BUREAU DIRECTORS – NOV. 1974 –
Three directors (Bill Story, T. C. Hawthorne and L. W. Tilden) and County Agent Moore died during the interim. Attending reunion left to right former Executive Secretary Florida Farm Bureau Federation John Ford, Montgomery, Alabama; Norman Benzing, Orlando; Cushman Radebaugh, Ft. Pierce – Orlando; Art Karst, Vero Beach; Fran Fawsett, Ft. Pierce; T. G. Lee, Orlando. Unable to attend: Wilfred Hedges and E. B. Conoley.

The urban growth of the county during the late 1950's and the 1960's brought zoning and planning regulations, water control, and pollution restrictions. Advisory boards were created to help Commissioners formulate policy concerning these areas of concern. These advisory boards were made up of citizens from all walks of life, including agriculture. The Commissioners called upon the "voice of agriculture" to recommend representatives from agriculture to sit on these various advisory boards.

When urban pressures intensified the "countdown" for agriculture, the impact that these pressures had on some of the charter

1974-75 ORANGE COUNTY FARM BUREAU DIRECTORS — (left to right)
Jack Ross, John Talton, Larry Hiatt, Lester M. Austin III, Jack Christmas,
George Howard, Dr. A. E. Willson, R. G. Pitman, T. G. Lee, Richard Risser, Mrs.
Margaret Vickery, Fred Dietrich III, Don Rybolt, Paul Faircloth, President
Henry Land, Charles Hawthorne, Billy Long. Absent — Mrs. Irene Day.

members of the Orange County Farm Bureau are noteworthy. Three
Directors of the 1944 Board moved their agricultural endeavors from
Orange County to other counties. Art Karst moved to Vero Beach,
Cushman Radebaugh and "Fran" Fawsett both moved to the Ft.
Pierce area, a severe loss to Orange County's agriculture!

The increasing activities and stature of the Farm Bureau in
Orange County prompted the Directors to undertake a program to

ORANGE COUNTY FARM BUREAU DIRECTORS NOV. 1944 — Seated,
Left to Right — John Ford Executive Secretary Florida Farm Bureau Federa-
tion, Bill Story, President Art Karst, Fran Fawsett, K. C. Moore, County Agent.
Standing, Left to Right — Claude Hawthorne, E. B. "Bounce" Conoley, Norman
Benzing, Cushman Radebaugh, L. W. "Bill" Tilden, T. G. Lee, Wilfred Hedges.

acquire modern office facilities for staff members and service agencies serving a membership of over 2,000. On June 6, 1966 the Orange County Farm Bureau staff moved into their $50,000 building at 2750 West Washington Avenue in Orlando.

As the urban demands of Commissioners and local legislators continually grow louder, the "voice of agriculture" must indeed speak more often and louder in order to be heard above the urban confusion. A larger Board of Directors, representing all commodity areas, can better express the needs of the entire industry. Furthermore, the issuance of a monthly newsletter keeps the entire membership of over 2,000 fully informed of the many activities of their organization. An annual dinner meeting provides a forum by which the entire membership can participate in the elections, transaction of business and hear various committee reports and financial reports.

Like any organization, some one has to head up the entire organization and assume the total responsibility of guiding the organizational activities toward certain predetermined goals. Recognition and thanks should be given to Presidents who have given of their time and talents in orchestrating the "voice". The following are individuals who have served as President of the Orange County Farm Bureau:

PAST PRESIDENTS OF ORANGE COUNTY FARM BUREAU

YEAR	NAME	ADDRESS	COMMODITY FIELD
1943	V. L. Bullis	Orlando	Citrus
1944	Art Karst	Orlando	Citrus
1945	Art Karst	Orlando	Citrus
1946	Art Karst	Orlando	Citrus
1947	Art Karst	Orlando	Citrus
1948	L. W. Tilden	Tildenville	Vegetable-Citrus
1949	L. W. Tilden	Tildenville	Vegetable-Citrus
1950	L. W. Tilden	Tildenville	Vegetable-Citrus
1951	Bob Pitman	Apopka	Citrus
1952	Bob Pitman	Apopka	Citrus
1953	Cushman Radebaugh	Orlando	Cattle
1954	T. G. Lee	Orlando	Dairy
1955	T. G. Lee	Orlando	Dairy
1956	Tom Mahaffey	Apopka	Foliage Plants
1957	C. A. Root	Winter Garden	Citrus
1958	Jack Ross	Oakland	Citrus
1959	Jack Ross	Oakland	Citrus
1960	Jack Ross	Oakland	Citrus
1961	Jack Ross	Oakland	Citrus
1962	Chester Karst	Orlando	Citrus
1963	Chester Karst	Orlando	Citrus
1964	Chester Karst	Orlando	Citrus
1965	Chester Karst	Orlando	Citrus

YEAR	NAME	ADDRESS	COMMODITY FIELD
1966	Don Rybolt	East Orange	Cattle
1967	Don Rybolt	East Orange	Cattle
1968	John Talton	Apopka	Poultry-Citrus-Foliage
1969	John Talton	Apopka	Poultry-Citrus-Foliage
1970	John Talton	Apopka	Poultry-Citrus-Foliage
1971	Dr. A. E. Willson	Maitland	Citrus
1972	Dr. A. E. Willson	Maitland	Citrus
1973	Jack Christmas	Apopka	Foliage Plants
1974	Billy Long	Apopka	Vegetables
1975	Henry W. Land	Tangerine	Poultry

PAST PRESIDENTS ORANGE COUNTY FARM BUREAU — Kneeling Left to Right — Jack Christmas (1973), Billy Long (1974), Chester Karst (1962-65), Don Rybolt (1966-67). Standing , Left to Right — John Talton (1968-70), Tom Mahaffey (1956), Jack Ross (1958-61), Art Karst (1944-47), T. G. Lee (1954-55), Bob Pitman (1951-53), Charlie Root (1957), Dr. A. E. Willson (1971-72).

III. SOIL AND WATER

The disastrous dust bowl of the early 1930's focused national attention on the need for an agency to work on the inter-related problems of soil and water. The Army Corp of Engineers had long been in existence but their efforts were directed primarily to water-use problems.

The dust bowl emergency prompted Congress to create the Soil Erosion Service which would concern itself with soil erosion problems as a branch of the United States Department of Agriculture. In this capacity the Soil Erosion Service supervised many of the activities of the Civilian Conservation Corps (C.C.C.) which carried on such activities as planting trees, grass and other conservation activities.

Congress soon recognized that soil conservation efforts should be oriented towards prevention, rather than corrective programs, if soil conservation efforts were to be meaningful in terms of cost-benefit ratios. Toward that end, Congress passed Public Law #46 creating the Soil Conservation Service and enabling legislation to let the states avail themselves of the technical services of this agency through the creation of Soil Conservation Districts at the grassroots level.

Provided with this legislative opportunity, the Florida Legislature, during the early 1940's, passed Chapter 582 which provides for the creation of Soil Conservation Districts. Chapter 582 provided the legal vehicle by which freeholders within a geographic area of the state could, by referendum, establish a Soil and Water Conservation District. Through nomination and election, five land owners would become Supervisors of the District. These Supervisors would serve on a staggered term basis either two or three years, without compensation, in developing a program to accomplish certain conservation goals and objectives within their geographical area or district. To implement this would require the technical services of the Soil Conservation Service. To acquire the services of the SCS, the Supervisors were required to sign a Memorandum of Agreement with the Department of Agriculture — USDA. To start the ball rolling for a new program such as this invariably requires the educational efforts of the County Agent because of his responsibility as being an educational officer of the USDA. In such a capacity his mission has always been to bring the facts to people and let them decide on the merits and what course of action to pursue.

In 1944, County Agent Moore started an educational campaign to arouse interest in the merits of a Soil Conservation District and of utilizing their technical services. The first exploratory meeting in this regard was held on September 7th. At this meeting C. D. Gunn and Bob Witherell of the Soil Conservation Service and K. S. McMullen, Extension Service Conservationist, presented information on forming a Soil and Water Conservation District for Orange County. This was followed by three conferences between Agent Moore, the County Farm Bureau officials and others.

On January 30, 1945, Agent Moore brought together all interested parties to determine whether an organized effort should be undertaken to establish a Soil Conservation District. Those in attendance recommended that steps be undertaken to form such a District. Officers of the Orange County Farm Bureau undertook the "leg work" necessary to secure twenty-five signatures for calling a hearing on this proposal. On March 1 a hearing was held with twenty-one land owners present. Testimony taken during this hearing brought out that those present were primarily interested in water conservation and control for the best interests of agriculture. A unanimous vote favored the establishment of the District and it was decided that the name would be Orange Soil Conservation District.

At that time machinery was set in motion to send out legal notices, establish five polls for voting, the hours of voting, and the date of the election — May 25, 1945. The vote was 90 "for" and four "against" establishing the District. Next, nominations for five Supervisors were made and sent to A. P. Spencer, Administrator, P. C. Peters, citrus grower, Winter Garden; L. W. Tilden, vegetable and citrus grower, Tildenville; Clarence Datson, dairy and cattle owner, Pine Castle; A. H. Reppard, citrus grower and ranch owner, Orlando; and H. A. Ward, citrus and vegetable grower, Winter Park. These nominations were approved by the State Soil Conservation Committee and an election was called for November 5, 1945. The nominees were duly elected and an organizational meeting was called for November 22, 1945.

In his 1945 Annual Report Moore commented on these activities in behalf of the District — "I have regretted that so long a time has been taken to accomplish this set up. I have held back hoping that the Farm Bureau's committee would actively interest themselves

SOIL AND WATER STEWARDS — The Board of Supervisors of the Orange Soil and Water Conservation District with Secretary and District Conservationist. (left to right) Secretary Henry Swanson, Supervisors Don Platt, Don Rybolt; Chairman G. E. Snow; Supervisor R. I. Wetherbee and Conservationist Fred Merrill. Absent Supervisor R. G. Pitman — January 30, 1975.

in putting it through. This they seemed too busy to do. Most of the work has fallen on me. I was too concentrated on other work during July, August and September to give any time to it."

The organizational meeting of these newly elected Supervisors — A. H. Reppard, P. C. Peters, Clarence Datson, L. W. Tilden and Harley Ward was held in County Agent Moore's office November 27th and the duties were informally discussed. A. H. Reppard was elected Chairman and County Agent Moore became Secretary.

Five applications for assistance had been received from farmers on February 21, 1946. The Board of Supervisors made a tour of inspection of these properties with R. E. Wetherell, District Conservationist. The legal Memorandum of Agreement with the U.S.D.A. was signed.

The first work unit technician assigned to the Orange Soil Conservation District by the Soil Conservation Service was W. B. Hutcheson. Those serving in various capacities with the Orange Soil and Water Conservation District during 30 years of existence are as follows:

CHAIRMAN OF THE BOARD OF SUPERVISORS
A. H. Reppard — Orlando
L. W. Tilden — Tildenville
Gary E. Snow — Orlando

SECRETARY TO THE BOARD
K. C. Moore, County Agent
Fred Baetzman, County Agent
Henry F. Swanson, County Agent

WORK UNIT CONSERVATIONIST (DISTRICT CONSERVATIONIST)
W. B. Hutcheson
Walter Shaeffer
W. Gayle Diamond
A. R. Swartz
Fred Merrill

INDIVIDUALS WHO HAVE SERVED AS SUPERVISORS
A. H. Reppard — Orlando — citrus grower and rancher
L. W. Tilden — Tildenville — citrus and vegetable grower
Clarence Datson — Pine Castle — dairyman
Phil Peters — Winter Garden — citrus grower
H. A. Ward — Winter Park — citrus and vegetable grower
L. B. McLeod, Jr. — Turkey Lake — cattleman
C. S. Radebaugh — Orlando — cattleman
Gordon Eunice — Fairvilla — dairyman
Glenn Datson — Pine Castle — cattleman
Gary E. Snow — Orlando — cattleman
Paul Teal — Winter Garden — cattleman
B. W. Judge, Jr. — Conway — dairyman
Donald F. Rybolt — East Orange County — cattleman

Cliff R. Freeman — Ocoee — citrus grower
W. D. "Bill" Hartzog — Windermere — citrus grower
Robert C. McColley — Orlando — foliage grower
R. M. Dilatush, Jr. — Barton Lake — citrus grower
Donald D. Platt — Bithlo — dairyman
R. I. Wetherbee — Boggy Creek — citrus grower
R. G. Pitman, Jr. — Apopka — citrus grower

Celebrating 30 years of existence in 1975, the District not only can reflect on the thousands of requests of land owners in the District for technical services that it has expedited, but it can also be proud of four historical accomplishments that will benefit untold generations.

One of the District's first and most lasting contribution was its leadership in getting a new soil survey made of Orange County. The partial soil survey made in 1936 was entirely inadequate for the soil information demanded in the post World War II period. After considerable prodding by the Board of Supervisors and County Agent Fred Baetzman, the Board of County Commissioners signed a request in 1950 for such a survey with the U.S. Soil Conservation Service and the University of Florida Agricultural Experiment Stations. This request was supported with a financial appropriation to pay part of the cost involved.

This urgently needed soil survey was completed and released in 1960, just in time to be a valuable resource document for the "sizzling sixties" when urban growth almost engulfed the county. Builders, planners, zoners, government leaders, and others found this guide extremely helpful in planning proper land-use.

No sooner had the Soil Survey Report been received than the Board of Supervisors began to campaign for a similar survey for the water resources of Orange County. Upon a formal request to the Board of County Commissioners for a water resources study, the Commission signed an agreement with the U. S. Geological Survey to support such a survey with a financial commitment.

A water resources investigation study was undertaken by the U. S. Geological Survey in 1959. The report was released in 1968 just in time for the Commissioners to use the findings of this important study in their land development policies. The most revealing fact of this survey was that *the prime ground water recharge areas in the county were definitely located.* Accordingly the county developed a low density plan of development for those vital recharge areas.

However, the Board of Supervisors realized that the county's Soil and Water Surveys were only resource tools and if utilized properly they must be used in connection with planning and zoning concepts. Consequently, the Board spoke in favor of establishing planning and zoning regulations for the county. They recommended to policymakers the drafting of such legislation and made their voice heard in many ways. They argued that misuse of the land in the 1930's by the agriculturists helped trigger the "dust bowl" and that history could well repeat itself in Orange County through urban misuse. Supervisors pointed out the unusual soil and water relations of Orange County and that misuse could contribute to flooding conditions, malfunctioning septic tanks and other problems associated with misused environment through urban overdevelopment. Their warnings were heeded and many recommendations were accepted in this regard.

The Board of Supervisors also encouraged the County Commissioners to print up a supplement to the Orange Soil Survey, a supplement entitled "Soil Interpretations For Urban And Recreational Uses". This guide has been most helpful to lay people to become more knowledgeable about the capabilities of Orange County soils for urban development.

When the county was "flooded" by two years of excessive rainfall in 1959 and '60, the policymakers drafted a water control bill to establish lake levels and build necessary flood control structures to cope with problems brought about by the tremendous urban growth experienced since the end of World War II up to 1960.

The Board of Supervisors recommended that this Water Control Bill have a Citizen's Water Advisory Board consisting of the five main users of water to act in an advisory capacity to the County Commissioners. It was recommended that members represent the agricultural segment of the economy, sportsmen, municipalities, industry, and the public at large. The citizen's lay board has performed a valuable service in helping the Commission to formulate water policy in agreement with public opinion as reflected by this representative body.

Thus, the custodians of Orange County's soil and water resources have played, and continue to play a major role in determining the policy behind the utilization of these two vital and interrelated resources.